# The Natural History of Palms

# The Natural History of Palms

## E. J. H. Corner
FRS, FLS

*Professor of Tropical Botany, University of Cambridge*

**UNIVERSITY OF CALIFORNIA PRESS**
Berkeley and Los Angeles · 1966

University of California Press
Berkeley and Los Angeles, California

© *1966 by E. J. H. Corner*

Library of Congress Catalog Card Number: 66-25698

*Phototypeset, Printed and Bound in Great Britain*

# Contents

# Plates

# Preface

WHEN THE *Wayside Trees of Malaya* was published in 1940, my intention was to add a companion on the larger monocotyledons. War and international responsibility led me to return to academic life. Though no longer within the spell of that richly endowed country, yet I have been able since 1958 through the generosity of the Royal Society of London to return on several occasions to the Far East. I found the thirst for natural history as burning there as it is in England. Here at Cambridge, since 1950, it has been my privilege to give every year to advanced students in botany a course of four lectures with practicals on the subject of the palms. I have learnt, in my endeavours to present to students the great feats of the plant kingdom, that palms should come first, not last or, as most often has happened, not at all in the study of monocotyledons. My intention has re-crystallized in this book, which is neither systematic nor taxonomic. The final chapter deals with the classification of palms in order to orientate the reader among their vast columns, for we are waiting this revision from across the Atlantic.

It is a pleasure to record my gratitude to Dr H. Gilbert Carter, former Director of the Botanic Garden of the University of Cambridge, who introduced me to palms, and to Dr C. X. Furtado of the Botanic Garden, Singapore, who cultivated this interest during our many years together in Malaya. In the preparation of illustrations for this book, I am indebted to the following colleagues who have supplied me with much local information: Dr P. S. Ashton, Forest Department, Sarawak, for plates 8, 12, 13; Dr E. F. W. Brunig, University of Hamburg, and formerly of the Forest Department, Sarawak, for plate 7; Mr Francis Hallé, Adiopodoumé, Ivory Coast, for plate 18; Dr Edwin A. Menninger, Stuart, Florida, for plates 17 and 19; Mr R. A. A. Oldeman, Institut Français d'Amerique Tropical, Cayenne, for plate 20; Dr T. C. Whitmore, Forest Research Institute, Malaya, and formerly of the Forest Department,

British Solomon Islands Protectorate, for plate 17 (bottom figure). Furthermore, I express my gratitude to Dr G. H. S. Bushnell, Curator of the Museum of Archaeology and Ethnology, University of Cambridge, for plate 20 (Oriya script); to Mr H. R. Creswick, Librarian of the University of Cambridge, for the illustrations in plates 1–4 and 21–24; and to the Royal Society of London for plate 15.

# Chapter 1

# The Palm Scene

OF ALL land plants, the palm is the most distinguished. A columnar stem crowned with giant leaves is the perfect idea, popular or philosophic, of what a plant should be. It suffers no attrition through ramification. In all the warmer parts of the earth this form stamps itself in grand simplicity on the landscape. It manifests itself in more than two thousand species and several hundred genera, every one restricted more or less by climate, terrain, and geographical history. The present distribution of palms resembles an immense chessboard on which we see the last moves of a great game of life. Kings and queens are Malaysian and Amazonian. The major pieces have moved into America, Africa, and Asia, and the pawns have reached the islands. There are fragments of the early moves in the Cretaceous rocks, dating back 120 million years. A fan-palm has been reported from the Triassic of Colorado, and we do not know when the game began or whence it was derived. All we can say is that the palms are as old, if not older, than any other form of flowering plant and that they have endured while the rest have pressed forward into modern trees, climbers, herbs, and grasses, ramified, extended, twisted, and simplified. We find palms in the meadows, steppes and deserts, on the mountains, and all through the tropical and subtropical forests. Whether surrounded by grass-blades, towering trunks, or tree-ferns they maintain their rigid character as if this great family had been pitched, as a block of special creation, into the Mesozoic world, and around, through, and over it the subsequent streams of life had flowed. The palm is an evolutionary challenge, primitive, standardized, and viable.

We approach a tropical shore and coconut palms extend along it. We enter a tropical river and other palms are drawn up on the banks. They burst from the canopy of the broad-leafed forest; they hide in its shade; they obstruct its walks; they entangle its trees; they line its rivulets. They dot the landscape of native agriculture. They dis-

I

tinguish the villages. They blot out the landscape under commercial agriculture. They troop across the derelict countryside and cluster at a water-hole. They are stationed along city streets and decorate the parks. We tread on their flooring, shelter beneath their roofing, rest on their matting, and eat of their substance. We should know well what palms are.

In warm climates the people have grown up accustomed to palms, using them in all these ways, playing under them from childhood and making playthings from them, perhaps reverencing them, but always caring for them. When the forest must be hewn back, the palms are spared by that primitive trait which mingles admiration with necessity. The local kinds are known through custom, story and legend, but no science or botany of a palm family has emerged. Strangers to the palm lands sketch and photograph, gather seed for their distant gardens and greenhouses, and rejoice generally in the realization of book-knowledge, but they find the palms too massive and intractable for ordinary scientific approach. It is necessary to live with the palms for many years in order to appreciate them. The rustle of the moorland grass lies overhead; the debris of fallen leaves and inflorescences is unaccommodating. So we find that few scientists have been able to cope with palms and that fewer still have made the effort to build up palm science. We find, in fact, no major group of plants so neglected in its study.

Commerce has perceived the output of palms. There are big estates of coconut palms, oil palms, date palms, sugar palms, sago palms, wax palms, ivory-nut palms, betel palms and wine palms, whilst others, such as the rattans, are still bountiful enough in the forests and it is scarcely time even for sylviculture to heed them. The palms are an immense source of raw material for they are part of the truly productive, photosynthetic income of the world. They offer good kinds and poor, high yielders and low, vigorous and weak, tardy and quick, disease-resistant and susceptible, and those which are easily marketed compare with others that, with spines, fibres, and old leaf-bases, present many practical problems. Research stations are growing up which require physiologists, pathologists, and geneticists, as well as estate-managers, engineers, and chemists. Thus a considerable body of practical and scientific knowledge of the commercial palms is coming into existence [1]. The search for oils, tannins, resins, and other products of plant industry is leading to a chemical understanding [2]. Horticulture, by raising seed and selec-

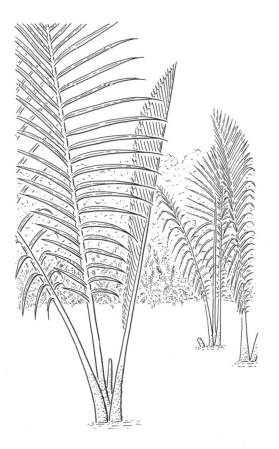

Figure 1. Nipa palms at high tide with dried mud on the leaf-stalks from previous floods; $\times \frac{1}{100}$.

ting the ornamental, is meeting its palm problems and attempting a scientific inventory [3]. As so often in human affairs, practice forces the pace and demands science. The philosopher may muse on the revolution among these Jurassic fruiterers which fattened reptiles, then mammals and birds, and now men, and the millions of years which have elapsed before the provision of palms comes to be exploited contemporaneously with the atoms. Cereals, legumes, vegetables, and other annual crops are proletarian; palms are capitalists. They store. They work not on the day to day running of a short season, but on the gross accumulation over many years. Where ground-nuts fail, palms may succeed. They prove that there has been no one way to organize the earth, though the palm way has prevailed.

All these aspects come and go in the natural history of palms, the purpose of which is to understand what they are, what they are doing in the progress of nature, and whence they have come. Palms, we read, are monocotyledons, but we shall learn that the converse may be truer. They are thought to have been derived from the concentration of herbaceous plants about the order Liliales, which embraces the lilies, tulips, hyacinths, asparagus and many tropical and subtropical allies, and it is assumed that they have engineered these simple plants into the most gigantic primary stems, leaves, inflorescences, and fruits of the whole world, but we shall learn that the truth may be the reverse [4]. As for what they are doing, they contribute more carbohydrate and oil in the form of leaf, pollen, honey, and fruit to tropical wild life than any other family of plants. There are said to be 'solid stands hundreds of square miles in extent' of the carandá fan-leaf palm *Copernicia alba* in south-west Brazil, the largest estimated to contain five hundred million of these massive palms [5].

Certainly it was a great discovery to have found that palms conform with other plants in their seedling ways. But we seldom think of palms as seedlings, and many other characters go with the simple one of monocotyledony. The leaves of monocotyledons grow mainly at the base, not at the tip, and about this all-important feature the monocotyledon is constructed. Then these leaves have parallel, longitudinal veins, conforming with their manner of growth and their cross-connections are by short transverse veins, not by the network of the dicotyledonous leaf. The floral parts of the monocotyledon are arranged in threes, not in fours, fives, or some higher number as in dicotyledons. The arrangement represents a limiting case of phyllotaxy, or the mechanism of leaf-production at the stem-apex, and it is more advanced in the sense of being more reduced than in the dicotyledon. Thus the palm flower has eventually three sepals, three petals, six stamens, and an ovary with three carpels or three cavities, such as are represented by the three eyes of the coconut. But we shall find that numerous palms show that this finality has been experimented with in many different lines of palm evolution from a greater number of stamens and carpels, and that these lines arrive in parallel, not in common inheritance, at the monocotyledonous formula; it is not primitive.

The veins, or vascular bundles, of monocotyledons are strands of phloem or xylem tubes within a sheathing of mechanical fibres. The bundles are usually less than 1 mm. wide and, as they do not have the cambial tissue of dicotyledons, they cannot be widened once they have been formed; they are lengthened, nevertheless, by new growth at the apex of stem or root and at the base of the leaf. The palm trunk

4

depends, therefore, for its supply of vascular bundles on the primary thickness of the growing points of stem and root [6]. There is no addition to the tissue of the trunk below the crown of leaves, which becomes in general columnar though, as we shall see, there are exceptions caused by dilations of the ground tissue, or by contractions of the stem-apex, and these are not referable to secondary thickening by means of a cambium. Likewise the palm root is devoid of secondary thickening. Its life is limited, perhaps in the same manner as that of the leaf. Old roots are continually being dismantled, as it were, and new roots developed from the base of the stem which swells into the elephant-foot as the characteristic pedestal to the larger palms.

As the monocotyledonous leaf grows in the bud, it enlarges and widens the lamina. It develops more vascular bundles. Some of these interconnect, but the maximum size of the bundle is soon reached and all the extra bundles must be continued down to the leaf-base and into the stem to connect with those carrying the water-supply from the roots. The base of the growing leaf must continue expanding to accommodate all these vascular bundles until the whole leaf has been laid down. A broad attachment is needed to carry the bundles into the stem and the attachment is made by thickening the leaf-stalk or petiole and by extending it to form a sheath round the stem. The sheathing leaf-base is, in fact, another characteristic of the monocotyledon and it shows up on the palm trunk as the conspicuous rings or nodes where the large leaves were attached. It follows from this arrangement that two leaves cannot be developed at the same level on the stem. The monocotyledon must lay down one leaf at a time. So the one seedling leaf, just as the parallel veining and the sheathing base, is the result of the basal growth of the leaf and its vascular system in the form of vascular bundles without cambial connection. The one cotyledon which, historically, defined the group is a subsidiary item on the agenda.

Because of their great size and enormous quantity of vascular bundles, palms exemplify the features of monocotyledony better than any other plants. This could not have been known, of course, until the anatomy of flowering plants was understood. Palms now turn the table. It is not that they are monocotyledons but that monocotyledons are palm-derivatives. Botanical theory has been beset with the minutiae of herbs. It requires vast structures such as palms to re-establish its magnitude. More than a century ago it was realized, however, that grasses were a sort of palm of a lower grade [7]. The

5

conclusion confirms the geological record. Given the equipment of a palm, it is possible to deduce by established precepts of plant morphology the other orders and families of monocotyledons. We shall develop this theory little by little as we discover the modifications which palms themselves have undergone. Through the process of neoteny, or maturation at an early or simpler state of development, many of their genera have become diversified towards the condition of the undergrowth herb that characterizes the majority of monocotyledons. The problem which must finally be faced is the ancestry of the palms.

The leading questions in biology are how the organism is made, how it works, how it reproduces, where it occurs, and whence it has come. The last becomes the first in explanation of the others. What knowledge is there of palm forerunners? Geologically there is none, but morphologically in structure there is plenty. The palm leaf betrays in its complicated development the manner in which the ordinary strap-shaped and basally growing monocotyledonous leaf is connected with the apically growing, compound dicotyledonous leaf. The palm inflorescence, in striking contrast with the palm stem, is a much branched structure ramifying on the same principles as the dicotyledonous, yet modified also with basal growth; it bespeaks an ancestry far exceeding the age of known fossil palms. The fruit relates unquestionably to the durian theory of flowering plants in general [8] and, by itself, is proof of the immense ancestry which lies behind the Cretaceous occurrence of palm-fossils. The distribution of palms bespeaks the antiquity of their family. The isolation of certain genera and species, both structural and geographical, indicates an age far exceeding that of the petty species and genera of the more recent herbaceous monocotyledons. *Phoenix, Nipa, Caryota, Borassus, Mauritia,* and *Phytelephas* cannot be equated with the genera of orchids, grasses, crucifers, or composites, nor even with oaks or durians. All these aspects, structural, geographical, geological, commercial, and ethnobotanical, illuminate the presence of palms on our planet, where they have been the precedents of its civilization. But the scene is incomplete without a knowledge of the other kinds of arborescent monocotyledons that grow with the palms and have somehow failed to make such an impression. It seems not to have been permitted to establish co-supremacy among the tree monocotyledons.

Conifers may be called soft woods or needle-leafed trees, dicotyledons hard woods or broad-leafed trees. The pandans or screwpines, the traveller's palms and banana-trees, the dragon's blood trees and their allies, the tree-aloes and tree-lilies, the grass-trees, the bamboos, and various rushes, sedges, orchids, aroids, and bromeliads are monocotyledonous trees without a unifying and familiar designation [9]. I have always thought of them as sword trees and I shall introduce the expression. The leaf is the main organ of the land-plant and distinguishes its kinds, as these names show. We recognize from their shape, structure, and manner of growth, moss-leaves, fern-leaves, cycad-leaves, conifer leaves, and dicotyledonous leaves. So we can recognize the monocotyledonous leaf, the basal growth of which projects it from the apex of the shoot to open from the tip, which is the oldest and first formed part, downwards to the base which is the youngest part and the last to mature. We see this in the white growing bases of onion and leek. We see it in the ageing of grass and sedge leaves, yellowing, browning, and dying from the tip basewards or, in botanical expression, basipetally. The monocotyledonous effect is to thrust the young leaves one at a time as a sword or dagger into the air from the centre of the crown or the rosette of leaves which terminates a branch. The bigger the leaf, as in palms, pandans, and bananas, the more conspicuous the thrust; in palms it is pre-eminent and it is the key to understanding what is going on in their heads. In a modified way the sword becomes the spear of the bamboo shoot and, in miniature, the quill of the spring crocus.

The blade of the palm leaf is folded together in the bud by longitudinal pleats. The sword has inside it the lamination of a fan, and it exposes this structure from above downwards, as a fan might do if it were not operated from the base. It is the plicate leaf of botany, frequent among various families of dicotyledons such as the oaks, mulberries, figs, dipterocarps and so on, but nowhere so exclusively and characteristically perfected as in that of the palms. Nevertheless it is one feature which allies the small tropical American family Cyclanthaceae indubitably with the palms, as we shall consider when reviewing the consequences of palm inheritance (chapter 11). The feature occurs in some grasses, sedges, allies of the lily, and other monocotyledons, and in a narrow or confined way it distinguishes the pandan leaf. It is a vestige, as we shall see, or a sort of memory of their past in these modernized groups where the plane strap-shaped leaf has taken over in the progressive simplification of vegetation.

When the palm sword opens, its folds split and separate into leaflets. If the leaf-axis is short, the effect is the fan-shaped or palmate leaf but if, as happens more often, this axis has been elongating and spacing the folds along it, there comes the pinnate leaf superficially like the feathery fronds of ferns and cycads. It is this compound form of the open leaf, having the original blade split into leaflets, which distinguishes the palm from other kinds of sword tree. The tattering of the old banana leaf, which was rolled up, not folded, in the bud, is a spurious analogy.

Fan and feather leaf, or palmate and pinnate, offer the readiest distinction for the classification of the palms. Yet it is not sufficient in itself for there are two kinds of each leaf form, namely the induplicate and the reduplicate, as will be explained in chapter 3. Moreover, the Lepidocaryoid palms, recognized from their scaly fruits, have a few genera with palmate leaves, while the majority has pinnate. The induplicate leaf splits to give gutter-shaped leaflets, as viewed from the upperside of the leaf, whereas the reduplicate splits to give roof-shaped or inverted gutter-shaped leaflets; and there is no inter-

Figure 2. The Coryphoid fan-leafed palm *Washingtonia*, with the dead leaves persistent as a skirt round the trunk; $\times \frac{1}{200}$ (after McCurrach 1960).

mediate between these two ways of splitting. It is this less obvious feature, therefore, which gives the primary basis for the grouping of palms. Then details of flower and fruit enter and it is customary now to distinguish nine subfamilies of palms, as shown in table 1. Three of these contain a single genus; two are relatively small, but four are large, pantropical, and as varied in vegetative and reproductive characters as most families of flowering plants. The names of the subfamilies are supplied by their most characteristic genera; thus, there are the talipot palm *Corypha*, the palmyra *Borassus*, the fish-tail *Caryota*, the coconut *Cocos*, the betel *Areca*, and the scaly-fruited *Lepidocaryum*.

Of all the sword trees which accompany palms, only the pandans or screwpines rival them in abundance and locally expel them (plates 5 and 6). There are tracts of rivers where the pandans prevail in serried and impenetrable ranks to the exclusion of palms and they may predominate again where the forest is passing into subalpine scrub at the tree-limits on tropical mountains. But these are peculiarities of the Old World, especially in the countries or islands of the Indian Ocean and the west Pacific; the pandans have succeeded little in the greater part of Africa and have not reached the Americas [10]. Their stout trunks, marked with the annular scars of the leaf-bases and reaching in the bigger kinds to a height of a hundred feet, lack also the method of cambial thickening. Unlike palm trunks, they are commonly branched and the branches curve upward in the manner of pachycaul rosette trees [11]. From the lower part of the trunk there issue very often stiff stilt-roots directed obliquely into the soil; this feature, almost habitual in the pandans, is so uncommon among palms as to call for special comment. And, whereas the palm-leaf expands into the open, the pandan leaf lengthens and maintains its vestigial folding in longitudinal furrows that give in cross-section the form of an inverted W. These leaves, like gigantic sedge-leaves, are set as densely on the thick stem and appear to succeed each other in twisting spires. This effect, together with their large cone-like fruits, give the pandans their nick-name of screwpines.

The long leaves are horribly barbed. The edges and the underside of the midrib have curved spines. In the upper or distal part of the leaf the thorns point upward and catch the hands moving in. In the lower or proximal part, the thorns point backwards and catch the hands as they withdraw. In the very young leaf, while still in the bud, the thorns are straight but as the lower part of the older leaf outside

Table 1. *Palm classification*

| SUBFAMILY | LEAF | LEAFLET | FRUIT | SEX | GENERA/SPECIES | DISTRIBUTION |
|---|---|---|---|---|---|---|
| Coryphoid | fan | induplicate | thin stone | monoecious | 33/330 | America, Europe, Asia, Australasia |
| Borassoid | fan | induplicate | thin or thick stone | dioecious | 6/22 | Africa, Asia |
| Phoenix | feather | induplicate | no stone | dioecious | 1/12 | Africa, Asia |
| Caryotoid | feather, fish-tail | induplicate | thin stone | monoecious | 3/38 | Asia, Australia |
| Cocoid | feather | reduplicate | thick stone | monoecious (mostly) | 27/600 | America (Africa 2, Asia 1) |
| Arecoid | feather | reduplicate | thin stone or none | monoecious (mostly) | 130/1,100 | pantropic |
| Nipa | feather | reduplicate | fibrous stone | monoecious | 1/1 | Asia, Australasia |
| Phytelephas | feather | reduplicate | many-seeded | dioecious | 1/10 | America |
| Lepidocaryoid | fan or feather | reduplicate | covered with scales | monoecious, dioecious | 25/500 | pantropic |

it begins to lengthen and ride over the inner leaf, the soft young thorns are deflected forwards. Then, as the lower part of the inner leaf begins to lengthen and ride over the rigid part of the outer leaf, the thorns are deflected backwards. Such details are important because they reveal how the leaves have been growing in the bud and, as we shall find, there is not a feature in the open palm leaf which does not indicate some peculiarity of its development. How different are the flat spiky leaves of the American *Agave* or the fleshy leaves of the African aloes on which the outlines of the spines or inner and outer leaves are sharply stamped! They have suffered no sliding growth.

The long pandan leaf usually bends or buckles at a point about half to two-thirds of its length from the base. The barbed tip hangs down and carries off the drips. The longer, proximal part carries the rain down the furrows to the wide and shallowly encircling leaf-base where a moat of vegetable and animal debris collects between the older leaves. Whether pandans can absorb the water or the products of decomposition through the membrane of these leaf-bases, as the pitcher-plants *Nepenthes* and the bromeliads can do, has not been ascertained. But the debris provides a niche for many epiphytes and little worlds for micro-organisms just as one finds with the palms.

Pandan flowers, male and female on separate plants, differ in numerous respects from those of palms but the most obvious is the way in which they are set, particularly the female flowers, in compact heads. They develop into the massive fruits which resemble stout cones or fibrous fleshy pineapples. Palm inflorescences are open, branching panicles or long spikes, except for the remarkable fruiting heads of the tropical American ivory-nut palms *Phytelephas* and the Indo-Pacific nipa palm, which botany has also transliterated as *Nypa*. On the principles of plant morphology the head is a compacted or neotenic and bud-like panicle. So these two palms are advanced in their family, whereas the pandans present a uniformly advanced condition which agrees with their progressively ensiform or sword-shaped leaves and their more restricted distribution. However, there occurs in some parts of the Philippines and New Guinea, and throughout the Solomon Islands, a pandan-ally *Sararanga* which is a normal pandan tree except that it lacks the stilt-roots and its trunk is remarkably like that of a palm, but its inflorescences are long hanging uncompacted panicles descending for five or six feet from the crown. In these respects here, on the outskirts of tropical progress, lingers a pandan-ancestor which, if its leaves were dilated, might almost be a palm [12]. We are alerted to the possibility of similar relics on the cosmopolitan outskirts of the older family of the palms. Comparative studies are the best spur to biological investigation. It is impossible to appreciate palms, or monocotyledons, without considering the differences between them and the other sword trees.

To mistake a pandan for a slender sedge would seem ridiculous. Nevertheless in the swampy ground under the shade of the tropical forest there are stalwart sedges of the genus *Mapania* which every botanist mistakes at first for thickets of pandans. The leaves are slightly thinner, but there is no obvious means of distinguishing them when sterile, though there are microscopic differences in leafstructure. These sedges, however, have lateral inflorescences hidden under the cascade of leaves, while pandans in the more usual monocotyledon way have terminal inflorescences rising from the centre of the rosette of leaves [12a]. The position of the inflorescence is an important matter in the study of monocotyledons and reaches its greatest and most problematic degree in the study of palms. The pandan-like sedges are not truly arborescent, though the smaller kinds can be mistaken for the palm seedlings with strap-shaped leaves which grow among them. There is, however, one species of sedge with a short stout trunk, namely the West African *Microdracoides*, which resembles a small grass tree *Xanthorrhoea* of Australia, but a terminal panicle of sedge-flowers rises from its rosette [13]. There is, also, the arborescent Nile papyrus, *Cyperus papyrus*, to show that the majority of sedges which extend to the polar regions are neotenic Cyperaceous herbs.

In the American tropics the place of pandans as competitors with palms is taken by the very different, unarmed or thornless, banana trees *Phoenakospermum* and *Heliconia*. They have two allies in the Old World, namely *Strelitzia* of South Africa and *Ravenala* which is the traveller's palm of Madagascar. This curious lapping of plant distribution round the Cape of Good Hope turns up in the problem of the coconut palm, and Madagascar stands out not only as the place where banana-trees, pandans, and palms contend, but as a peculiar centre of palm evolution. It is not unique, however, in the first point because the banana-trees *Heliconia*, palms, pandans, and *Sararanga* contend in the Solomon Islands, where the only major contribution to palm life seems to have been the sago-palms of the genus *Metroxylon*. Pachycaul geography, being that of the relics of mono-

Figure 3. Sword trees. The traveller's palm *Ravenala madagascariensis*, tufted and with wind-tattered banana-leaves set in two rows. Two dragon-trees *Dracaena* with simple sword-shaped leaves on thickening trunks; $\times \frac{1}{100}$.

cotyledonous ancestry, displays about the broad tropical spread of palms all the perplexing modes of plant and animal distribution; these perplexities seem to have been subsequent to the primary differentiation of flowering plants.

The broad blade of the banana type never splits of its own accord. Wind and weather do that when it has expanded. Nor is it plicate, but the two halves are inrolled on the upper side of the midrib in such a way that the one is wrapped within the other. When this bulky baton, rather than sharp sword, begins to open it unfurls from above downwards and finally displays the unequal base caused by the dissimilar rolling of the two halves. At the tip there is the short withered string corresponding with the spiny tip of the pandan leaf, the blunt tip that is disengaged from the palm leaf, and the long tip which the climbing palms or rattans process into a barbed prehensile whip; we shall need to consider what is this vestige of leaf construction

13

employed by the rattans. The expanded leaf is smooth, pliant, slippery from wax, and rather succulent, unlike the stiff dry palm leaf; and the tissue, when crushed or cut, has always the characteristic banana smell. Nevertheless, there is the midrib from which hundreds of vascular bundles in the form of parallel veins pass to the margin just as in the folded palm leaf. This type of blade distinguishes the whole of the great alliance of the order Scitamineae which has evolved from banana trees into an immense variety of herbs, gingers, arrowroots, and cannas, under the palm trees. They have learnt to manipulate fine structures and slight tissues in a manner which the massive palm has never achieved. It is revealed in their elegant flowers, beautifully petalled, which are at last beginning to conform with the popular idea, unlike the plain structures of palms and pandans. The true bananas, *Musa*, occupy in this order the inter-mediate position between trees and herbs. They have no trunks until a massive stalk thrusts the inflorescence up through the tight rosette of giant leaf-sheaths which makes their false stem. They have no corresponding modification among the palms. In fact the whole order breaks away completely from palm engineering [14].

On the muddy, tidal, and freshwater banks of the Amazon and Guiana rivers, in front of the columnar trunks of the *Mauritia* palm, there are long stands of the tree-aroid *Montrichardia* [15]. Its smooth heart-shaped leaves are borne in a lax spiral along the tapering green stem which may reach a height of fifteen feet; the base is daily inundated by the tides and at times of exceptional flood the whole plant may be submerged. In front of them floats the spreading fringe of the free-living water hyacinth *Eichornia* which, as a liliaceous derivative with delicate ephemeral flowers, completes the evolu-tionary symbolism from arborescent palm to aquatic herb. The aroid family with its special inflorescence, that functions as if it were a flower, has almost entirely passed on to herbaceous forms. A con-nection with the palms was once thought possible through the almost herbaceous species of *Geonoma* in the South American forests (p. 307), but this is clearly an instance of parallel evolution. The aroid leaf is never plicate but inrolled upon itself like the banana leaf; the veins, however, curve upwards in their passage to the leaf margin, and it never tatters into false leaflets. Always among the arborescent mono-cotyledons there are profound differences in the manner of leaf development which are not met with among the dicotyledons. The distinction may seem trivial in the herbaceous and derived mono-

tyledons, such as orchids, rushes, grasses, and sedges, but they are
:oblems of monocotyledonous construction of which the single
otyledon is merely the seedling beginning.

Bamboos, as tree-grasses, are unlikely to be mistaken for palms [16].
.evertheless, in that vast region of Malaysian affinity from Thailand
New Britain there are climbing bamboos, the slender, leafless,
trailing stems of which on the forest floor may be mistaken for those
of climbing palms. The grass leaves are very different from the thorny
compound leaves of the rattans, and these bamboo stems are hollow
whereas those of palms are always solid.

A big cluster of sword trees centres on the two orders *Liliales* and
*Agavales* [17]. They are often called palms but no botanist would
make the mistake because they have simple strap-shaped leaves
which are never plicate or, even, inrolled in the bud. Some of them
also branch freely in the pachycaul manner of the pandans. Their
botany is intricate but it is necessary to mention them if only to correct

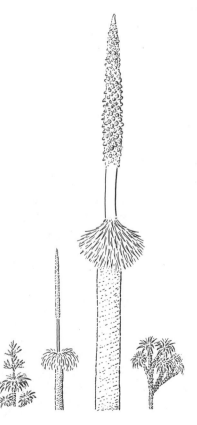

Figure 4. Sword trees. From left to
right the rush-tree *Prionium*, the grass-
tree *Xanthorrhoea*, the Bromeliad *Puya*,
and *Vellozia*; × $\frac{1}{100}$.

15

the popular notion that they are palms. We shall have to correct also the botanical notion that they may be the ancestral stock of the palms (chapter 11). The genera are the aloes *Aloe* of Africa, Arabia, Socotra, and Madagascar; the dragon's blood trees *Dracaena* and *Cordyline*, distributed throughout the tropics and subtropics, and often planted in warm temperate regions, where they are mistaken for exotic palms; the central and North American allies of these two genera, namely *Yucca*, *Nolina*, *Dasylirion*, and *Furcraea*; and, lastly, the complex of Australian grass-trees ranged about the genus *Xanthorrhoea*. A unique peculiarity of all these genera is that they thicken their trunks in the secondary manner of dicotyledons but the cambium by which this is done acts in an unusual way. Instead of forming secondary wood on the inner side and secondary phloem on the outer side, entire new vascular bundles separated by new ground tissue are developed on the inner side. Thus the monocotyledonous pattern of many 'scattered' vascular bundles is retained without their union into a block of wood [18]. The trunks of these sword trees thicken downwards, therefore, like the dicotyledons and lose gradually the annular leaf-scars which distinguish the pachycaulous sword trees without secondary thickening. However well known this is in botany, it is still a surprise to discover that a seventy foot trunk disappearing into the dicotyledonous foliage of the forest canopy belongs to a *Dracaena*. There is nothing of the kind in palms, pandans, banana-trees, or aroids. Whether they have lost the property or never possessed it remains an enigma.

Similar in general appearance to the grass-trees and the sedge-tree *Microdracoides*, there is the short rush-tree *Prionium* with one species in South Africa. Known locally as palmita, it has a trunk three to five feet high topped with a crown of thorny-edged, *Yucca*-like leaves, and a terminal grass-like panicle of rush flowers [19].

South America adds a parallel in the tree-bromeliads of the large genus *Puya*, which is mainly Andean from Colombia to Chile and Argentina [20]. The largest specimens belong to the Peruvian *P. raimondii*; its trunk grows to twenty feet high; there is the crown of thorn-edged leaves like an enormous pineapple rosette, for the pineapple belongs in *Bromeliaceae*; and the immense spike of humming bird flowers is nearly as tall as the stem. The genus is usually regarded as the most primitive of the family which has specialized in epiphytic rosette-plants.

To show, finally, how arborescent forms exist among the most unlikely monocotyledons, there are more or less tree-like orchids [21]. The shrubby species of *Sobralia* in South America and the slender, sapling-like *Corymborchis* of western Malaysia, the erect stems of which may reach to twelve feet in pencil-thickness, resemble the small species of the palm genus *Pinanga*. Their flowers, of course, are orchid flowers and their copious minute seeds, so unlike the large seeds of palms, show that they exploit quite different niches in the forest. It is customary to dismiss the resemblance in plicate leaf as a parallel evolution, but the argument is unsupported. To the contrary, when palms are understood as the fullest expression of forest mono-cotyledonous life and orchids as the very specialized herbaceous undergrowth, the plicate leaf becomes the palm bequest that is then translated by neoteny into the commoner strap-leaves, fingers, and triangular flanges on the orchid stem; it reduces even to the minute, non-photosynthetic scale-leaves of the epiphytic *Taeniophyllum* which has delegated the chloroplasts to its green roots, and to the scale leaves of the saprophytic ground orchids which are entirely devoid of chlorophyll. The plicate leaf distinguishes the little family Apostasiaceae, so indicative of the origin of orchids. It is the neglect of palms through their intractability which has led to the misconception of monocotyledonous theory, and to the popular idea of the botanist as the flower gatherer.

What, then, is to be thought of the Velloziaceae with the strange distribution from Peru, Bolivia, and south tropical Brazil to south and east Africa, south Arabia, and Madagascar? Space and time, for it takes time to plant seeds over such a domain, spell evolution. The family scarcely enters botanical theory. But the distribution is an ancient one. Their small tree form without internodes is a primitive one. The scarcely folded leaves carry vestiges of the plicate. The flowers resemble those of Apostasiaceae to which, as relics of orchid ancestry, the Velloziaceae add the arborescent habit necessary for a successful evolutionary line in the primitively upsurging flowering plant forest [22]. I am not dismayed at the wealth of plant life but thankful that so much has survived to enlarge our understanding and appreciation. The longest view from the beginning to the present must be taken when considering the nature or the natural history of any family. If there are fragmentary sign-posts on and off the route, so much the better.

The chief scene of plant evolution on land has been the forest. The successful plants are those which overtop and overshadow others, fill more space, and seed enough to maintain and spread their line. This means big forest trees, but such cannot have sprung fully equipped into station. They must have come from trees of lesser stature. How they may have grown up is the theory of the pachycaul tree and how they may have subsided into the herbaceous [23]. The stock of flowering plants diverged in vegetative construction into dicotyledons and monocotyledons, the seedling leaf being only the initiation of this great difference. Unlike the dicotyledons which have evolved much further and diversified into so many lines that their classification is baffling, the monocotyledons fall into about a dozen orders. Among these the palms and pandans have maintained the primitive pachycaul habit, though even they show the inevitable tendency to relinquish the struggle and become herbaceous. Most of the orders have withdrawn from the rising canopy of the flowering forest, yet many retain arborescent relics. The Dracaenas have succeeded with their secondary thickening, the bamboos with their hollow elongating internodes, but there are merely forty genera of bamboos compared with some five hundred of herbaceous grasses. These arborescent forms accompany the palms in different parts of the tropics. How they work together or in competition we do not know, but the miscellaneous sword trees reveal by their presence where the palms have gone ahead and what they could not bring about in the circumstances which they helped to build. Only the palms display the primitive and unspecialized ubiquity.

## Chapter 2

# Palm Pioneers

*'In palmis semperparens juventus; in palmis resurgo'*
MARTIUS, *Historia Naturalis Palmarum*

WHEN WE go collecting palms from a motor vehicle, supplied with oil-burners for rapid drying of the specimens, polythene tubing for their despatch, fixatives for their preservation in plastic bottles, duplicate notebooks for their recording, tie-on labels, biro-pens, secateurs, and other modern equipment, we should think of the difficulties that beset the early botanists and admire their achievements.

Palms began to be presented to science through the Dutch development of the Far East. 'The Dutch had discovered very considerable interest in Botany; their Universities were equipped with Botanic Gardens; and at Leiden, which is close to Amsterdam, there was a heated house from the year 1600 for the cultivation of tender plants. Their interest in Botany was so nation-wide as to reach a high administrator Heinrich van Rheede tot Draakenstein (1637–92) who had been made Governor of the Dutch possessions in Malabar in 1667' [24]. Van Rheede commissioned the publication of the *Hortus Malabaricus* in twelve immense folio volumes. It appeared during the years 1678–1703 under the supervision of Jan Commelin (1629–92), professor of botany in Amsterdam. We should call it economic botany for it figured and described the plants of cultivation and detailed their uses, their vernacular names in the native scripts, the manner of cultivation, the fables and the legends; it is how botany began. The text is in Latin and the figures by native artists are astonishingly good (Plates 1 and 2). It described only the common palms which had been in cultivation from time immemorial. So we find in the first volume the coconut, betel palm, palmyra, and fish tail palm; in the third volume the talipot and the wild date palm; and in the ninth volume there are two rattans and a Salacca. None is given a botanical name.

About the same time in Amboina, which is one of the Moluccas or Spice Islands, the leading Dutch merchant Georg Everhard Rumpf (1627?–1702) was writing his *Herbarium Amboinense* [25]. He started in 1662, but never saw its publication; he never saw, indeed, the final manuscript. Tragedy upon tragedy beset this unfortunate man who has become known to botany as Rumphius. In 1670 he grew blind. On 17 February 1674, an earthquake destroyed the larger part of the town of Amboina. His wife and his youngest daughter were killed; and a clerk, in his account of the devastation, has recorded these words: 'Very sad it was to perceive that man sitting near these his bodies, and to hear his lament, both on this accident and his blindness' [26]. In 1687 a fire ravaged the town and Rumphius' library, manuscripts, and illustrations for the *Herbarium Amboinense* were destroyed. He commenced to repair the loss by means of assistants who were put at his disposal by the authorities, to copy out what he could remember. The first six books were despatched in 1690 to Holland via Batavia in Java, but the ship was sunk by the French and the cargo lost. Fortune smiled because the Governor General of Batavia, Camphius, had caused a copy to be made, and this arrived in Holland in 1696. Rumphius completed his task in 1701, and the last books safely reached their destination. On 19 May 1702, the Governor of Amboina wrote that 'nothing more was to be expected of that old gentleman, having lived his years.' His grave was destroyed by a party of English soldiers who hoped to find gold buried under the stone. A second monument, erected in 1824 to honour the pioneer naturalist, 'remained till it was hit by a bomb in the last world war and was smashed' [27].

The *Herbarium Amboinense* was eventually published in six volumes by the Dutch botanist Johannes Burmann (1706–79) in the years 1741–55, and an index was supplied in 1769. It consists of Latin and Dutch texts in parallel columns over 1,660 pages, with nearly seven hundred plates and descriptions of about one thousand two hundred species of plants. There have been numerous efforts to interpret these plates and to identify the plants for the purposes of modern botanical nomenclature [28]. The plates, though better than those of the *Hortus Malabarius*, are still crude and, through force of circumstances, they were never scrutinized by the author (plate 3). About fifty species of palms are described; about thirty are illustrated, and twenty-five of these have passed into botanical literature with botanical names established on the illustrations. Besides the coconut, betel, palmyra, and nipa palms, there are the first illustrations of a *Livistona* (*L. rotundifolia*), a *Licuala*, the fish-tail *Caryota rumphiana*, the sugar palm *Arenga pinnata*, the sago *Metroxylon*, and ten species of rattan (*Calamus, Daemonorops*).

By 1753 these palms of India and Amboina had been assembled by Linnaeus (1707–78) according to his binomial system of nomenclature under the now well known generic names *Areca, Borassus, Calamus, Caryota, Cocos*, and *Corypha*, representing respectively the betel, palmyra, rattan, fish-tail, coconut, and talipot palms. He added, too, the Mediterranean palmito *Chamaerops* and the date palm *Phoenix* [29]. Ten years later five Caribbean palms were added by Nicolaus Joseph Jacquin (1727–1817) who, born at Leiden, went on an expedition to the Dutch colonies in tropical America before returning to an academic career in Vienna [30]. Jacquin created the genus *Bactris* with two species, and it has now expanded into one of the very large genera of thorny American palms; he added two species of *Cocos*, and first discovered as an *Areca* the well-known *Euterpe oleracea* of South America [31]. Later, Jacquin made the genus *Elaeis* for the African oil-palm.

During the years 1778–88 two Spanish botanists Hipolito Ruiz (1754–1815) and José Pavon (d. 1844) were travelling with many adventures and misfortunes in Peru and Chile, not the least disastrous being the partial loss of their collections through fire and shipwreck. Nevertheless, they brought to botanical knowledge the ivory-nut palm *Phytelephas* and two genera *Martinezia* (now referred to *Aiphanes*) and *Morenia* which has been reduced to *Chamaedorea*.

Such were the tributaries of palm science when they were swept into a mainstream by Alexander von Humboldt (1769–1859) on the return from his famous journey to tropical America (1799–1804). Inspired in his youth by the narratives of his predecessors, constantly in conversation and study with the great scientists of his time, and possessed of unbounded interest in every aspect of nature, he strove for ten years after leaving his university of Göttingen to accomplish a world task himself. The *Personal narrative of travels to the equinoctial regions of America*, translated into most languages of Europe, became the inspiration of his successors, and has remained the most eloquent of all narratives of scientific travel.

The opportunity came when the Spanish Government magnanimously decided to send him, a foreigner, with his botanist friend Aimé

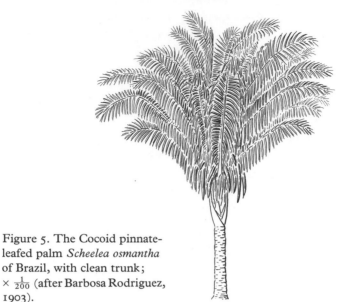

Figure 5. The Cocoid pinnate-
leafed palm *Scheelea osmantha*
of Brazil, with clean trunk;
× $\frac{1}{200}$ (after Barbosa Rodriguez,
1903).

Bonpland (1773–1858) on a voyage of scientific investigation to the
Spanish colonies in America. Humboldt prepared himself as
geographer, astronomer, geologist, meteorologist, botanist, zoologist,
anthropologist, and artist, which was no easy accomplishment even
in those days. He looked into the sky, the ocean, the mountains, the
rivers, the rocks, the desert, their plants, their animals, and men. His
books, seldom read now for the style is gone and the glorification of
nature deemed unseemly, are still quickened with the animation with
which he sought to enliven them. We can supply scientific explana-
tions for many of his problems, but the sagacity of his conclusions
remains. Science is fact-collecting and fact-presenting. After so many
new sights, experiences, and discoveries, he strove in gentle sentences
to impress on his fellow scientists in Europe that their whole world
was richer, grander, and more inspiring than the familiar parish [32].

His early essay on the *Physiognomy of Plants* opened in this way.

We will begin with palms, the loftiest and noblest of all vegetable forms,
that to which the prize of beauty has been assigned by the concurrent voice
of nations in all ages; for the earliest civilization of mankind belonged to
the countries bordering on the region of palms and to parts of Asia where
they abound [33].

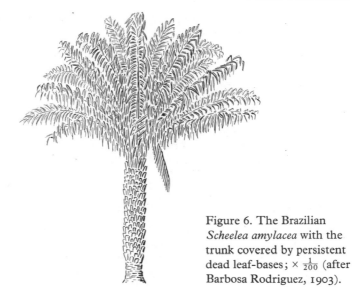

Figure 6. The Brazilian *Scheelea amylacea* with the trunk covered by persistent dead leaf-bases; $\times \frac{1}{200}$ (after Barbosa Rodriguez, 1903).

Many years later he inserted a postscript.

It is remarkable that, of this majestic form of plants . . . only fifteen species had been described up to the time of the death of Linnaeus. The Peruvian travellers, Ruiz and Pavon, added only eight; whilst Bonpland and myself, traversing a greater extent of country, from 12° south lat. to 21° north lat., described twenty new species, and distinguished as many more which we named, without however being able to secure their blossoms in a perfect state. At present (forty-four years after my return from Mexico) more than 440 species of palms, from both continents, have already been scientifically described, including the East Indian species arranged by Griffith. The *Enumeratio Plantarum* of my friend Kunth, which appeared in 1841, contains no fewer than 356 species.

Further in this postscript he recounted the ways in which palms should be studied as living plants. He perceived the significance of the *Caryota* leaflet and that of *Martinezia* (*Aiphanes*), and he knew well from his own experience the difficulties attending the study of palms.

I confess it would hardly have been credible to me before I left Europe. How interesting a work might be produced on palms by a traveller in South America who could exclusively devote himself to the delineation, in their natural size, of the spathe, inflorescence, and fruits! (Thus I wrote many years before the Brazilian travels of Martius and Spix, and the appearance of the admirable work on Palms by the former) [34].

C

Martius followed but it was Barbosa Rodriguez two generations after who fulfilled Humboldt's wish.

When considering the ways in which the Guaraon Indians depend for food, shelter, implements, and other necessities on the fan-palm *Mauritia flexuosa* of the Orinoco, which the early Spanish missionary Gumilla had called the tree of life, Humboldt remarked:

It is curious to observe in the lowest degree of human civilization the existence of a whole tribe depending on one single species of palm-tree, similar to those insects which feed on one and the same flower, or on one and the same part of a plant [35].

Then, of the same palm in the hot dry llanos:

The plain was undulating from the effects of the mirage; and when, after travelling for an hour, we reached the trunks of the palm-trees, which appeared like masts on the horizon, we observed with astonishment how many things are connected with the existence of a single plant. The winds, losing their velocity when in contact with the foliage and the branches, accumulate sand around the trunk. The smell of the fruit, and the brightness of the verdure, attract from afar the birds of passage, which love to perch on the slender, arrow-like branches of the palm-tree. A soft murmuring is heard around; and overpowered by the heat, and accustomed to the melancholy silence of the plains, the traveller imagines he enjoys some degree of coolness on hearing the slightest sound of the foliage. If we examine the soil on the side opposite to the wind, we find it remains humid long after the rainy season. Insects and worms, everywhere else so rare in the llanos, there assemble and multiply. This one solitary and often stunted tree, which would not claim the notice of the traveller amid the forests of the Orinoco, spreads life around it in the desert [36].

There is more of what we call the ecology of palms among the incidents of the *Personal Narrative* than in any modern book.

To the preceding genera Humboldt and his collaborators Bonpland and Karl Sigismund Kunth (1788–1850) added *Attalea*, *Ceroxylon*, and *Jubaea*, for they were not splitters of genera; and in 1815 they summarized the knowledge of palms [37]. Yet, strangely, misfortune led Humboldt to revel in the palms. A disease in the ship in which he travelled with Bonpland from Spain forced them to disembark in eastern Venezuela, whence they were led to explore the Orinoco. If Martius discovered so many more South American palms, it was the fire in Humboldt, like the volcanoes which he admired, that kindled the enthusiasm. The *Physiognomy of Plants* ended with this passage:

These and many other enjoyments which nature affords are denied to the nations of the North. Many constellations and many vegetable forms . . . remain for ever unknown to them; for the puny plants pent up in our hothouses give but a faint idea of the majestic vegetation of the tropics.

Humboldt's travels and publications, and his contacts with scientists and nobility in Europe, stirred up a lively interest over South America. The King of Bavaria, Maximilian Joseph, who had himself visited Brazil, organized an expedition to that country (1817–20) for the purpose of securing objects of natural history. The zoologist was Johann Baptist von Spix (1781–1826). The botanist was Carl Friederich Philipp von Martius (1794–1868). Born in Bavaria and destined for a medical career, he had turned to botany

Figure 7. The date palm *Phoenix dactylifera*, tufted, the trunk rough with the stubs of dead leaf-bases, and the leaves turning to set the leaflets in a vertical plane; $\times \frac{1}{200}$.

and was soon to become one of its leaders. In 1826 he became professor at the University of Münich and, in 1832, director of the University Botanic Garden where he had first met Maximilian Joseph. In 1854 he retired to immerse himself in his final and immense undertaking.

The Brazilian expedition had three results of increasing magnitude [38]. First came the joint account of the expedition by Spix and Martius [39]. Then the *Historia Naturalis Palmarum* was published by Martius in three immense volumes; they constitute the most magnificent treatment of palms that has been produced. Thirdly, Martius enlisted the help of many other botanists and commenced the biggest and most sumptuous tropical flora, the *Flora Brasiliensis*, which was not completed until 1906, sixty years after the publication of the first part and thirty-eight years after the death of its founder. It consists of forty volumes which, in a recent reprint, are priced at $1,750 [40]. A person entered the botanical world, not with the restless omniscience of Humboldt, but with dignity commensurate with palms and their surroundings.

Martius was the first botanist to explore in the light of Humboldt's synthesis Amazonia, which is the richest palm region of the world. He travelled, collected, sketched, and noted with incredible energy, depicted in one of the fine plates of the *Historia Naturalis Palmarum*. On return he set about putting palms, as one would now say, into current botanical thought. He engaged the astute microscopist and physiologist Hugo von Mohl (1805–72) to investigate the minute anatomy and the working of palms. The palaeobotanist Franc. Unger (1800–70) contributed the remarkable section on fossil palms. Martius himself described the Brazilian palms in the second volume and, in the third, those of the rest of the world, so far as he was able to draw on the researches of others. He made the well-known genera *Acrocomia, Brahea, Copernicia, Desmoncus, Gulielma, Hyospathe, Leopoldinia, Lepidocaryum, Maximiliana, Oenocarpus, Plectocomia, Syagrus,* and *Trithrinax*. He set the outlines of the modern classification of palms and prepared the first maps of palm geography, which were later elaborated in 1882 by O. Drude (1852–1933) when he revised the palm family for the *Flora Brasiliensis*. In the first part of this flora, with *Tabulae Physiognomicae* after the style of Humboldt, he introduced the ecology of palms (plate 4). The landscapes, illustrated in this work and in the *Historia Naturalis*, are classical and many can be revisited, for instance 'Fontes fluvii Paraguay' (Plate LIV) and

'Palmetum Mauritiae Viniferae' (Plate LIII), which is by the flat-topped mountains Paredões (Sierra dos Parecis) between Goiaz and Cuyabà.

As for the *Historia Naturalis*, we gain the impression as we peruse and re-peruse this colossal study that there was not an aspect of the life of palms which the authors did not endeavour to elucidate. They set themselves to learn all that was in their power about palms, so eminent in vegetation, to test this knowledge with enquiry into other large monocotyledons, and to impart their discoveries and conclusions in a manner worthy of their subject. The magnificent illustrations of von Mohl have never been surpassed whether in the microscopic examination of trunks, leaves, and roots or in such details as the development of the scales on the Lepidocaryoid fruit (plate 3, 21–23) I am privileged to be able to show these volumes every year to botanical students as a source of inspiration. The text is in Latin, but the illustrations suffice, even that of the huge inflorescence of *Maximiliana regia* which, like an old German helmet, symbolizes the royal patronage.

In 1818, when Martius had arrived in Brazil, Carl Ludwig Blume (1796–1862, born in Brunswick) went to Java where, from 1822 to 1826, he was director of the institute which was to become the Mecca of tropical botanists, namely the Buitenzorg Botanic Garden. His travels were limited to that industrious and populous island but, in his day, the forest was far more extensive than it is now when its relics have to be guarded as national parks. Studying all kinds of plants, as was then possible and the custom, he collected specimens, drawings, paintings, and notes to lay the foundation of the intensive botany of Malaysia – the archipelago from Malaya and the Philippines to New Guinea. He returned to Holland and became in 1829 director of the Rijksherbarium at Leiden [41]. There he marshalled his material and began to publish in the sumptuous manner of the times. Those giant folio books went, I think, to people's heads, for he became martial and magisterial, figuring himself in the tight fashionable cut of the day at study with the muses on the flora of a portion of Paradise. His illustrations and coloured plates are certainly amongst the finest of their kind and so, when Martius on his return was stumbling over the Asiatic palms in his third volume, Blume with first hand knowledge was delineating them precisely in his great publication *Rumphia* [42]. Its plates of Asiatic palms have never been excelled. His description of the nipa-palm is still the standard reference. He introduced the familiar palm genera *Calyptrocalyx, Ceratolobus, Cryosophila, Cyrtostachys, Daemonorops, Iguanura, Kentia, Korthalsia, Oncosperma, Pholidocarpus, Pinanga,* and *Salacca.* Bespectacled and aquiline he attacked plants with impeccable Latin, and set the pace which quickened over the century for splitting genera in fine detail. He became the herbarium botanist.

A contribution to the anatomy of palms was made in 1847 by the German botanist Hermann Karsten (1817–1909) from the material that he had collected in South America. He made several expeditions to Venezuela and Colombia 1843–52, and began to publish his great work on the flora of Colombia in 1856. In the first volume of this work he described and illustrated several new species of palm and to him we are indebted for the generic names *Jessenia, Pyrenoglyphis, Scheelea,* and *Socratea.* He was the first after Humboldt to visit the high Andean altitudes of the wax palms *Ceroxylon,* where he discovered several new species (p. 289). His writings were for the most part tersely botanical and, after the zest which followed Martius' *Historia Naturalis Palmarum,* Karsten devoted himself chiefly to the vast number of other plants which comprise the rich Colombian flora.

The year 1850 saw the publication of another great palm book. It was the posthumous *Palms of British East India* by William Griffith (1810–45). Though far from the sumptuousness of the volumes of Jacquin, Humboldt, Martius, and Blume, it remains a stupendous product from one who had begun to excel in many other aspects of tropical botany. Had it not been for malaria from which he died in Malacca, this young man of prodigious energy would have become one of the leaders in botany of last century; as it was, he was one of its makers [43]. As a student of John Lindley (1799-1865), professor of botany at University College in London, his Indian career began when three botanical illustrations of his introduced him to Nathaniel Wallich (1786-1854). This Danish surgeon, pupil of Martin Vahl (1749–1804) who was professor of botany at Copenhagen, went in 1807 to serve the Danish community at Serampore, up river from Calcutta. He became superintendent of the Calcutta Botanic Garden 1828-33. He sent Griffith, also a surgeon, to Assam in 1832 in connection with the development of tea-growing. Then Griffith followed Wallich at Calcutta 1842–45. Griffith devoted his energy to exploring, collecting, anatomizing under the microscope, and drawing. Most of his papers were edited posthumously by his friend John McClelland (1808–85) who had gone to Assam with him [44]. He was a free and rebellious thinker, impatient and quarrelsome, yet possessed of enormous patience for his life's work; it was to have been a *Flora Indica*. His palms have been rescued as a unique contribution. Martius received many of Griffith's collections which enabled him to treat the Indian palms so fully in the *Historia Naturalis Palmarum*.

Having toiled, anatomized, and drawn in like way in the eastern tropics, but with all the advantages of the twentieth century, I wonder unceasingly how Griffith accomplished so much (plates 23 and 24). Sir George King (1840–1909), his successor at Calcutta in the years 1871–98, wrote:

No botanist of India ever made such an extensive exploration nor himself collected so many species (estimated at nine thousand) as Griffith did during the brief thirteen years of his India career; none ever made so many descriptions of plants from living specimens. His botanical predecessors and contemporaries were men of ability and devotion: Griffith was a man of genius [45].

He insisted on viewing even the biggest plants microscopically, which is done now with the aid of specialists. He brought to light the problematic genus *Eugeissonia*; he studied deeply the anomalous nipa palm; and he described with great care many of the rattans which begin to abound in the Indo-Malayan forests from Assam south-eastwards. Two of his more forceful remarks apply especially to the classification of Cocoid and Arecoid palms. 'Give me a large genus and several subgenera, rather than the modern way. This, by the bye, is most illogical, for a genus, being a genus, should have a certain amount of character, but we have no certain amount, but a most uncertain one; one genus having several distinct marks, another one only, another half a one, and so on' [46]. 'Botanists don't know that a plurality of marks is required for a genus, a deviation from any one or two of these will only constitute a subgenus, not a genus' [47]. Beccari dedicated his monograph of Asiatic palms to the memory of William Griffith.

The scene shifts continually from east to west and back again, never pausing in the African continent. A little book appeared in 1853 from the pen of Alfred Russell Wallace (1823–1913) on the palms of the Amazon. It was the second in the English language to be devoted to palms, and the smallest ever. Zoologist more than botanist, above all a naturalist, Wallace travelled in 1848 to South America with his friend Henry Walter Bates (1825–92). During four years he explored

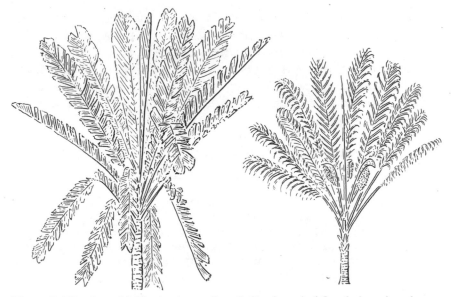

Figure 8. The Arecoid *Manicaria saccifera* (left) of tropical South America, the entire leaves becoming tattered by wind and rain in the banana-leaf manner; the Cocoid *Astrocaryum giganteum* (right) of Brazil with the spathes persistent over the erect bunches of fruit; × $\frac{1}{200}$ after Barbosa Rodriguez, 1903).

mainly the region of the Rio Negro and the Upper Orinoco, thus impinging on Humboldt's southward journey from Venezuela. The grandeur and elegance of palms impressed him alike. Without camera, he sketched and, living in the native camps, became aware of the dependence of the American Indian on these versatile trees. His book staged by these lively sketches, is a work on ethnobotany in which he bravely described as new those palms which he could not identify. He illustrated forty-eight species, of which fourteen were new, but he created no genera. Martius had not visited this territory. The collections of Humboldt and Bonpland had suffered greatly from damp and decay during the journey to the Rio Negro via the Casiquiari, and they had the misfortune to meet with many kinds of palm not in flower or fruit. We know now that this region differs fundamentally in soil, topography, and geological history from the main Amazon plain and that its flora is unusually rich, vast and flat though a great part of the country is. Wallace's book will need revising for it should be known in all the schools of Amazonia. What he wrote of the uses of palms applies to all countries; few have perceived so well the contribution of palms to the beginnings of villages.

Suppose then we visit an Indian cottage on the banks of the Rio Negro, a great tributary of the river Amazon in South America. The main supports of the building are trunks of some forest tree of heavy and durable wood, but the light rafters overhead are formed by the straight cylindrical and uniform stems of the Jará palm. The roof is thatched with large triangular leaves, neatly arranged in regular alternate rows, and bound to the rafters with sipós or forest creepers; the leaves are those of the Caraná palm. The door of the house is a framework of thin hard strips of wood neatly thatched over; it is made of the split stems of the Pashiúba palm. In one corner stands a heavy harpoon for catching the cow-fish; it is formed of the black wood of the *Pashiúba barriguda*. By its side is a blowpipe ten or twelve feet long, and a little quiver full of small poisoned arrows hang up near it . . . it is from the stem and spines of two species of Palms that they are made. His great bassoon-like musical instruments are made of palm stems; the cloth in which he wraps his most valued feather ornaments is a fibrous palm spathe, and the rude chest in which he keeps his treasures is woven from palm leaves. His hammock, his bow-string and his fishing-line are from the fibres of leaves which he obtains from different palm trees, according to the qualities he requires in them – the hammock from Mirití, and the bow-string and fishing-line from the Tucúm. The comb which he wears on his head is ingeniously constructed of the hard bark of a palm, and he makes fish hooks of the spines, or uses them to puncture on his skin the peculiar markings of his tribe. His children are eating the agreeable red and yellow fruit of the Pupunha or peach palm, and from that of the Assaí he has prepared a favourite drink, which he offers you to taste. That carefully suspended gourd contains oil, which he has extracted from the fruit of another species; and that long, elastic, plaited cylinder used for squeezing dry the mandioca pulp to make his bread, is made of the bark of one of the singular climbing palms, which alone can resist for a considerable time the action of the poisonous juice. In each of these cases a species is selected better adapted than the rest for the peculiar purpose to which it is applied, and often having several different uses which no other plant can serve as well, so that some little idea may be formed of how important to the South American Indian must be these noble trees, which supply so many daily wants, giving him his house, his food, and his weapons [48].

From South America Wallace went to the Far East and travelled in the same humility for another eight years (1854–62). He dwells again in his book on the Malay Archipelago on the ethnobotany of palms but refers in detail only to the seven main kinds – the sugar palm (*Arenga*), the rattans, the fan-palm (*Livistona*), the coconut, betel (*Areca*), sago (*Metroxylon*), and nipa palms. Concerning *Livistona*, which Robert Brown (1773–1858) had introduced as a genus from his journey with Joseph Banks to Australia, Wallace wrote that it had 'the most complete and beautiful fan-leaf I have ever seen, serving admirably for folding into water-buckets and impromptu baskets, as well as for thatching and other purposes.' The native people with a minimum of implements, supplied from stones, teeth, and bones, cast around and discovered, applied, and imitated the natural phenomena of the forests. These leaves catch rain, hold water, serve as natural umbrellas, and make string, fibre, cord, and sacking to hold themselves together. They have done so since the Mesozoic era, but it is only in very recent times that primitive men have found in them the resources which have led to civilization.

Describing the coconut palms at night, illuminated by bonfires of their old leaves on the principle that still rules for the periodic clean-up of the village, Wallace writes: 'The effect was most magnificent – the tall stems, the fine crowns of foliage, and the immense fruit-clusters, being brilliantly illuminated against a dark sky, and appearing like a fairy palace supported on a hundred columns, and groined over with leafy arches.' No doubt there was native music to this *son et lumière*; yet what a glimpse of architecture! I am reminded of a contrast. On the island of New Georgia in the Solomons group, during the last war, the Japanese used this 'fairy palace supported on a hundred columns' to conceal the aerodrome which they were making: the trunks were cut, but the crowns were supported by cross cables. One day there was a coconut plantation and the next revealed to American aviators an air-strip in use.

Wallace's description of rattan-forest gives the first and best insight into this wild tangle. He wrote of Celebes:

The chief feature of this forest was the abundance of rattan palms, hanging from the trees, and turning and twisting about on the ground, often in inextricable confusion. One wonders at first how they can get into such queer shapes; but it is evidently caused by the decay and fall of the trees up which they have first climbed, after which they grow along the ground till they meet with another trunk up which to ascend. A tangled mass of twisting living rattan is therefore a sign that at some former period a large tree has fallen there, though there may be not the slightest vestige of it left. The rattan seems to have unlimited powers of growth, and a single plant may mount up several trees in succession, and thus reach the enormous length they are said sometimes to attain. They much improve the appearance of the forest as seen from the coast; for they vary the otherwise monotonous tree-tops with feathery crowns of leaves rising clear above them, and each terminated by an erect leafy spike like a lightning conductor.

This is the unopened sword leaf, which may serve as a lightning conductor. The enormous weight of these rattans can pull trees down, and the transpiration stream winds along these coils to the invincible growing points.

Of betel-chewing, Wallace wrote in the Matabello Islands of the Moluccas: 'All the little children here, even such as can just run alone, carried between their lips a mass of nasty-looking red paste, which is even more disgusting than to see them at the same age smoking cigars, which is very common even before they are weaned.' Concerning 'the great sago district of East Ceram, which supplies most of the surrounding islands with their daily bread,' he described how entire houses were built from the palm and detailed at length the making of sago flour and its baking. So may have begun bakeries and confectioners! He concluded:

It is truly an extraordinary sight to witness a whole tree trunk, perhaps twenty feet long and four or five in circumference, converted into food with so little labour and preparation. A good-sized tree will produce thirty tomans or bundles of thirty pounds each, and each toman will make sixty cakes of three to the pound. Two of the cakes are as much as a man can eat at one meal, and five are considered a full day's allowance; so that, reckoning a tree to produce 1,800 cakes, weighing six hundred pounds, it will supply a man with food for a whole year. The labour to produce this is very moderate. Two men will finish a tree in five days, and two women will bake the whole into cakes in five days more; but the raw sago will keep very well, and can be baked as wanted, so that we may estimate that in ten days a man may produce food for the whole year. This is on the supposition that he possesses sago trees of his own, for they are now all private property. If he does not, he has to pay about seven and sixpence for one; and as labour here is five-pence a day, the total cost of a year's food for one man is about twelve shillings. The effect of this cheapness of food is decidedly prejudicial, for the inhabitants of the sago countries are never so well off as those where rice is cultivated. Many of the people have neither vegetables nor fruit, but live mostly on sago and a little fish.

I have quoted at length because Wallace proved what Humboldt had glimpsed, the almost complete dependence of early humanity on the palm scene. It is of historical interest to botany that these splendid essays roused so little interest that we wait sixty years until Blatter revived them in his book on the palms of India and Ceylon. The observer Wallace has not been excelled. Bates concluded his book on the river Amazon with these words:

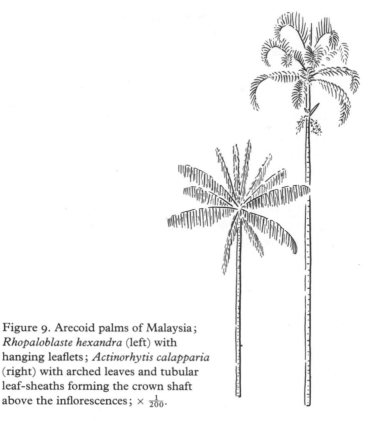

Figure 9. Arecoid palms of Malaysia;
*Rhopaloblaste hexandra* (left) with
hanging leaflets; *Actinorhytis calapparia*
(right) with arched leaves and tubular
leaf-sheaths forming the crown shaft
above the inflorescences; $\times \frac{1}{200}$.

About four hundred miles from the mouth of the main Amazons, we
passed numerous patches of floating grass mingled with tree-trunks and
withered foliage. Amongst these masses I espied many fruits of that
peculiarly Amazonian tree the Ubussú palm (*Manicaria*); this was the
last I saw of the Great River.

Hard upon Wallace and Bates came the Yorkshireman Richard
Spruce (1817–93). Of all the explorers of the Amazon valley, he
travelled furthest by the humblest means and botanized the longest.
His is another story of arduous tenacity, inspired by the achievements
of Humboldt and Martius. In opening his tale of the Amazon palms
which he studied during the years 1849–60, he wrote of Martius,
whose visit to the Amazon was limited to eleven months (1819–20).

Protected by the Emperor of Brazil, and provided by the government of
that country with all possible aids in the prosecution of his enterprise
(rarely lacking numerous Indians to row his boats and to cut down or
climb the trees of which he desired to secure specimens) he possessed

advantages seldom enjoyed by a solitary botanist travelling and working in so modest a way as myself. And it must be admitted that he made the best possible use of those advantages, and that the amount of work performed by him in that short space of time was enormous . . . I confess to have followed the steps of this great botanist with ever-increasing admiration [49].

But Spruce brought a new insight and began the ecology of palms, studying the situations where they grew, their distribution throughout the valley to the eastern slopes of the Andes, and their regional geography. Through his field-knowledge, gathered from living under the palms and continually handling their massive parts, he added numerous points to the theory of their classification which, if not accorded the pre-eminence that he expected, yet opened the mind and improved the work of his successors.

He divided the Amazon valley into five palm-regions, and these have still to be reassessed. There was the vast coastal region where, on mud and sand, inundatable and with scarcely a rock or stone for hundreds of miles, the banana-like *Manicaria saccifera*, the prickly *Acrocomia sclerocarpa*, and the scaly-fruited *Raphia taedigera* abounded. The granite region about the Casiquiari river contrasted by its thin soil with low caatinga-vegetation and was distinguished by such palms as *Leopoldinia piassaba* 'with its long brown beard (of fibres from the leaf-bases) reaching the ground and giving half-grown trunks the appearance of bears rampant,' *Leopoldinia major* with blood-red fruits, *Mauritia caraná*, and the genus *Lepidocaryum* of elegant little scaly-fruited fan-palms which 'seem also to have originated in the Granite Regions, not on the river-banks.' He intercalated a Diamond-Region, as the elevated rocky heart of Central Brazil, which he was unable to explore. The western end of the great valley, where its rivers combined from their Andean clefts, he called the Subandine Region 'remarkable for being the headquarters of palms with broad praemorsely-cut (raggedly tipped), and often laciniate leaflets with which are nearly always associated a stem supported on an emersed cone of roots that resembles the spokes of a half-opened umbrella.' It was the region of *Iriartea* and its allies, that continues into Peru, Ecuador, Colombia, and Venezuela. '*Iriartea ventricosa*, the noblest species of the genus, known from its congeners by the fusiform swelling, or belly, midway of its trunk' and 'a much lowlier species, *I. setigera*, whose stems furnish most of the blowing canes used in Amazonland.' Between these extremes lay the Amazon

35

Region proper which 'abounds in Palms quite as much as the regions that border it on all sides, but seems to have derived most of its species from them – its Iriarteas from the Andes, its Leopoldinias and Lepidocaryums from the Granite, and so on.'

That noble palm *Maximiliana regia*, Inajá of the Brazilians, Cocurito of the Venezuelans and of Humboldt, one of the most conspicuous ornaments of the primitive forests of the Amazon, is still more frequent in the Casiquiari Region and (besides being dispersed over the whole plain) is commonly seen perched on the granite peaks, where there is a ledge or hollow on which the decay of less noble vegetation has furnished a matrix for its roots. . . . It probably existed there at a period when the surrounding low country was one great lake, or a series of lakes, out of which stood these island peaks.

Thus Spruce began to relate the palms of the Amazon to its geological history as its delta advanced in the Tertiary Period eastwards between the Guianas and the shield of Brazil. The picture of *Maximiliana* suggests what must have been the ancient scene about the double coconut palm *Lodoicea* in the Seychelles (p. 311).

In two pages he delineates what would now be called the autecology, or particular natural history, of the fan-palm *Mauritia flexuosa* as 'the most universally distributed palm throughout the basins of the Amazon and Orinoco or, say, from the Andes of Peru and New Grenada to the shores of the Atlantic.' Over the savannahs it goes 'with a double winding line, which marks the course of a rivulet' down to the swampy lakes and mudbanks of Pará. The shade of the enormous leaves, and the drip from them, 'often surrounds each stem of Mauritia with a little pool or morass of its own, which is best seen on the savannahs of the Upper Orinoco.' He rediscovered Humboldt's observation, and he investigated the origin of Humboldt's Peach Palm, *Gulielma gasipaes*, the Pupunha of Brazil, as the most widely cultivated 'native' palm of the Amazon valley, and he decided that its origin must also have been in the Andean region (p. 282). So he developed Humboldt's geography of palms, as Wallace his ethnobotany, and Martius his systematic botany. His brief essay is the pith of palm ecology in Amazonia [49].

In 1856, Berthold Carl Seemann (1825–71), of German upbringing, wrote the one and only popular history of palms in the English language. It was dedicated to his friend Humboldt, and carried the un-Humboldtian boast that 'there is no work in existence, in any language whatever, in which an equal amount of information, such as

here given, is to be met with.' He gathered with least acknowledg-
ment the fruits of his predecessors, contributed his experiences from
the voyage of the *Herald* (1845–51) which had sailed westwards from
Plymouth round the globe, and he borrowed most of the worst of
their illustrations. It is good reading just so far as one does not go to

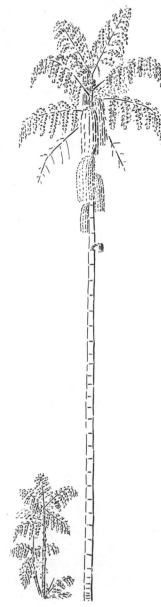

Figure 10. The fish-tail palm *Caryota*, with
doubly-pinnate leaves; a lofty solitary species
(right), flowering along the trunk from the
apex downwards toward the base; the small
tufted *C. mitis* (left); $\times \frac{1}{200}$.

37

the original sources. It has not been republished and it seems to have had little impact upon the study of palms.

Odoardo Beccari (1843–1920), the Florentine botanist, impelled into the twentieth century the science of palms which Martius had launched. His interest in tropical nature was aroused at the universities of Pisa and Bologna where he studied. He went to Borneo from April 1865 to the beginning of 1868, and turning to the study of palms developed a character proportionate with their grandeur [50]. He went to Eritrea on palm-studies in 1870, to New Guinea via Java, Celebes, the Moluccas and the Aru Islands in 1872, returning in 1876 to take charge of the Botanic Garden and Herbarium in Florence. The next year saw his final palm-expedition to Australia and New Zealand with a stay in Sumatra on the return voyage. During one of these expeditions he contracted elephantiasis of the arm, but managed to fight it off when settled in Italy.

If Wallace was naturalist-zoologist, Beccari was naturalist-botanist. He contributed to the ethnology of the east and became an authority on the natural history of the orang-utans. His great travel work *Nelle foreste di Borneo*, translated into English as *Wanderings in the great forests of Borneo*, was not written till thirty years after his return and, then, only at the insistence of the Rani of Sarawak. It lacks the freshness of Wallace's *Malay Archipelago*, but it has the maturity of all Beccari's contributions, which are classics in botany.

As the author of thirty-five genera of palms, he contributed many scientific papers on them and a number of massive monographs of which the most notable are that on the Lepidocaryoid or scaly-fruited palms of Asia, particularly the rattans [51], and that on the Arecoid palms of the Old World, edited and published posthumously by Pichi-Sermolli [52]. Through his friendship with Sir George King, the earlier monographs were published sumptuously from the Botanic Gardens at Calcutta.

As an evolutionist, Beccari expressed the first ideas about the phyletic interrelation of the main groups and genera of palms. He perceived the relative fixity of modern genera and species from a past long ago, when, he considered, their ancestors had been highly plastic, unformed and formative or, as he wrote, 'plasmatic'. They were irritable and the irritations produced the modern adaptations. He applied the idea to all manner of tropical plants and was led to statements that now read teleologically. Thus, in his introduction to the big genus of rattans *Calamus*, he wrote:

I suppose therefore that the spinosity of Palms, especially that which besets the leaf-sheaths, was originated by the stimulus induced in the very sensitive peripheral tissues by animals in search of nutriment in the youngest and most tender parts of the plants. I suppose therefore that the young central parts of every spinous Palm must have been coveted for nourishment by numerous animals, had they not been defended by spines [53].

He viewed the rattans in a different light from Wallace, as the following quotation shows:

On account of the difficulty in collecting and in preserving these plants, botanists usually content themselves with very imperfect specimens, and do not keep the long filaments armed with hooked spines which enable these rampant plants to ascend and hold on to trees; nor do they preserve the leaf-sheaths which envelop the stem and are the parts most covered with thorns. Yet these are precisely the parts which it is most essential to have and to study, for they present the characters on which specific distinctions are principally based, and by which the species of the genus *Calamus* can be distinguished. It may be laid down as a general rule that where plants are provided with spines or thorns they possess nutritive qualities, and are sought after by animals. The Calami, and other thorny palms, have a central bud or 'cabbage' (*umbut*, Malay) – a most delicate morsel, much relished by many animals, monkeys amongst others; and if this most essential portion of the plant were not well defended, it would be easily damaged or destroyed [54].

Monkey, orang utan, and honey bear tug the young sword leaf from the bud of those palms that they can reach in order to eat the soft base and disrupted parts of the stem-apex: then insects and fungi enter to complete the destruction of the whole stem, which cannot branch, and indeed of the whole palm if it cannot sucker from the base. The thorns certainly ward-off the larger animals.

To a like plasmatic effect exerted by ants upon the ancestral species, Beccari attributed the special ant-shelters developed by the rattan *Korthalsia*. He regarded them as 'hereditary pseudo-galls or ant-homes. In Borneo several species of hospitating *Korthalsias* occur – indeed, it is in their ant-shelters that the characters are found which serve to distinguish the formicarian species of this most difficult genus.' [55]

From Borneo he recorded 130 species of palm, most of which he had found during his sojourn in Sarawak and had then described as the pioneer of the palm-flora of this great island. He observed that no tree-palm over-topped the level of its high forest. The enormously

Figure 11. The ivory nut palm
*Phytelephas* of tropical
America; the female plant
with fruit-heads (left), the
male plant with cylindrical
inflorescences (right); $\times \frac{1}{100}$
(after Seemann, 1854).

high Dipterocarp trees, which cover most of the lowlands of Borneo
and the rest of Malaysia, with a canopy at a height of 150–200 ft,
exceed that which the palm trunks can reach with the exception of
the rattans that use the trees as hop-poles. Yet, in this rich island, he
discovered only one endemic genus, the Arecoid *Gigliolia*. He was
attracted to Griffith's genus *Eugeissona* with five new species in
Borneo. Two of these, at least, *E. insignis* and *E. utilis*, were the main
sago-producing palms for the forest-dwellers, the eastern *Metroxylon*
having been introduced to the coastal villages. The Malay name for
raw sago is *lemantah*, and he suggested that from this the Indonesian
name for Borneo Kalamantang (Kalimantan) had been derived [56].
He described the process of sago-manufacture and observed in
*E. utilis*: 'Even the pollen, which has the aspect of a violet-coloured
meal, is utilized, being eaten as a condiment both with rice and sago.'
He continued:

The flowers are formed in such a manner as to offer an efficient protection to the pollen, which, on account of its nutritious properties, might be
sought after by different animals and thus destroyed before the flowers
open. Indeed, the flowers of *Eugeissona utilis* hardly come up to the usual
conception of a flower at all. They are very slender, but as much as three
and a half inches in length, and their petals are extremely hard and of a
dark funereal colour, much resembling leather. The corolla forms a sheath
to the stamens of great toughness, and at the same time does not attract the
attention of animals.

We may smile at these notions and even ridicule them, but the genus
is a very problematic one, intermediate between the Cocoid and

Lepidocaryoid palms as Beccari showed [57], and we must develop this thesis in a later chapter. No one else has studied or thought about these primitive palms, or the nature of primitive palm flowers, their pollen, or their pollination. Throughout Beccari's writings there are many hints for naturalists to pursue. The ways of palms must be discovered; and there will be found in Borneo, as in Malaya, Anonaceous trees of the genus *Polyalthia* with similar funereal flowers and richly coloured pollen.

These sago palms (*Eugeissona*) are not cultivated in Borneo. They seed freely and develop rapidly about the dwellings of the forest people who take care only that they should not be destroyed. A kind of symbiosis with useful plants has been established, which Beccari developed into a theme of man and his crops, anthropophilous in a 'system of naturalism', not as cereals but as cereal forerunners in remote antiquity of forest men.

As a final example of his intimate perception of the environment, I will mention the narrow leaf-shape of riverside plants to which he drew attention. He called them stenophyllous (narrow-leafed) plants, the willow (*Salix*) being the temperate instance [58]. But many genera of tropical trees, herbs, climbers, and ferns have this character among their riparian species and it distinguishes some small stream-side palms locally common on the flood-banks in Borneo (*Pinanga calamifrons, P. rivularis*). It is an unsolved problem that cannot be referred simply to the selective action of torrential floods stripping off the broader leaves and favouring, therefore, the survival of the narrow-leafed; it distinguishes tall trees and their lofty climbers which overarch the ravines far above the flood level.

Beccari presented the Asian and Australasian palms with first-hand knowledge. He attempted the African and the American from the herbarium; and, reading in the minutiae which Blume had introduced, he was less successful [59]. As Martius had failed where he had not travelled, so Beccari. It is the lesson of palms that Mahomet must go to the mountain. The latest reviews of the world flora of palms come from the school of Adolf Engler (1844–1930) at work in Berlin on the African flora [60].

Contemporary with Beccari and acquainted surely with him for he received a doctorate from the university of Florence, the Brazilian botanist João Barbosa Rodriguez (1842–1909) has the distinction of being the first native of a palm country to have promoted palm science in his own country [61]. This versatile man of the French school of

Brazil, poet, artist, teacher, business man, and botanist, turned to the palms when he was sent on an official mission to the Amazon region 1871–74. He revisited its centre in Manaos, where the wild rubber industry was booming that city into splendour, during the years 1883–89. He became director of the Botanical Museum and Garden of Amazonas, which have long since disappeared, but his studies of the palms which he measured, drew, and painted in their natural surroundings are bequeathed to us in the two magnificent volumes of *Sertum Palmarum Brasiliensium*, published after his return to Rio de Janeiro. Here he ended a truly Brazilian career as director of the city's Botanic Garden.

If his landscapes seem a trifle crude, they have captured with vigour scenes and events that are now fast disappearing; and he fulfilled Humboldt's wish that a botanist should dwell in Amazonia and depict at life-size the fronds, flowers, and fruits of its palms. Parts of his classification were severely criticized by Beccari [62], yet vindicated subsequently by Bondar who spent many years with the Brazilian palms in the land of his adoption [63]. These are the conflicts of uncertainty that in no way diminish the contributions of those whose lives were devoted to the study of palms, but should act rather as a stimulus to future investigators. The library of Barbosa Rodriguez, with its priceless volumes from the last century, was still safe in the school of his patron Pedro Segundo at Manaos in 1948. Students research into the old documents of European families and institutions to discover lost histories. Amazonia should be explored from Belem-do-Pará to Iquitos, and Esmeralda to Santa Cruz de la Sierra for the traces of its pioneers; even in that ruthless climate there may be records substantiating events that are almost fabulous.

## Chapter 3

# The Palm Crown

*'Now my idea is, first of all, study growth and structure:*
*then make use of terms, or names of the structures.'*
GRIFFITH, 1848

THE LAST thing to be perceived is commonly the obvious. The nature of the palm crown was conveyed to me very gradually. Engineered by giant fronds, it has no twigs. My introduction came on the toothed railway which ascends Penang Hill in the midst of that tropical isle. In a few minutes there is the view over the tops of the coconut palms. Aeroplanes now glide past too rapidly for contemplation. But these giant grey-green cabbages have remained in my memory for many years and there came at length some understanding.

By the house where I lived in Singapore there grew a slender pinnate-leafed palm *Actinorhytis calapparia* (figure 9). I gazed at it every day from the first light of dawn. At times a new leaf would open and disclose the next and shorter sword leaf thrusting from the centre. It would open as the lowest leaf on the crown began to die. This palm, therefore, kept in its crown the same number of open leaves and timed the rotation of them from the centre to the outside. I timed them. At intervals of 27–29 days, the successive sword-leaves would open and successive lowest and oldest leaves would turn yellow, then orange, and brown before falling off in a day or two. The crown had twelve leaves. Between the opening and the falling of one leaf, there would come twelve sword leaves at intervals of a month. In twelve lunar months, therefore, the crown would completely renew its fronds. I watched this palm over several years and began to wonder whence and in what order the unopened leaves were developing within the crown. But, as ever in the tropics with incessant calls in other directions, I did not return to the problem until the late Kwan Koriba (1882–1957) took charge of the Singapore Botanic Gardens

43

during the last world war [64]. He wished to learn how palm leaves grew, and I recalled these observations.

The same orderly sequence must continue within the palm bud as in the open crown unless some congestion of developing leaves should increase their number, or some acceleration in development reduce it. Presumably when a leaf dies and the sword-leaf opens, a new leaf is started. The palm crown should have as many developing leaves as it has open leaves. *Actinorhytis* should have eleven developing leaves in addition to the sword-leaf. I was never able to prove this for want of a specimen on which to operate; destruction of the central bud kills these solitary palms, and the bud cannot be opened without cutting away all the outer leaves in order to arrive at the microscopic stem-apex. I had opportunity to examine six other species of pinnate-leafed palm.

Two coconut palms (*Cocos nucifera*) had 20 and 22 leaves on the crown (not 26–36 as usual) and each had exactly this number in the bud, the smallest being as microscopic as the stem-apex. An oil palm (*Elaeis guineensis*) had 40 open leaves and 38–39 unopen leaves; the bud snapped in dissection and damaged the soft apex. The Australian *Ptychosperma mcarthuri* had 8–11 open leaves and as many in the bud, the exact number depending on the thickness of the stem. For three species of small Malayan palms of *Pinanga*, I found by dissecting numerous specimens 4–5 leaves in crown or bud (*P. simplicifrons*), 5–6 leaves (*P. furfuracea*), and 6–8 leaves (*P. kuhlii*).

A diagram can be made to show the clockwork of the palm crown by representing the leaves as if they formed on one side of the stem-apex (figure 12). If the interval between successive leaf-openings or leaf-yellowings is $p$ days and the number of open leaves in the crown is $n$, the working life of the leaf is $np$ days; its period of development must also be $np$ days. Therefore, the total age of the leaf is $2np$ days. In other words it is necessary merely to time the opening of leaves, or their ageing, and count the number of open leaves in the crown to discover the apparently recondite age of any leaf. In *Actinorhytis*, $2np = 24$ months; so the leaf takes a year to grow and a year to function. For the oil palm, $p$ is about sixteen days and, because of this short interval in a crown of many leaves, there are two sword-leaves in the centre, one shorter than the other by half a month's growth. If, therefore, $n = 40$ and $p = 16$, $2np = 1,280$ days or about three and a half years. A recent treatise on this palm gives the age of the leaf at $c$. four years [65]. In the case of the coconut, which I did not explore fully,

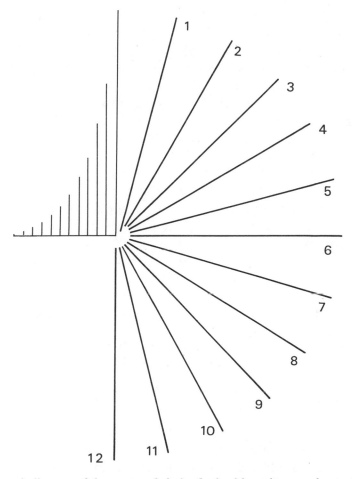

Figure 12. A diagram of the crown of *Actinorhytis* with twelve open leaves (heavy lines, right), and twelve developing leaves (thin lines, left) spaced at equal intervals of time and of length proportional to their age; as a new leaf begins all the leaves grow into the next stage, the open leaves rotate on the crown, and the oldest leaf (which would become the thirteenth) falls off.

$p$ is said to be about one month [66] and if $n=30$, $2np=60$ months or five years. The Indian palmyra palm (*Borassus*) seems to have a similar rhythm and age of leaf [67]. In the huge fan-leafed (*Lodoicea*) there are said to be about twelve open leaves in the crown and, at least in young plants, new leaves are said to open at intervals of nine months [68]. These figures give the stupendous age of eighteen years for the leaf, nine years being spent in the bud; but it may not be too fantastic for this monstrous plant. The Mediterranean *Chamaerops* has 30–35 leaves in the crown and is said to have as many in the bud but, as always in descriptive botany, field-notes are missing that would enable us to understand its working. It would be interesting to know the figures for the date palms *Phoenix*, one species of which *P. canariensis* is said to have two hundred open leaves in the crown: the smallest species have merely a dozen. What a fascinating generic evaluation may be possible! Do all palm leaves develop at the same rate and does their age depend upon their bulk? This key will unlock many palm problems.

   If $s$ be the number indicating the station of an open leaf in the crown as reckoned from the centre, the age of that leaf will be $(n+s)p$, for there are $n$ leaves in the bud and $s$ leaves in order of opening. Similarly the age of any leaf in the bud is $sp$. The whole age of the palm will be the age of the crown ($2np$) plus the trunk-age, plus a sapling period before the trunk began to rise. To determine the trunk-age, the number of leaf-scars or old leaf-bases along the trunk must be counted or estimated and multiplied by $p$, which is the time-interval between successive leaves. The sapling age can be determined only by observation; for slender palms it may be six to twelve months, but for stout palms it may be as many years. Coconut palms begin to form the trunk after five years from germination. The Indian palmyra palm (*Borassus*) does not develop the trunk until the nineteenth year [69]. In the talipot palm (*Corypha*) this period is about twelve years.

   We perceive, as a corollary, to this working out of the palm crown, that leaves requiring six months to several years for their growth and functioning cannot be shed annually. Palms could not afford to lose their leaves seasonally and become deciduous; and, of course, they are not.

   A more complicated deduction enables us to understand the differences in stature among palms. If, for simplicity, all palm-leaves are assumed to grow at the same rate, a big leaf will take longer than a small leaf and it will have a longer working life equal to its growing time. But a big leaf needs a thick stem to support it and a big food supply to develop it. A thick stem in palms means a stout stem-apex and, other things being equal, a stout stem-apex will develop more leaves around it than a small apex. Therefore, palms with stout trunks should have large crowns of many large and long-lived leaves whereas those with slender trunks should have small crowns of few, small, and relatively short-lived leaves. This is exactly what is found

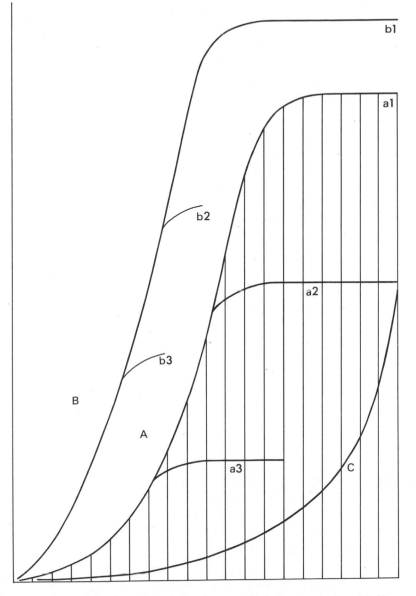

Figure 13. A graph to show the relation between leaf-size (vertical) and leaf-succession (horizontal) in the palm crown at different rates of leaf-growth A, B, C, and at different stem-thicknesses *a* 1–3, *b* 1–3. Flattening of the curves indicates leaf-opening. Stem-thickness is measured by the number of developing leaves. A, medium growth-rate with 13 leaves in the bud and in the crown *a* 1, 10 leaves *a* 2, and 7 leaves *a* 3. B, fast growth-rate, with similar variations in crown-size *b* 1–3. C, slow growth rate, giving a massive trunk and crown of many large leaves.

in large genera of palms such as *Areca, Pinanga, Bactris,* and *Phoenix*. We begin to see how specific differences in stature depend on quantitative differences in stem-bulk, and, since this is a developmental matter, we begin to see how species may arise by arresting or prolonging the enlargement of the stem-apex. The principle is shown in figure 13, where the curves A, B, and C represent three growth-rates for leaves; the corresponding proportions of trunk-thickness can be read along the base-line. The shape of these curves will be explained presently.

A wider inspection of palms in this light shows, however, that they do not all conform to one growth-curve, such as curve A (figure 13). For instance, a *Raphia* palm with trunk comparable in thickness to that of a coconut-palm carries 14–15 leaves 50–60 ft long, or more, instead of 26–36 leaves 20–25 ft long as in the coconut. Leaf-length is a prime measure of leaf-size and period of growth. We must assume that other factors enter and that the stem-apices in palms may work in different ways. Variation in $p$, only, may affect leaf-size, but they will not cause fewer bigger leaves to appear on a trunk of the same thickness. For this we may suppose differences in rate of growth such as curve B (figure 13) which is faster and this suggests curve C which is slower; it may explain why *Chamaerops* has as many leaves as the coconut-palm on a more slender trunk. However, all these variations will affect the stem-apex and there is not the information wherewith to explain. Nevertheless it is clear that to appreciate palm-form, palm-stature, palm-effect, palm-station in vegetation and, therefore, palm-evolution we must go further into the organization of the stem-apex and its leaf-arrangement. We must study phyllotaxis which is the bugbear of botany, so simple yet so profound as to be incomprehensible. It is pre-eminent in palms which have championed the giant leaf and the single apex and, just because palms have not been available for study, the master-key may not have been found. Leaf-number, relative bulk of leaf initial to stem-apex and their relative growth rates, as well as leaf-interval (or plastochrone), are the main factors in phyllotaxis, as they are manifested gigantically in the diversity of palm-crowns. A few exceptional palms have the leaves in two alternating rows, namely *Hyospathe elegans* and *Oenocarpus distichus* of Brazil, and *Wallichia disticha* of Assam. Others have, in phyllotaxis notation, leaf-systems of $\frac{1}{3}$, $\frac{2}{5}$ and so on up to the high fraction $\frac{13}{34}$ in the fan-shaped *Copernicia*. Generally the number is specific but there may be varietal differences as in the oil palm *Elaeis*.

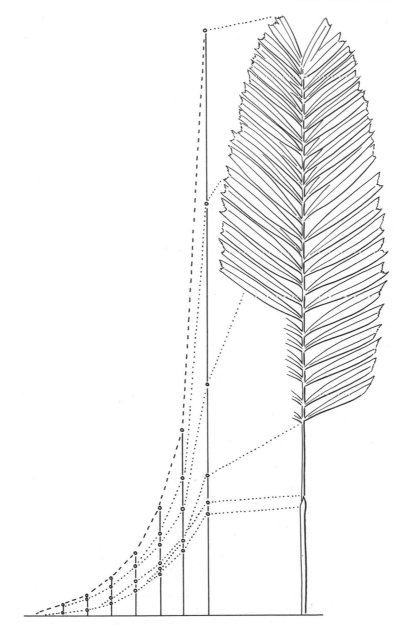

Figure 14. Leaf-growth in the bud of *Ptychosperma*. Left, the first seven successive leaves drawn to scale with points of reference to the right hand figure. Basipetal growth is shown by the delayed lengthening of the lower parts of the leaf; the leaf stalk (petiole) is the last part to develop. Left-hand figure $\times$ 5; right-hand figure $\times \frac{1}{16}$.

49

At least two genera, *Neodypsis* of Madagascar and *Syagrus* of South America, have the curious twist of the leaf-arrangement to give the appearance of three ascending spires of leaves, as in the pandans [70].

In cutting up palm-buds to count developing leaves, we meet the strange forms of unopened palm-leaves. There are no young leaves so weird and complicated, and the wizardry is another manifestation of the big-leaf character. To conceive what the young state must be like, the open palm leaf must be closed up, shut down, squeezed into the narrow tube between the leaf-bases in the centre of the bud, fitted as a little night-cap round the stem-apex and, then, merged into it. Yet the developing leaf must leave room for the next, just as the preceding one made room for it. We must think not only of the shape that a closing and shortening fan must take but of the space into which it must fit and the chinks that it will leave; the growing tissue will bulge wherever it can. So the gaps are the negatives in which the growing leaf is moulded.

No palm has been studied in sufficient detail to relate how all this occurs. Von Mohl and von Martius tried but could not get to the critical minuteness. The best account is that of the great German morphologist Eichler, written in 1886 with the transparent universality of a clear mind, but it is now old, buried in succeeding volumes, and generally inaccessible; it suffers, too, from the same difficulty which beset von Mohl [71].

The first thing to be noticed in the developing palm leaf is that it opens from above downwards. The second is that no progress can be made in the study without cutting open the bud and, so, sacrificing that trunk. It must be chopped down and the crown chopped off below the oldest leaf; the saw is useless in these fibrous plants. Then the outer leaf-bases must be chopped away, and there will be revealed the softer yellowish white bases of leaves that in their distal parts have fully matured. They can be cut off with a stout knife: and, suddenly, the delicate bud will snap across. It cannot support the weight of the developing leaves. We learn with chagrin that, though the leaves are maturing and hardening distally and apically, they still have very tender growing basal parts supported and protected by the mature and tough leaf-bases that have been hacked off. We have to start again because it is difficult and often useless to try and piece together the broken bits; palms must be studied that can be sacrificed in plenty.

By this time we shall have noticed that, as the leaf opens, a strip of dry tissue separates on each side from the tips of the leaflets as they

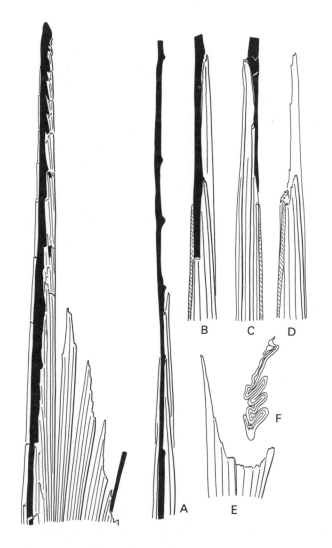

Figure 15. Leaf-opening in *Ptychosperma*, with fish-tail leaflets. Left figure showing the upper side of the frond-tip with the leaflets breaking away with their marginal strip (in black) from the median strip (black) to which the other marginal strip remains attached. A, a lower leaflet with a long piece of marginal strip from which other leaflets have detached. B the upper side and C the lower side of a leaflet still attached to the marginal strip; D, the same as B but with the marginal strip removed; the midrib of the leaflet hatched in all three figures. E, the leaflet tip A opened out; every tooth was an attachment to the marginal strip; every sinus was a minor fold of the leaflet. F, cross-section of leaflet A near its base. A, E × ½; B–D × 1; F, × 5.

begin to spread; that the strips join at the dried tip of the leaf which is also shed; and that, as the strips are traced downwards, they join the leaflets together by their tips. In younger leaves the strip becomes more and more conspicuous as a fine strut under which the leaflets bulge as folds on either side. Each leaf has two strips and two sets of folds to each strip, the outer folds and the inner folds (figure 16). Though ending as dry twisted threads or merely fragmenting as the leaf begins to work, the strips are a prime structure in the development of the palm-leaf. Eichler called them the marginal strips, and every palm-leaf develops about a median axis or rachis, two marginal strips or original leaf-margins, and a pointed apex which joins all three. So we pick off one by one the unopened cylindrical leaves, cutting them off now with a scalpel from the stem-apex, carefully so as not to sever the inner, younger, and softer leaf, and the youngest leaves must be dissected under the binocular microscope. The oldest in the coconut-palm may be ten feet long, the smallest less than a millimetre. They cannot be drawn satisfactorily to scale because of this enormous range in length. In figure 14 the lengths of successive leaves of the small-leafed *Ptychosperma* are shown in the form of a graph alongside the adult leaf.

We may pause to deliver an item of experience. There is no detail, however trifling it may seem, in the form or structure of the developing palm leaf which does not become characteristic of the open leaf, as growth magnifies it. The slender marginal strips may hang as long threads or curtains of hair from the leaves or they may fragment and remain on the pointed tips of the leaflets in *Pinanga*, except its terminal compound leaflet from which they break off. The shape of the gap into which the very young leaf first grows defines the tip of the sword-leaf. Microscopic rows of cells set the leaflets into their characteristic directions. Hairs and chaff from the epidermis may garnish leaves distinctively and lubricate their escape.

Reversing the order of dissection and starting with the smallest leaf on the stem-apex, we find that there is only one leaf forming at a time. There are no palms with paired or whorled leaves. The leaf-primordium, as its earliest stage is called, is too big to allow another to arise along with it. Hence the single file of leaves in the bud. Successive primordia develop in a spiral order round the stem-apex except, apparently, in those few striking palms in which the leaves are set in two rows, like those of the Traveller's Palm *Ravenala*, and which must develop in two alternate rows with the leaf-primordia at 180° to each

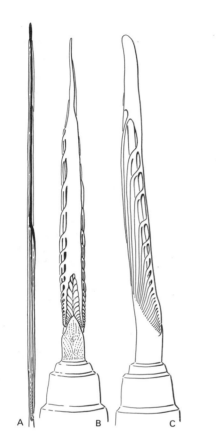

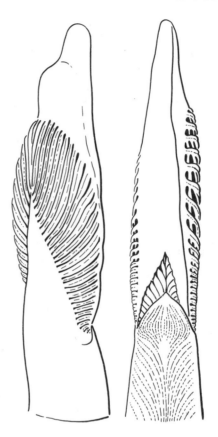

Figure 16. Young leaves of *Ptychosperma*. A, the 9th leaf from the stem-apex, showing the junction of the marginal strips into the median strip (heavy black line), the petiole just beginning to lengthen, and the 8th leaf enclosed in the sheath at the base, $\times \frac{1}{6}$. B, C the 8th leaf from the stem-apex in front and side views to show the ligule (at the top of the sheath), the short marginal strips divergent from the relatively long median strip, the secondary folding (fish-tailing) of the leaflet folds, the basal (basipetal) development of new leaflet folds, and the absence (as yet) of a leaf-stalk; $\times 1\frac{1}{2}$.

Figure 17. *Ptychosperma*. The 8th leaf from the stem-apex of another plant from that of Fig. 16, and at a younger stage with less elongate upper part; the external folds show the translucent splitting lines; the venation of the ligule and front of the leaf-sheath visible; $\times$ 3.

53

other. The distinctive arrangement is a limiting case of reduction from the spiral arrangement in palms, as in grasses, but it is not popular among the palms.

The primordium has the shape of a small crescent, or sand-dune, the arms of which extend round the hump of the stem-apex and meet on the other side. They would seem to be exactly transverse but

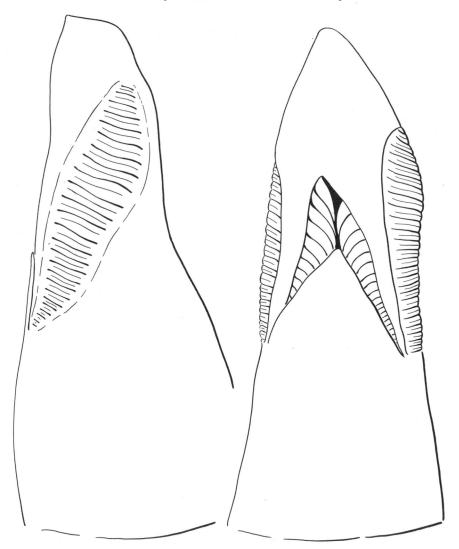

Figure 18. *Ptychosperma*. The 7th leaf from the stem-apex of the same plant as Fig. 17; the external folds showing the splitting lines but without, as yet, the secondary folding; × 15.

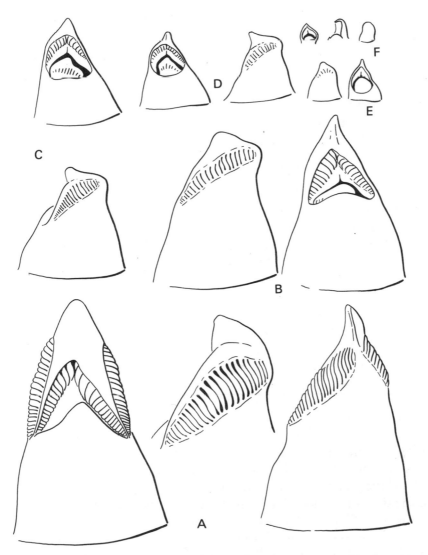

Figure 19. *Ptychosperma*. Younger leaves from the same plant as Figs 17 and 18;
× 15. A, 6th leaf from the stem-apex in front view (left), side-view, and back-
view (right); note the short median strip and the basipetal development of the
leaflet folds, the outer folds not having defined the splitting lines. B, 5th leaf with
the 4th leaf C inside the sheath; all the leaflets have been started as folds. C, 4th
leaf with the ligule beginning and the leaflet folds showing their succession
apically and, mostly, basally, from the first longest fold. D, 3rd leaf with the 2nd
leaf E in its sheath. F, the first leaf without folds, and the rounded stem-apex.
Note, if the leaves of Figs 17–19 are put one inside the other, the bud is
reconstructed.

E

examination of the adult trunk shows that this is not so; one arm is slightly higher than the other and, if a string is put around the lower margin of the leaf-scar on a palm trunk the two ends will not be at the same level. One arm leads slightly up the trunk because, while that arm was growing round the stem-apex, the apex was growing itself upwards, and this arm is the one which leads on towards the next leaf. For this reason palm-leaves, while appearing symmetrical, are really slightly asymmetric; one half of the primordium is slightly older than the other and grows for a bit longer; it commonly has an extra leaflet or two.

The crescentic primordium arches over the stem-apex and becomes hood-shaped. The cavity of the hood gives the space for the next leaf. Hence young palm-leaves form a series of hoods, or snuffers, one inside the other and, while studying the development of one, we have to think of the preceding and succeeding leaves. I will call them leaves 1, 2, and 3. They arise sufficiently apart in time so as not to interfere.

As the base of leaf 1 lengthens and dilates, it makes room for leaf 2 to extend its apex upwards and to expand the sides of the hood. Leaf 2 now has the beginnings of all its parts (figure 19). The apex is solid and will form the very tip of the projecting sword-leaf in the crown. It has a particular shape in most genera, if not in most species, determined by the shape of the gap made by leaf 1. The squat neck of the hood, extending round the stem-apex, forms the stalk of the leaf. The sides of the hood develop the leaflets. The edges become the marginal strip. The narrow back, or spine, extending from stalk to apex and joining the sides, becomes the rachis or leaf-axis.

Now the leaflets begin to develop, not as outgrowths, but as folds on the sides of the hood [72]. An obliquely longitudinal bulge appears and is soon followed by two others, one on each side, parallel to it. More folds develop and their order can be made out from their size, the largest being the prior. Soon, however, there is no more room to develop folds in the direction of the spine or leaf-apex because this distal part has already begun to differentiate; more folds are added in the opposite direction towards the stem-apex, because the young leaf is growing rapidly in this basal part. The folds are separated by furrows and they heighten, widen, and deepen without intercalating other folds. The botanist will recognize in the few folds which develop towards the spine (five to seven in *Ptychosperma*) a vestige of apical growth, while most of the leaf-growth becomes basal.

56

The young leaf now begins to lengthen because the sheath of leaf 1 is lengthening, and out of the basal pocket of leaf 2, the tip of leaf 3 begins to appear. The base of leaf 2 begins to grow and raise the arms of the original crescent as a tube round the stem-apex and leaf 3, within which leaf 4 will arise. Yet still more folds develop at the basal end of the row until, in *Ptychosperma*, there are as many as there are leaflets in the open leaf; that is thirty-one on each side of the leaf-axis. The older leaflets have lengthened considerably and, even when

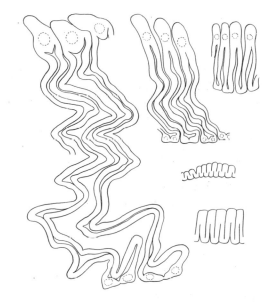

Figure 20. Cross-sections of the leaflet folds of *Ptycho-sperma* in young leaves 2·5, 4, 6, 11, and 29 mm. long; the inner folds are uppermost and the outer folds show the development of the thin splitting line between two vascular bundles; note the development of secondary folds; × 25.

the leaf is ready to open, they are longer than the lower folds: indeed, in many palms they are much longer, and that is why the lower leaflets on the frond are usually the smallest. In *Phoenix*, the lower leaflets have so little time to develop that they form merely the pointed spines which characterize the leaf-stalk of the date-palm and its wild allies. In *Ptychosperma* the oldest leaflets are placed about the sixth below the apical; hence, as they are the longest, the open leaf has an egg-shaped outline widest towards the apex in a form called the obovate.

The leaf-axis is now distinguishable into four parts. There is the thin spine and the stouter rachis as the pedestal of the folds. It widens downward into the region which will become the leaf-stalk below which the tubular leaf-sheath, so characteristic of Arecoid palms, is developing. This sheath always retains the thin part where the two

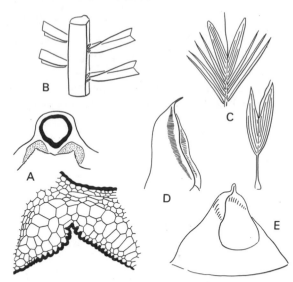

Figure 21. *Cocos nucifera*, A–D, and *Borassus*, E. A, cross-section of the midrib of a leaflet with the pulvinar tissue (hinge) stippled and the woody sheath of the vascular tissue in black, × 1; lower figure, the hinge-tissue enlarged with the cuticle in black. B, the lower side of part of the frond to show the pulvinus at the base of each leaflet on the side towards the leaf-apex, × ½. C, the apex of a mature leaf and a seedling leaf to show the median filament (median spine) from which the uppermost leaflets separated; much reduced. D, a very young leaf; × 4. E, a very young leaf of the fan-leafed *Borassus*; mag. (A, after Copeland, 1906; C–D, after Venkatanaraya, 1957; E, after Periasamy, 1962).

arms of the crescentic primordium met and, because of this, the sheath ruptures along this weak line when the leaf dies and falls off to make another scar on the clean trunk of these neat palms. If there is a stalk between the sheath and the lowest leaflets, it forms from the original leaf-axis where no folds could be developed. The leaf dies from the tip downwards, as it was constructed.

The great problem, however, is in what way the leaflets can be extricated from the continuously folded lamina of the unopened leaf. Cross-sections of unopened leaves must be studied (figure 20). They show that the folds, originating on the two flat sides of the primordial hood, develop into more and more strongly zig-zag lines. Each line consists, in fact, of two sets of folds. There are those developed on the outside, which are visible in side-view of the young leaf, and those developed on the inside, which can be seen in front view of the leaf along with both marginal strips. Close inspection of the cross section

58

shows that the outer folds have very thin angles (three to four cells thick) whereas the inside folds have thick angles strengthened by the development of vascular bundles. The thin outer angles can be seen as fine translucent lines along the centre of the outer folds. We turn to the opening leaf and discover that, as the folds expand, they split apart down the thin lines of the outer folds and that the inner folds become the leaflets. The outer folds, in fact, are splitting folds; the transverse parts of the folds make the lamina of the leaflet, and the inner angle of the inner folds becomes the midrib. The folds are gathered at their ends by the marginal strips and each side of the leaf-rachis, with which their tissue is confluent. Thus each double set of folds resembles a curtain fixed to a rod at each end and comprising so much material that it is thrown into longitudinal folds.

Another problem presents itself. Plant organs split usually in one or two ways, either by the swelling or by the drying and contracting of one tissue to rupture another. The only drying tissue in the opening leaf is the marginal strip, but its contraction will not separate the folds. There must be some swelling tissue. The leaflets have been swelling all along, so they cannot supply the new force. We turn to the leaf-rachis and discover that in the lengthening, but unopened, leaves its general elongation becomes restricted to the intervals between the folds. The intervals lengthen into internodes, as it were, which separate the folds and, in so doing, part them at the base and split the outer folds from the base upwards to the tip. But we observe in the opening leaf that the tips become separated downwards towards the base of the folds while the basal splitting is still in progress. There must be another force which causes the folds to diverge from each other so that the tips are stretched apart; there must be some swelling which rotates each fold away from the rachis. We look in the axil where the fold joins the rachis and discover a small cushion which swells as the leaf opens and finally hardens into a sort of wart in the open leaf. This swelling consists, at first, of thin-walled cells but they greatly enlarge until, on reaching full size, their walls thicken and become rigid. Localized swellings like this, which operate movements, are called pulvinuses (or pulvini). They function in the same way as an air-cushion placed in the armpit, will, on inflation, raise the arm, but they are water-cushions and incompressible. They not only rotate the folds about their junctions with the rachis and split the outer folds from the apex downwards, but they pull these apices from the marginal strips, thus freeing the

59

leaflets entirely, and eventually they set the leaflets at their characteristic angles from the leaf-axis which, in its turn, has spaced them at
their characteristic distances.

What, then, forces the two sides of the inner folds apart to open the
leaflets? Where the sides join the leaf-axis, they are close together, but
further from this axis they diverge and the mature leaflet is flat
throughout most of its length. The leaflet must be studied microscopically in transverse section. There will be found on each side of
the underneath of the midrib a patch of swollen cells which, clearly,
have greatly enlarged and, as they form two strips along the whole
leaflet, they have lifted the sides about the midrib and thus flattened
the leaflet (figure 21). These strips of pulvinar tissue were found by
von Mohl, and have been called hinges because their mobility persists
throughout the life of the leaf unlike that of the pulvinus at the base of
the leaflet [73]. In the heat of the day, water is withdrawn from the
cells of the hinge to the transpiring mesophyll and the sides of the
leaflet move gradually together. The deficiency is made good towards
evening and during the night; by sunrise the leaflets have recovered
their position. Thus, when seen from below, the glitter of the palm
crown increases as the leaflets droop towards mid-day.

We learn that the palm leaf is deliberately opened. Its exact
outline, shape, and direction in space are manoeuvred. It is a fairly
rigid structure that is pushed open by the intermittent lengthening of
the leaf-axis and the hinges of its parts. Thus, every kind of palm
develops a characteristic set to its leaf-stalk and leaflets. The number
of leaves and leaflets is specific to every palm and they are put into the
air in such a way that it is usually easier to recognize the species from
afar than close at hand. In some palms, as the coconut and the South
American alliance of the massive *Attalea*, *Maximiliana*, and *Scheelea*,
the leaf-axis turns gradually along its length through a right angle;
the leaflets are conveyed from a horizontal to a vertical plane, and the
periphery of the crown presents the leaves as knife-edges; in doing
this, the leaf-axis changes in shape from a cross-section that is
rhomboidal to one that is semi-circular and, finally, lenticular
(figure 54). It remains to be discovered how this tilt is related to the
whole succession of leaves up the stem, whether it is with or against
the ascending spiral [74].

The variety of leaflet position is shown ¹                ion species
of the tufted, spiny palms *Oncosperma* of A              *ntosa* of the
west Malaysian swampy forest the leaflets              y on both

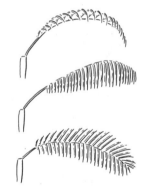

Figure 22. Fronds of the Arecoid *Oncosperma*. Upper figure, *O. fasciculata* of Ceylon with arcuate leaflets: middle, *O. filamentosa* of Malaysian mangrove with drooping leaflets; lower, *O. horrida* of Malaysian lowland forest with stiff leaflets held in a vertical plane; $\times \frac{1}{200}$.

sides of the leaf-axis. In *O. horrida* of the hill-forests, the leaflets are set stiffly from the axis which curves them into the vertical plane. In *O. fasciculata* of Ceylon, the leaflets are directed obliquely upwards from the axis and arch fussily towards their hanging tips. In most of the royal palms (*Roystonea*) every second or third leaflet is stood up, or less displayed, and the whole leaf seems to have four rows of leaflets. Then in some palms, notably the rattans, the leaflets are bunched in groups along the leaf-axis. It is not easy to see how this can happen. The bunches of leaflets may alternate on either side of the leaf axis so that a bunch on one side comes opposite an internode on the other, yet there is no curving of the leaf axis: it is like stretching the body on one side, while keeping it straight on the other. There is less opportunity for such differences in the fan-palms where the degree of splitting and drooping of the leaflets is more characteristic, and the upcurving of the sides of the frond. Herbarium specimens give no proper idea how the palm fills space according to its particular kind.

The pulvinus, or its elongation under the lamina into a hinge, is in fact the motor which opens most parts of monocotyledonous parts from their cramped positions in the bud. Thus the bracts which enwrap the palm inflorescences are spread; thus, the branches of the inflorescence are spread; even the lateral inflorescence itself is displayed in this manner from its initial upright position in the bud. It was in fact, the starting of this pulvinus at the base of the inflorescence which finally detached the old leaf of *Actinorhytis*; the opening inflorescence in its axil pushed it off, showing thereby that not only the leaves but the inflorescences are timed and the two co-ordinated in the palm crown. The inflorescences of grass, sedge, rush, and lily are displayed by pulvinuses. They open grass flowers and, as hinges, flatten, roll-up, and flatten again the grass leaves. Thus the banner-like leaves of the banana are held flat, to droop as palm leaflets in the afternoon and revive at night. These structures, pulvinus and hinge, seem relatively uncommon in dicotyledons, but they may have been overlooked; thus, they occur as small tumid triangles in the axils of the main veins on the underside of the leaf when it has been folded in the bud.

Looking back on the ins and outs of the young palm leaf, we detect other points of general interest. The spine of the young leaf becomes the median fold joining the two series of folds that form under the marginal strips. In most pinnate-leafed palms, such as *Ptychosperma*, it splits longitudinally and liberates the pair of apical leaflets. It is, however, often thicker than the other splitting folds and in the fish-tail palms (*Caryota*) and their allies the sugar palms (*Arenga*) it fails to split; their leaves in consequence have undivided terminal leaflets. In the coconut, the spine detaches from both apical leaflets and dries up as a fine brown median tail. In the rattans, however, the stouter leaf-axis is continued through the spine to form the whip by which the leaf climbs (figure 111).

Most of the Arecoid palms have long tubular leaf-sheaths which fit closely inside each other to form the green crown-shaft at the tops of their elegant stems. Other palms may appear to have no leaf-sheath, yet it is always present in some degree, as revealed by the annular scar of leaf-attachment. The nature of the sheath is almost certainly characteristic of big generic groups of palms, for it is a very complicated structure in the arrangement of its vascular bundles [75]; it is a subject in which we wait studies on leaf-base development. In the largest fan-palms such as *Borassus* and *Corypha*. the sheath is slight; the thick broad leaf-base, supported by the other leaf-bases, takes up the immense strain of the opening and swaying frond. *Phoenix* has a short sheath which splits, as usual, from above downwards along the thin mid-line opposed to the leaf-stalk, to which it gives the frayed and fibrous edge. In *Livistona* and many other fan-palms the sheath is longer, even two to three feet long, and dries up into a very tough, brown, fibrous sacking. *Caryota* has a fibrous gusset (figure 23), which is widened in the coconut palm to include the whole of the sides of the sheath, but in this case it is peculiar for the sacking is toughened along the mid-line where it should split; it detaches from the sides of the leaf-stalk which appears as a naked petiole. In the Cuban *Zombia* and its allies the main external vascular

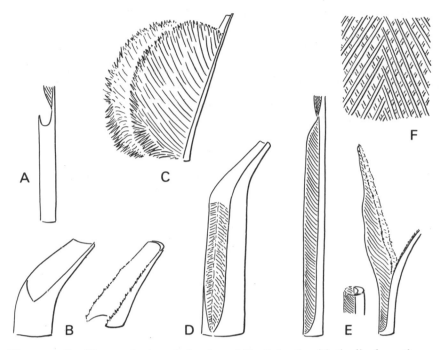

Figure 23. Leaf-bases. A, the tubular Arecoid leaf-sheath with the ligule on the side opposite to the frond. B, *Phoenix* with the sheath splitting to give the fibrous edges to the leaf-base. C, the fan-palm *Livistona* with broad fibrous sheath splitting into halves. D, *Caryota* with fibrous sheath not splitting. E, *Cocos nucifera*, the fibrous sheath detaching from the leaf-axis from above downwards to give a 'false petiole'. F, the pattern of fibres (vascular bundles) along the mid-line of the sheath of *Cocos nucifera*; mag. A–D, × $\frac{1}{10}$; E, × $\frac{1}{20}$ (after Tomlinson, 1962, 1964).

bundles of the sacking end in long spines which, on drying, become recurved (figure 53).

This fibrous sacking is a most remarkable tissue. In supporting the leaf-axis by wrapping round the bud as a kind of bandage it has to withstand great strain. As the leaf opens, the ground tissue of the sheath dries up and disintegrates. The brown epidermis flakes off to reveal the fibrovascular bundles woven in an intricate pattern. There are two sets of fibres, an outer crossed by an inner and both held together by small interconnections. The result is an exceedingly strong texture. The construction has been investigated in the coconut [76]. Thousands of fibrovascular bundles are employed which take oblique, not longitudinal, courses and it is quite impossible, as yet, to understand how they have been laid down at the base of the developing leaf. The temptation is to think of them 'running up' the sheath whereas they were, in fact, developed downwards as the leaf grew at its base, and somehow they link with the fibrovascular bundles in the stem. The smooth, broad, flexible sheets of sacking which can be rasped off the *Livistona* palms of Asia may have given the idea of weaving in the first place, inasmuch as they are used for clothing, matting, bands, bags, and baskets by primitive inquisitive people. The toughness and durability of the fibres is shown by the curious use to which the black fibres of the sugar palm *Arenga* have been put. They have been laid as mattresses under coastal roads in

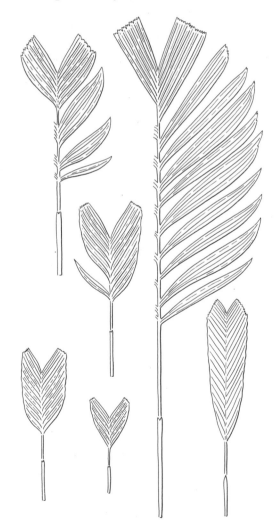

Figure 24. Leaves of *Pinanga kuhlii* from seedling to adult form and (bottom right) the adult unsplit leaf of the slender *Pinanga simplicifrons*. Note the compound leaflets of *P. kuhlii* composed of several unsplit folds (7–8 in the apical leaflets and alternately 2–3 in the lower leaflets); the leaf expands from its small seedling state by basal growth of the lamina and the splitting off of leaflets from the base; $\times \frac{1}{10}$.

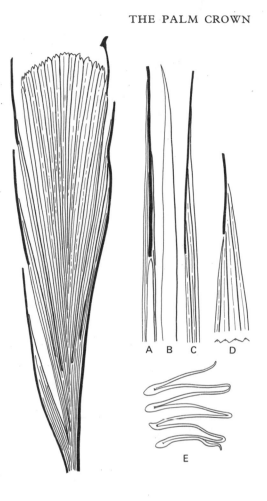

Figure 25. The opening of the leaf in *Pinanga furfuracea*, the marginal strip (in black) adherent to the tips of the compound leaflets; × ½. A, the tip of a leaflet from the outer side, B from the inner side, C from the underside. D, the leaf-tip of A opened out to show its composition from four leaflet folds. E, the base of leaflet A in section with the inner folds to the left. A–D, × 1; E, × 5.

South-East Asia to stop the burrowing prawns from working their way through the road metal and piling their mud heaps on the surface. The thick brown coating of leaf-base fibres of the piassába or chíqui–chíqui palm *Leopoldinia piassaba*, which Spruce remarked upon, are made into ropes and these, as Humboldt recorded, have the extremely useful property for river folk of floating on water [77].

In *Ptychosperma* all the internal folds of the young leaf become splitting folds. Every internal fold, therefore, becomes a leaflet the midrib of which, formed by the sharp and thickened angle of the fold, projects from the upperside of the leaflet, not from the underside as is usual in dicotyledonous leaves. A number of palm leaflets have several midribs, as it were, coursing parallel to each other in the lamina. It can be seen from the opening of the leaves that every

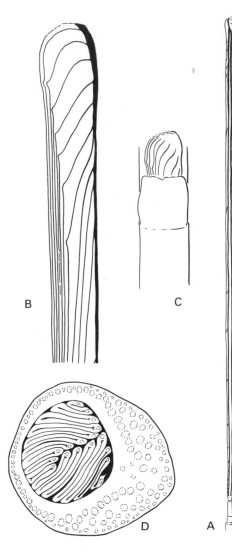

B

C

Figure 26. Young leaves of *Pinanga furfuracea*. A, the 8th leaf from the stem-apex, showing the long marginal strips and short, apical, median strip; × ½. B, the apex of this leaf in side view; × 3. C, the ligule of this leaf with the 7th leaf just emerging from the sheath; × 3. D, cross-section of the sheath of this leaf to show the folds of the 7th leaf; × 10.

D        A

midrib represents the angle of an inner fold and that, in such cases, the splitting folds occur at every second, third or higher number of external folds. In fact, these leaflets are compound in the palm sense of being composed of two or more complete folds which have not been split apart. *Pinanga furfuracea* has a splitting fold at every third or fourth complete fold; *P. kuhlii* has one at every sixth or seventh. In both species the terminal leaflet is larger than the others and has six to twelve folds on each side; they represent the apical part of the folded

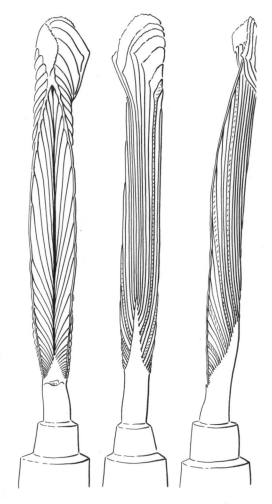

Figure 27. *Pinanga furfuracea*, the 7th leaf from the stem-apex; 5·6 cm. long when the 8th leaf is about to open. Note the short median strip, the splitting outer folds (hatched), and the very short leaf-stalk region. Left, from the front or future upper side of the leaf; centre, from the back; right, from the side; × 2.

lamina which has not split into leaflets but has been divided centrally into two halves by a split down the spine of the young leaf. The organization of the splitting folds is extremely regular. The first external fold to develop in the young leaf becomes a splitting fold, but none of the folds then developed acropetally towards the leaf-apex split; hence the unsplit terminal leaflet. It is only the basipetally developed folds which introduce splits every so often to give the compound leaflets. The splitting folds are recognized easily in the young, unopened leaves because, being thin and without airspaces between the cells, they appear translucent and dull compared with the glistening white non-splitting folds (figures 27–29).

67

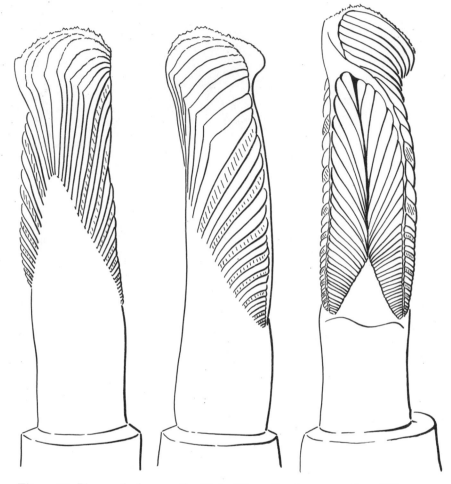

Figure 28. *Pinanga furfuracea*, the 6th leaf from the stem-apex, the splitting outer folds hatched;

The small *Pinanga simplicifrons* of Malaya and Sumatra, with slender stems merely a few feet high, has small leaves that are completely unsplit except where the median spine has been cleft to give the V-shaped apex. The leaf has about twenty inner folds, on either side of the leaf-axis, and each would be a leaflet with one midrib if the corresponding external folds split. This small entire leaf borne on a thin stem brings the study of adult palm leaves down to that of the seedlings and saplings which build up to the adult complexity. The succession of leaves from the seedling in *P. kuhlii* is

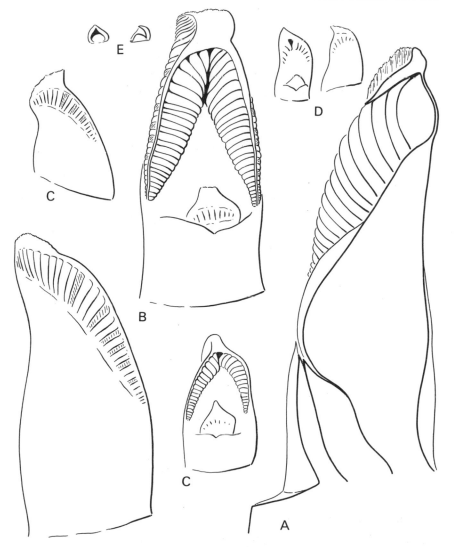

Figure 29. *Pinanga furfuracea*. A, 5th leaf from the stem-apex, in longitudinal section with part of the 4th leaf between its ligule and leaf-axis. B, 4th leaf with the full number of leaflet folds. C, 3rd leaf with the leaflet folds developing apically and, mostly, basally; the splitting outer folds hatched as in B. D, 2nd leaf. E, 1st leaf with rounded stem apex; × 15.

shown in figure 24 where they are drawn to scale. The simple young leaf corresponds with the compound terminal leaflet of the adult leaf, while the lateral leaflets are added basipetally as the stem thickens, the leaf primordium becomes larger, and the leaf growth increases.

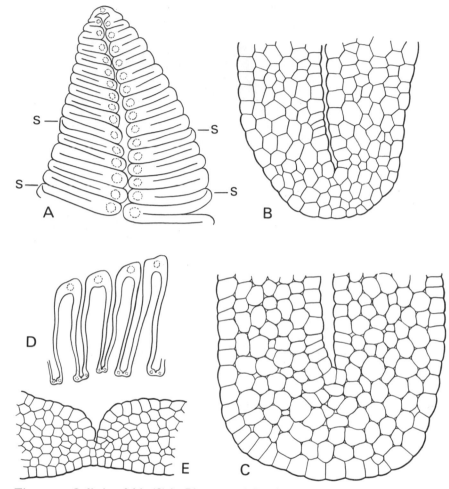

Figure 30. Splitting folds (S) in *Pinanga* and *Ptychosperma*. A, cross-section of the young unopened leaf of *Pinanga kuhlii*; × 45. B, the edge of a splitting outer fold, and C the edge of a non-splitting outer fold of *P. kuhlii*; × 380. D, cross-section of leaflet folds of *Ptychosperma* showing the thin splitting line of every outer fold; × 5. E, the splitting fold of D; × 380.

The simple frond of *P. simplicifrons* is, in fact, a juvenile leaf form persistent in the adult state of this small, persistently juvenile, or neotenic species of the genus.

Now this explanation for the evolution of the leaf in *Pinanga*, the species of which show the full range from large wholly split leaves with many leaflets to variously compound leaflets and simple unsplit leaves, applies equally well to many other pinnate-leafed genera of

Figure 31. Leaf of the Brazilian *Geonoma brachyfoliata* with compound terminal and basal leaflets and, occasionally, an intermediate leaflet; 16 leaflet folds on one side, 15 on the other; much reduced (after Barbosa Rodriguez, 1903).

palms. Thus *Bactris*, *Chamaedorea*, *Geonoma*, *Iguanura*, and *Reinhardtia* have evolved small palms with simple leaves. These are simple because they have not been developed up to the larger hereditary state; their species are no longer trees but undergrowth shrubs, tending to the herbaceous condition evolved by so many arborescent monocotyledons in the forest; and what they have lost in stature they gain by access to small stations in the forest which allow their quick turn-over. They are often mistaken for primitive plants, but their simplicity is secondary and juvenile; their flowers and fruits show the advancement which their genera have inherited. In the American forest palmlet *Reinhardtia latisecta*, the simple leaves have vestigial splits appearing as 'windows' in the lamina; they are not to be confused with the holes in the leaves of the aroid *Monstera*, which are caused by patches of necrotic tissue.

Nevertheless, neoteny is not the whole story. There are a few massive palms that bear large, unsplit leaves. For instance, the Amazonian *Manicaria saccifera* has leaves up to 30 ft long and 4–5 ft wide which are unsplit when they open: later, as they weather, they become torn into leaflets, possibly along the vestigial splitting folds; the two related species in the genus have normally split leaves.

Another case is the huge, unsplit, diamond-shaped frond of *Teysmannia* [78]. In these cases we must suppose that, although the leaf is fully developed for the genus, it has lost its power of splitting.

Generally in pinnate leaves the splitting occurs in the manner of *Pinanga* and *Ptychosperma*; that is, the external folds split and the internal folds form the leaflets. In section they are Λ-shaped, and this form is called reduplicate. In the date palms *Phoenix* and the fish-tail

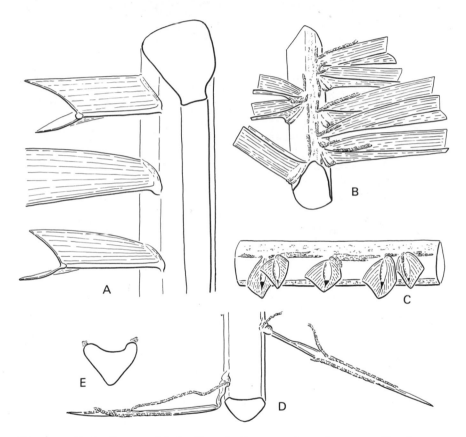

Figure 32. Reduplicate and induplicate leaflets, seen from the upper side. A, reduplicate leaflets of *Scheelea*, the leaf-apex upwards, the pulvinus at the base of the leaflet. B–D, induplicate leaflets of *Phoenix* without midribs, the brown scurfy strips of dried tissue mark where adjacent leaflet folds were attached together. B, the leaf-apex downwards. C, in side-view to show how a pulvinus between the folds of each leaflet splits the folds apart at the base. D, the abortive leaflets, transformed into spines, towards the base of the leaf-axis, each with a strong basal pulvinus. E, cross-section of a leaflet-spine. A, × ½ (after Barbosa Rodriguez, 1903). B–D, × 1. E, × 5.

palms *Caryota*, with its ally *Arenga*, it is the inner folds which split so that the outer folds make the leaflets and their cross-section is V-shaped; such leaflets are called induplicate. All fan-leaves are induplicate except for three genera of Lepidocaryoid palms which are reduplicate like their pinnate-leafed allies. They are the American

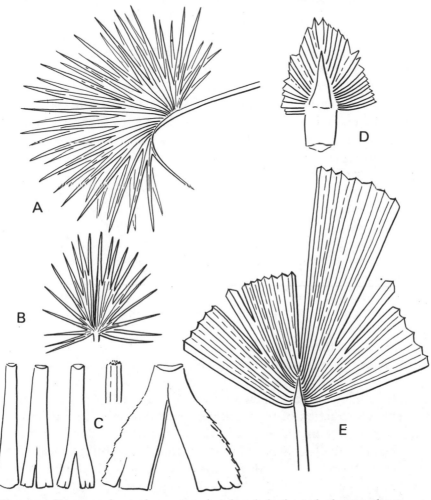

Figure 33. Fan, or palmate, leaves; much reduced. A, the arched costapalmate leaf of *Sabal* (induplicate). B, the truly palmate leaf of *Sabal minor*. C, the bases of young and old leaves of *Sabal palmetto* to show the splitting of the leaf-base, and the part of the leaf-stalk where the dead frond breaks off. D, the base of the blade of *Sabal* with its triangular ligule on the upper side. E, the reduplicate fan-leaf of *Lepidocaryum*, seen from underneath (A–D, after Bailey, 1944; E, after Barbosa Rodriguez, 1903).

genera *Mauritia*, *Mauritiella*, and *Lepidocaryum*, allied with the pinnate-leafed *Raphia* of Africa and *Metroxylon* of the west Pacific. The distinction between the reduplicate and the induplicate is profound and admits neither an intermediate state nor a mixture with some leaflets of the one kind and others of the other kind. The names, however, are easily confused. I remember them by associating reduplicate with roof-shaped (*r*) and induplicate with gutter-shaped (*i* and *g*). The classification of palms sets those with reduplicate leaflets against those with induplicate, but we have no idea why the pinnate leaf should favour the reduplicate, the palmate leaf the induplicate. We wait for the comparison between *Mauritia* (reduplicate fan-leaf) and *Corypha* or *Sabal*, which are induplicate.

This palmate leaf of the fan-palm differs from the pinnate or feather-leaf mainly because the leaf-axis does not elongate to the same extent during development. It does not space out the leaflets along an axis, but they radiate from it on opening. Most massive palmate leaves are called costapalmate because the midrib, or costa, extends for some distance along the folded blade, usually about half-way. The truly palmate leaf has no such elongation into the fan which is supported solely by its own rigidity. The costapalmate, therefore, is the stage in shortening of the leaf-axis which leads to the truly palmate. We suppose this evolutionary direction from pinnate to palmate because it is that which occurs in dicotyledons and because the basally growing leaf pre-supposes the apically-growing which, by virtue of its apical growth, develops a leaf-axis. What apically developed axis there is in palm-leaves is merely the spine between the apical folds but we shall see that this is improved in the Lepidocaryoid rattans.

The palmate, or costapalmate, leaf is opened and split into leaflets merely by the action of the pulvinus at the base of the folds and the hinges along their undersides; there are no spacing internodes developed by the leaf-axis. It follows that the stretching and splitting will be most forcible towards the margin of the whole lamina. In fact, most fan-leaves are split into leaflets only in the outer half of the open blade and here it is that their splitting folds occur. There are exceptions, nevertheless, in which the truly palmate leaf is divided into leaflets down to their attachment, for instance in *Licuala* and *Rhapis* (figures 34 and 35). The Malaysian genus *Licuala* of undergrowth palms is peculiar, also, because its species have compound leaflets as in *Pinanga* and these leaflets widen outwards from their attachment

74

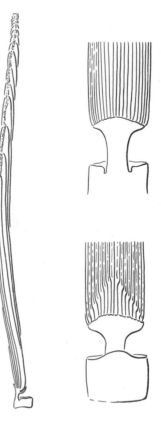

Figure 34. A young, unopened frond of the induplicate fan-leafed *Chamaerops* in side-view, showing the two ligules at the top of the stalk, × ½. On the right, the base of this frond in back view (above) and front view (below), × 2. Note the absence of a midrib, and the presence of splitting lines along the inner folds (lower right figure).

into a very characteristic, narrowly wedge-shaped (cuneate) form by which the genus is at once recognized: one or two of its species have, as we should expect, completely undivided and almost orbicular leaves. Then, when the fan-leaf is only partially divided, there can often be seen hanging from the sinus between the leaflets a marginal strip. This is odd because the pinnate leaves do not develop such strips between the leaflets, except in the case of *Caryota* which we shall mention presently. This detail, along with several others, gives the impression that the nature of the fan-leaf is not yet properly understood. Thus fan-leaves never develop the neat tubular leaf-sheath of Arecoid palms. They have stout fibrous leaf-sheaths with the complicated textile veining, and their leaf-bases are commonly split into two halves by the expanding trunk without detriment to their function; the split may in fact be a convenience and allow the inflorescences to escape easily from their axillary position through the arch in the leaf base: it is the way of the double coconut *Lodoicea*

75

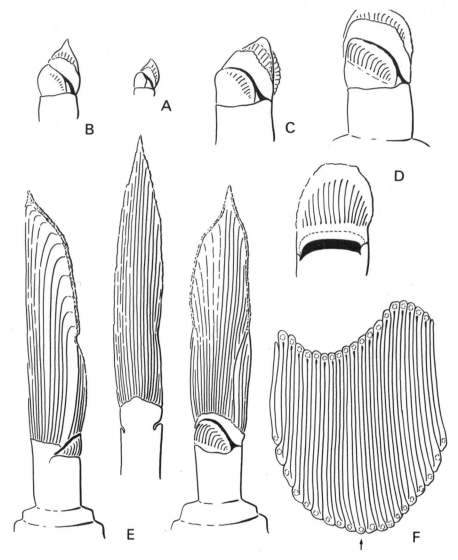

Figure 35. Young unopened leaves of the induplicate fan-leafed *Rhapis*. A, 3rd and 4th leaves from the stem-apex. B, 6th and 7th leaves. C, 7th and 8th leaves. D, 9th leaf, the lower figure with the ligule cut off. E, 9th and 10th leaves in side-view (left), back view (centre) and front view (right). F, cross-section of the 10th leaf, the mid-fold or spine marked by the arrow. A–D, × 8; E, × 5; F, × 15.

(figure 127). Furthermore, fan-leaves have a small flange (ligule or hastula) at the top of the leaf-stalk on one or other side of the blades, sometimes on both sides. In the pinnate-leafed a ligule occurs only on the edge of the tubular leaf-sheath opposite to the leaf-stalk. There have been no modern studies on the development of the fan-leaf to help in these comparisons.

A problem is set by the fish-tail palms *Caryota*. Alone in the family they have doubly pinnate leaves. The axis of the leaf bears not leaflets but secondary axes along which the leaflets are spaced; and these leaflets have not the long, narrow, tapered form but are dilated

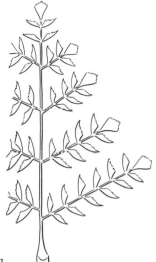

Figure 36. The doubly-pinnate leaf of *Caryota*.

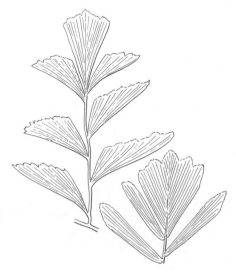

Figure 37. Left, a branch of the *Caryota* leaf with its fish-tail leaflets. Right, the apex of the frond of the allied *Arenga* with oblong fish-tail leaflets. Note the terminal leaflets.

77

outwards with many veins radiating to a jagged, toothed margin: they appear as broadening fish-tails and hence arises the common name for the genus. Its smaller species have leaves six to eight feet long, but they are over twenty feet in the larger and spread as the branches of a tree.

When the bud is dissected, the young leaf is found to start in the

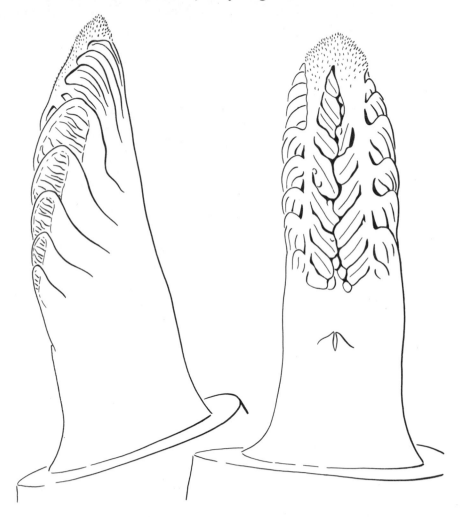

Figure 38. *Caryota mitis*, 6th leaf from the stem-apex (the third leaf internal to the opening leaf); showing the arched primary folds becoming stalked as the branches of the leaf-axis, and becoming themselves folded into leaflets. The right-hand figure in front view to show the fine splitting lines along the inner folds of this induplicate leaf. × 7.

78

same way as any other pinnate palm-leaf. Folds develop below the marginal strips but, as successive leaves are examined, these folds are seen to become folded themselves. Primary folds must be distinguished from secondary folds. The primary correspond with the folds of the *Ptychosperma* leaf, but they form the branches of the leaf-axis, not leaflets; these are made from the secondary folds arising from the parts of the primary folds near the marginal strip (figures 38–40). Then, this feature must be called the primary marginal strip because the secondary folds develop under their own, secondary marginal strips. At length, in an older leaf, the secondary folds are seen to be thrown into small and uneven tertiary folds. Thus each primary fold acts as if it were another pinnate leaf and develops folds which in turn have the semblance of folding. When the leaf extends and opens, the leaf-axis spaces its branches; they space the leaflets; and the leaflets flatten out their folds into the wedge-shaped form. There is a pulvinus at the base of every branch of the leaf-axis and of every leaflet but what in the way of a hinge runs along the leaflet is not known.

The splitting folds are all inner folds and the leaf is thoroughly induplicate. Consequently the outer primary folds make the branches of the leaf-axis; the outer secondary folds make the leaflets; and the tertiary folds make the jagged margin, every tooth of which marks

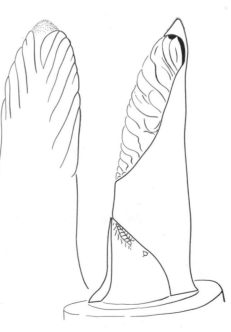

Figure 39. *Caryota mitis*, 5th leaf from the stem-apex with the primary folds beginning to develop secondary folds; right hand figure in longitudinal section to show the 4th leaf within the sheath; × 7.

Figure 40. *Caryota mitis*. Bottom row, 4th leaf from the stem-apex, the left figure in longitudinal section, × 7; top-row, 3rd leaf, × 15; middle row, 2nd and 1st leaves, × 15.

where a fold detached itself from the tertiary marginal strip. There is a terminal leaflet to every branch of the axis because there is no means of splitting it in the reduplicate manner. The description is difficult because this is the most complicated leaf in the whole plant kingdom. But we are helped in the understanding by a detail that has been over-looked in *Ptychosperma*. Its young leaf has the beginnings or, may be, vestiges of secondary folds just where the leaflet folds join the marginal strip on its outer side (compare figure 16 with figure 38). *Ptychosperma* goes no further than this but its leaflet has also the jagged ending like that of *Caryota*. It is the praemorse leaflet that occurs as a lengthened fish-tail in several other genera of palms such as the Cocoid *Aiphanes* of the Andes, the complex of *Iriartea* in the Arecoid palms, and the rattan *Korthalsia* among the Lepidocaryoid palms; Spruce noted it as a peculiarity of the Andean palm flora. We shall have to enquire further into this leaflet when considering the evolution of the palm leaf as one of the main features of the family. Here are diverse genera with once pinnate leaves tending towards the doubly pinnate construction, or are they receding from it?

Sapling leaves of *Caryota* pass quickly through a stage in which they are once pinnate. Its ally *Wallichia* of Assam has once pinnate leaves with typically fish-tail leaflets. Their ally *Arenga* of Malaysia has once pinnate leaves with oblong leaflets more like the normal form of palm leaflet, yet still ending in the jagged praemorse tip. A subdivision of this genus, once separated as *Didymosperma*, has leaves like those of *Wallichia* but also with a tendency to become doubly pinnate. If, as commonly supposed, the *Caryota* leaf were the most highly evolved state of the palm leaf, it is surely not in keeping with this hypothesis that, after a hundred million years of palm success, only *Caryota* should excel and that its allies, as well as various genera in other successful groups of palms, should be stumbling as it were on this discovery. It seems more likely that *Caryota* alone possesses the doubly pinnate leaf as the ancestral form from which the once pinnate has been derived as the more universal in the family, while these miscellaneous genera inherit relics of the greater construction, just as *Caryota* has indications of the trebly pinnate. Palm theory is to be tested by the *Caryota* leaf; it is either the most primitive palm leaf in existence or the most advanced.

## Chapter 4

# Trunk, Root, and Spine

THE PALM trunk appears to be a simple structure but when information is gathered from all over the palm world how it is varied, and when one considers what it is not, the simplicity disappears. There comes, instead, a strange problem – what can be done with a pole? It is usually upright, but it may lean and bend, and it can be laid horizontal, even inverted into the earth. It can be raised on stilts above the flood and it can be sunk in the mud. It bears the tremendous weight of the crown and in a gale the movement of the crown about the base becomes colossal. It must be supported, but not in any way that an engineer would design. It can proliferate and build a clump of poles. It can space these daughter poles apart and stalk, but stalking palms are small compared with stalking gingers. It can be big or little, thick or thin, and thin poles can become supple; if they lengthen rapidly, they can sprawl over other vegetation and be turned into rattans. The pole can practically disappear and the result is the so-called stemless palm. What it never does, with one exception, is to branch like a tree. This is where its internal construction fails. It can be climbed; it can be waxed as a greasy pole; it can be barbed. It can be naked and it can be clothed; and the vestment is primitive. We should start with the covered pole but it is too complicated for a beginning.

The pole is formed by the stem of the seedling. As it grows, the stem-apex thickens, producing bigger leaves until the size of stem and leaf reach that characteristic of the species of palm [79]. The base of the palm is, at first, a wide inverted cone on top of which the pole is raised from ground level. From the base roots grow, for the seedling root is short-lived, and these roots are the cables holding the pole upright. As they arise in large palms from higher up the trunk from a foot or two under the so-called bark, they gain purchase as low stays, and they dilate the base so that its original form completely disappears. But there is no tree bark, such as develops from the bark-cambium in the dicotyledonous tree, just as there is no wood-cambium and no secondary thickening to augment the water supply. All the construction of the trunk is confined to the apex, hidden and protected by the big leaf-bases. There the new stem-tissue is laid down and expanded, finely but thoroughly piped with the innumerable vascular bundles, strutted and tied by their fibrous sheaths, encased by their accumulation at the surface, connected below with the mature tissue, and adapted above to the active crown. So, as it were, block by block the stem is heightened. These blocks are the leaves, whose scars can be counted, and because no more elaboration can happen below them, their contacts with the soil are limited. The number of active leaves cannot be increased; an expanding crown cannot be built. As one leaf opens, the oldest is disengaged, and the adult crown maintains its quota. Ultimately, as the maximum height is reached, the stem peters-out and the leaves become smaller, but it is so rare to find palms dying of old age that their senescence calls for investigation.

The surface of the trunk is not exposed until the leaves have fallen. The process may be long. The leaves of Arecoid palms with tubular sheaths are readily detached and so are those of the oil-palm with simple leaf-base or those of the coconut in which the fibrous sheath becomes separated. Others have difficulty because this fibrous sheath may hold them and they may be unable to form a clean abscission layer. In these cases the stalk of the dead or dying leaf ruptures unevenly at some distance from the base; the exact place may be pre-determined by a structural weakness in the arrangement of the vascular bundles [80]. The old brown leaves dangle for a time and, when they fall, the jagged stump remains. The crash of a palm leaf in the tropical forest is one of its particular sounds; the botanists must scatter as it smashes its way through the foliage; a gale in a palm grove is brobdingnagian. In quiet contrast, when all is still, a palm leaf will start to wave in an unfelt current of air. Lastly heavy rain and limbs falling from other trees combine to denude the trunk of its mouldering leaf-bases. *Washingtonia*, living in pockets of the arid region of California to Mexico, is one of the few palms in which the dead leaves persist and obscure the trunk in a weather-proof skirting or petticoat as it is sometimes called. In young palms which have not attained a loftiness, the leaves tend to hang on, just as they do in young trees like the beech.

There are so many small differences in the structure and overlapping of the leaf-bases which affect the leaf-fall, that the investiture or the nakedness of the palm trunk is often a means of specific recognition. Pinnate leaves let the rain through, and their trunks, if set with old leaf-bases, allow many ferns, orchids, figs, and small climbers to develop as epiphytes. Palmate leaves act more as umbrellas and what epiphytes grow on them are such as prefer the drier conditions. The roots of the epiphytes bind the old leaf-bases together and retard their fall; much rubble collects and small animals take up their niches, such as ants, beetles, spiders, centipedes, scorpions, lizards, and frogs. Bees and wasps build in the drier parts; and he is a brave man who climbs a rough palm. Of the palmyra, it is written: 'The tree is well adapted for sheltering animals and hence it is resorted to by birds at night and by rats, squirrels, mongooses, monkeys, etc., during the daytime. When the leaves of a tree are undisturbed, the number of bats occupying it is sometimes incredibly great' [81]. Living palms, as well as hollow trunks and caves, are the dwellings of bats, some of which live on the palm fruits and distribute the seeds in a loose manner of symbiosis. Clean trunks develop patches of lichen and encourage more select epiphytes which require root-exposure on a firm surface; then many small orchids grow on them and various root-climbers, such as the peppers, asclepiads, rubiaceous climbers, vanilla-orchids, and in Tropical Asia creeping figs, ascend them from their seedling states on the ground. Clean trunks, as the later stage in evolution, entrain the more specialized and later evolved epiphytes.

Figure 41. The dichotomously branched Borassoid fan-palm *Hyphaene*, × $\frac{1}{200}$. Note the dichotomies in alternating planes.

84

The exception to the rule of the unbranched palm is the fan-leafed genus *Hyphaene*, several species of which in Africa and north west India develop a branching crown superficially resembling that of a pandan. The single stout trunk of the young plant, which may have taken many years to form, divides into two branches, each a little narrower than the main trunk. After a period of leaf-production they branch again into slightly smaller branches. With each branching the leaves also become slightly smaller. Finally the crown consists of numerous stout branchlets ending each in a rosette of leaves. There has been much speculation about the way in which *Hyphaene* branches. No one has seen the actual branching in the process of happening and we can only follow the latest account which seems confirmed in all respects [82]. Firstly, neither branch at the fork of the trunk is a lateral branch, that is, coming from the axil of a leaf; this is the way in *Pandanus* where lateral branches replace the terminal bud when it has formed an inflorescence. In *Hyphaene* every leaf has an axillary bud as in palms generally, but this, as usual, is the bud of an inflorescence which may or may not develop; leafy side-shoots are never seen on the trunks of *Hyphaene*. Secondly, there is no evidence that the terminal bud of the main stem or of its subsequent branchings ever desists in its growth and gives way to such an axillary bud. Thirdly, the system of leaves on the stem is continuous from main trunk to branch and branch to branchlet; there is no sign of intermittent growth with a new build-up of leaves as happens with lateral branches. Lastly, the internal structure confirms the conclusions from the external appearance that the stem-apex has divided into two and each half contrived to produce without cessation in any way the normal palm leaf. The inevitable conclusion is that the trunk and

Figure 42. Abnormal branching.
Left, *Borassus*; right *Cocos nucifera*;
$\times \frac{1}{200}$ (after Morris, 1892).

branches of this palm are dichotomous. This is extraordinary. Dichotomy, or the division of the stem-apex into two apices, is common enough in seaweeds but among the land-plants only the primitively organized club mosses *Lycopodium* and *Selaginella*, like their Palaeozoic ancestors *Lepidodendron*, have this manner of growth. *Hyphaene* is the only seed-plant and, certainly, the only flowering plant possessed of this primitive branching. Yet *Hyphaene* is a typical Borassoid palm and some of its species are sparingly dichotomous, others unbranched. The retention of this primitive way emphasizes the fundamental primitiveness of palms among the flowering plants. The loss of dichotomy in some species may well indicate how the solitary, unbranched palm pole has come into existence.

Freak branchings occur in various palms, such as the coconut and the palmyra, which is the ally of *Hyphaene*. Some very striking examples are figured by Barbosa Rodriguez for the coconut allies in Brazil, *Cocos romanzoffiana* and *Astrocaryum jauary* [83]. In these cases the branches seem to be caused by injury to the terminal bud, causing its death, to be followed by abnormal outgrowth of truly lateral, axillary branches. A few palms, such as the Madagascan *Chrysalidocarpus lutescens* often in cultivation, habitually develop one or a few lateral branches on the stem some distance below the crown, as if they were suckers displaced up the trunk. The many tufted palms such as the sago palms *Metroxylon*, *Oncosperma*, *Pinanga*, *Caryota*, *Bactris*, *Phoenix*, and so on, habitually branch from the base of the stem, commonly from underground, by means of these suckers which are lateral axillary buds developed in the normal way. None of these methods is dichotomous. Nevertheless there seems to be some unusual branching in the dwarf, tufted *Nannorrhops* of Afghanistan and India, which is an ally of the massive unbranched talipot *Corypha*. As in that genus, the inflorescence of *Nannorrhops* terminates the main stem which then produces leafy branches which terminate themselves in inflorescences; it is not clear, however, that the branching may not precede the flowering.

An unusual cause of damage or death to palms is that from lightning. The sword-leaf undoubtedly acts as a lightning conductor through which the discharge may take place from the ground. Lightning strike is well known as a 'disease' in coconut estates. The crown of a palm that has been struck appears scorched; longitudinal splits may appear on the trunk, as though it had been split by steam generated in the discharge; and sap exudes from these splits. The palms seldom recover but, if they do, these may be the rare ones that give the freak branchings where the main bud has died [84]. It is certainly unwise to stand under an isolated palm or group of palms during a tropical storm.

The suckering palms build up clumps in the same manner as the bamboos, bananas, and traveller-palms. It is the habit, too, of grass, and the sago-palms behave as gigantic grasses. Planted in the villages

Figure 43. The Brazilian Arecoid *Oenocarpus distichus* with the leaves in two rows (centre); the slender Lepidocaroid fan-palm *Mauritia limnophila*; and the tufted Cocoid *Bactris*; × $\frac{1}{200}$ (after Barbosa Rodriguez, 1903).

G

87

of Malaya, Borneo and further east, they encroach slowly but surely by means of their massive tillers on the borders of rice-fields and fertile valleys, which have the appearance of being threatened with a gigantic sward.

If the suckers, clad with scale-leaves instead of foliage leaves, grow horizontally for some distance before ascending into trunks, a more open clump is developed. The habit, often referred to as the soboliferous, occurs in other species of the same genera and is often connected with still smaller aerial stems. It is a common form of herbaceous degradation among monocotyledons, paralleled in the gingers and the rhizomatous or soboliferous grasses. A small species of *Pinanga* on Mt Kinabalu in North Borneo forms underground runners up to twelve feet long and a crowd of such palmlets has the appearance of scattered seedlings; indeed, I mistook them for such until I never found the parent and began to dig them up. Nevertheless there are lusty species of *Cocos*, or an allied genus, in South America that spread by underground rhizomes; some develop normal trunks at the ends of these prolonged suckers, and others are stemless, content with a rosette of leaves at ground level [85]. Caution must be exercised, however, especially in botanic gardens, in supposing that every clump of palms has arisen by suckering; commonly the crowded stems have each grown from a seed that has lodged at the foot of its parent stem or, indeed, two or three seedlings may have grown from one nut.

The eastern rattans, centred on the Lepidocaryoid *Calamus*, have another method. The seedling grows into a stemless rosette of pinnate leaves, eight to ten feet long in the larger kinds, and from the midst of the rosette several climbing stems ascend. They develop, it seems, from axillary buds, but whether the main seedling stem lengthens into the first climbing stem is uncertain. The American climbing genus *Desmoncus* is a Cocoid palm allied closely with *Bactris*. It develops suckers or short underground runners, as in *Bactris*, and these turn up to form the climbing stems. The inherited and generic habit is different in each case, but adapted in parallel.

By now we become aware of a difference between palm and grass, or bamboo, which shows that they too have evolved the tufted habit in parallel. The grasses and bamboos build by developing larger and larger branches until the requisite size for flowering is reached. The palm builds its main and flowering stem on the seedling stem after which it branches from the base of this stem. Bananas, gingers, and

Figure 44. The tufted Arecoid
*Oncosperma filamentosa* of Malaysia;
× $\frac{1}{200}$.

others of the alliance Scitamineae, as well as aroids, build tufts in the palm-way; orchids, rushes, and sedges follow the grass-method. The difference seems fundamental, and the big group of Liliales needs to be dissected according to this method.

The inclined pole seems an accidental, rather than an habitual feature, but it is another way of traversing space between tree trunks. It is the character of nearly all ginger plants to thrust the leafy stems upwards and forwards; and very aggressive they can be. Palms are too massive for this light engineering; yet the oblique stem, becoming decumbent towards the base, distinguishes the American ivory-nut palms *Phytelephas* and the oil-palm *Elaeis melanococca*, the African ally of which *E. guineensis* has a tall upright trunk. Thoroughly decumbent, creeping stems merge, of course, into the soboliferous. The most notable and commonest is that of the nipa palm which balances enormous stemless rosettes on the treacherous semi-liquid mud of estuaries by means of a stout horizontal trunk. It is the habit more or less, of the saw-palmetto *Serenoa* and the

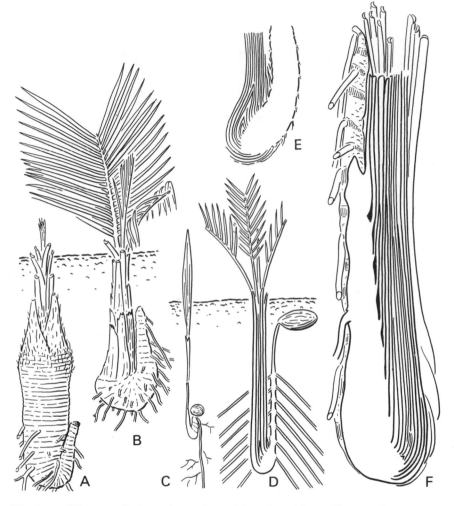

Figure 45. The so-called stemless palms of America with seedling trunks descending into the ground before upcurving. A, the Cocoid *Acanthococos* with its seedling C, and its trunk, E, in longitudinal section. B, a young plant of the Cocoid *Attalea* and its seedling D. F, a young plant of the Coryphoid *Sabal*. A, E, × $\frac{1}{20}$; B, × $\frac{1}{12}$; C, D, × $\frac{1}{4}$. (A–C, E, after Rawitscher, 1948; D, after Bondar, 1964; F, after Mohl, 1823).

creeping palmettoes *Sabal* of the south-east United States, but they prefer firmer sandy soil and tend still to develop erect trunks.

More remarkable and unusual are palms which grow stem downwards. It seems an American peculiarity to start the palm upside down. Apparently stemless tufts of pinnate leaves, belonging to some

90

species of *Cocos (Acanthococos)*, *Attalea* and its allies break the monotony of the dry savannas and *campos cerrados* of Brazil [86]. Unearthed, the stem is found to have grown to a depth of some fifty centimetres and then to have turned up, though remaining underground (figure 45). The cotyledon-stalk of the seedling thrusts the young stem into the loose soil. As the leaves develop, very short internodes are formed which continue to thrust the stem apex downwards while the older part of the stem is held by the lateral roots. The crown is curved at the base by lengthening of the lower leafstalks which take the slow friction of the thrust. The habit has a survival value when in dry seasons fire may start and burn off the superficial vegetation leaving the underground stems unharmed; with their capital reserves they can soon replace the scorched leaves. But, for the origin of the habit, there must be enquiry into the gravity-perception, or geotropism, of the stem which acts as a tap-root. To start life in this cryptic manner seems to be a general characteristic of the American palmettoes *Sabal* but, in most cases, their stems soon rectify and develop aerial trunks, even to a hundred feet high; the negative start is soon lost, though prolonged into creeping stems in a few of the more derived species.

A few palms strive to avoid the ground on which they must start. They elevate their stems on stilt-roots. While the seedling stem is expanding, it is also lengthening and putting out roots which grow down through the air-gap into the soil. The early part of the stem begins to die and these processes continue along with the formation of more stilt-roots until there may be a gap of one to several feet between the base of the trunk and the ground. The stilt-roots, arched and strong, branch in the ground and act as the stays to this ambitious pole. It is the habit of most species in the tropical American complex of *Iriartea* [87]. They grow in swampy places and elevate the trunk above the normal floods, and their stilt-roots may reach eight feet long (plate 20). Wallace wrote of them: 'In the forests where these trees grow, numbers of young plants of every age may be seen, all miniature copies of their parents, except that they seldom possess more than three legs, which gives them a strange and almost ludicrous appearance' [88]. So the monocotyledonous three extends to the roots. Many dicotyledonous trees of swampy forest develop stilt-roots, from the mangrove trees near the coast to the stilted *Eugenia* in high mountain swamps, and they have this same faculty of gradually widening the stem while it is being stilted, so that it tapers downwards even to a finger-point. It never dies away, however, in the dicotyledons because it is thickened to some degree by cambial growth. This is the trunk-form, also, in many buttressed trees; at least in their early life before the trunk thickening has had time to catch up with the buttresses. It is an unexplained deviation from the normal method of trunk-making.

The Seychelles palm *Verschaffeltia* has stilt-roots even when planted in dry ground, but there is no generic complex in the Old World so distinguished as that of the Andean *Iriartea*. In Celebes there is a stilt-rooted species of *Areca*, *A. langloisiana* [89]; another is said to occur in the Solomon Islands. That land of botanical wonder Borneo has the majority of species of the problematic Lepidocaryoid genus *Eugeissona*, and one of these has the appearance of a giant myriapod. The larger form stout erect stems and, seated on rocks and mounds in the forest, send their stiff roots for ten to twelve feet through the air in a variety of directions until they meet, or sink into, the ground (figure 93). Another has a small creeping stem, as in the one Malayan species, but it dwells in the swampy forest and it slowly grows this stem upwards, all the while developing sprawling stilt-roots; eventually the stem may ride seven or eight feet above the ground (Plates 12, 13). This strange habit is strongly developed in the pandans, and occurs in some gingers (*Hornstedtia*) and a few forest sedges of the genus *Mapania*. It renders the definition of the ground layer in the tropical forest as vague as the concept of litter when applied to a heap of palm debris.

The tallest palms occur not in the lowland forest in competition with the tall trees, but in the Andes where a species of wax palm *Ceroxylon* has trunks over two hundred feet high and bears the crown far above the dwarfed dicotyledonous vegetation at this altitude of ten to twelve thousand feet. The giant fish-tail *Caryota* in the Malayan mountains reaches 120 feet and exceeds the canopy of the oak-laurel forest. This is about the maximum height which any lowland palm attains and the majority are less than one hundred feet [90]. However, so much of the lowland forest has been cut over for timber or cleared, while the palms have been left, that they are rendered more conspicuous than was natural. The shortest palms are the stemless and those which descend into the earth with negative stature. The thickest trunks, about three feet in diameter, occur in the Chilean wine palm *Jubaea*, which is an ally of the coconut, and in the Indian talipot *Corypha* [91]. The slenderest are those of forest undergrowth, to be measured in millimetres. Beccari claimed to have found the most diminutive palm *Iguanura palmuncula* in Borneo with four to five fronds the size of a man's hand, at the top of a stem a few inches high and a goose-quill thick [92]. The thickest trunks are not the tallest, the slenderest not the shortest; and the longest are not self-supporting. There are reliable records of climbing rattan stems, *Calamus*, 550 feet long, trailing through the trees as the lengthiest bit of plant-engineering on land; they are rivalled only by the South Atlantic brown seaweed *Macrocystis* of much simpler construction (p. 204).

The palm trunk grows only in the apical part, where two regions must be distinguished. There is the very small growing point proper, or apical meristem, where the cells are dividing, enlarging, and ex-

Figure 46. Sections of the sunken apices of massive palm trunks. Left, *Washingtonia filifera*; × 10 (after Ball, 1941); right, *Livistona chinensis*; × 20 (after Helm, 1937).

tending vascular bundles to fit both the growing leaf-bases which surround it, and the lengthening stem. The whole is the creamy, succulent, and crisp mass bearing the celery-like young leaves, as the forbidden cabbage which the palm does its utmost to protect. It is deeply hidden in the heart of the crown, like the control room in a man-of-war, and the crown is walled with thick, tough, sharp-edged, or thorny leaf-bases which tooth and claw cannot penetrate, though boring beetles may work their way in and prehistoric man with flints force open. Not all palm-cabbages are edible. Some are bitter; others are unsavoury or poisonous; a few have irritant needle-crystals of calcium oxalate in the cells, as in the leaves and tubers of many aroids. The desirable and the undesirable are known to native people who, on occasion, may not scruple to rid themselves of intruders by this means; thus unwanted soldiery was dealt with in Borneo during the Second World War.

In slender palms the stem-apex is conical, but in thicker palms it becomes saucer- or basin-shaped through the great expansion of the subapical tissue. In the centre of this depression the peg-like apical

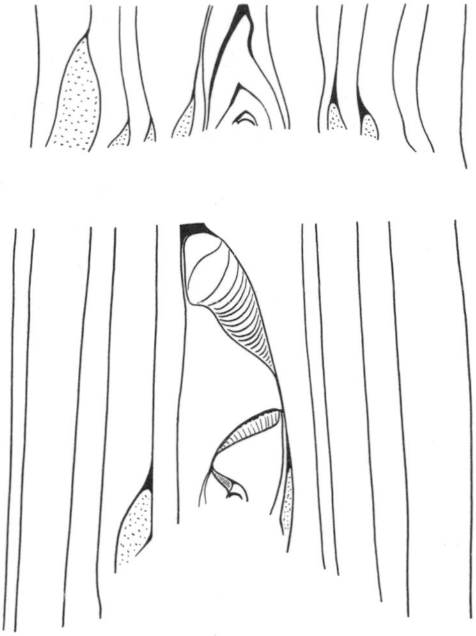

Figure 47. The apices of slender palm stems, the rounded growing point in the centre, the axillary inflorescences stippled. Above, *Ptychosperma*; below *Pinanga furfuracea*; × 6.

meristem is concealed. It measures 70–550μ wide according to the species of palms, and in one case, *Phoenix canariensis*, it has been found to enlarge from 75μ wide in the embryo-plant to 550μ in the adult with stem forty-five centimetres in diameter [93]. The size is much greater than occurs in dicotyledons (30–100μ) and from it results the large mass of growing tissue. There have been few studies on this critical tissue, and we cannot hope to understand fully how palm stems develop and their vascular bundles are arranged until there are many more comparative researches [94]. Someone must sit down in a tropical laboratory with abundant fresh material at hand to work and think it out. What can be said in general is that some palms complete their stem growth within the apical bud, such as most Arecoid palms with their crown-shaft, whereas others variously prolong the process until some time after the leaves have been shed. In this case the trunk does not reach its full size until some distance below the crown. The Arecoid royal palms *Roystonea* happen to show this well (figure 131). It is shown, too, by the fan-leafed palms, the mature leaf-bases of which are split by the slow thickening of the trunk. Such delays in primary growth have been called secondary thickening but the term is misleading because there is no secondary thickening by a cambium, and all primary thickening in multi-

94

cellular plants involves cell-division followed eventually by cell-enlargement. Cell-division multiples the operations which initiate the structures, and cell-enlargement brings them to their working size. The processes are usually in step in both leaf and stem, but the second is delayed in palms, perhaps through the long period required for basal growth of the leaves and it throws trunk and crown out of step. The final adjustment concerns chiefly the increase in amount or bulk of the ground-tissue, particularly in the central region which is the storage tissue for the trunk; there is no development of extensive new vascular tissue, which is the character of cambial secondary thickening. Primary growth is, however, complicated by internodes.

Stem-lengths between leaves are the internodes; where the leaves are attached are the nodes. The internodes often continue to grow after leaf and node are fully formed. In such cases the very short stem-region between two successive leaves keeps its meristematic property of cell-division, thereby adding to the stem-tissue, but in a peculiar basal way. The uppermost cells of the internode, adjoining the node and leaf-base, begin to enlarge and mature, and this second stage of growth passes down the internode until its base, just above the node

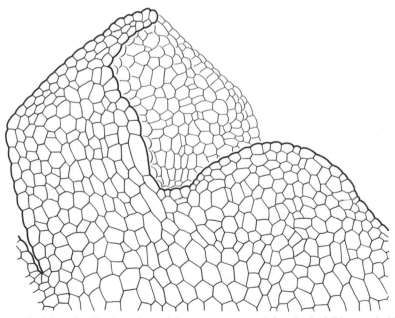

Figure 48. A longitudinal section of the stem-apex and first leaf of *Pinanga kuhlii*; × 350.

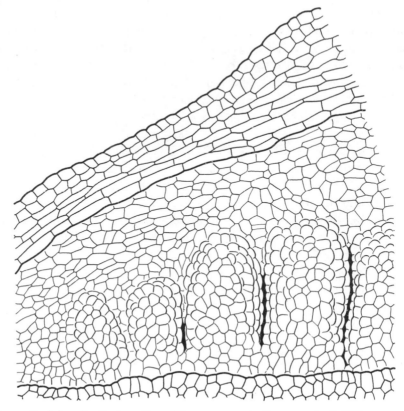

Figure 49. A longitudinal section of the upper part of a young leaf of *Pinanga kuhlii* showing the first stages of the leaflet folds; × 350.

below, is the last to cease growing. The internode is inserted below a leaf and belongs to it, not to the leaf lower down the stem; thus, the internode has the extensions of the vascular bundles of the leaf above, and on its surface ridges or lines of hairs may be carried down the internode from the leaf-base; they are not continued above the leaf-base because that is the internode of the next upper leaf. Internodes become a ready means of lengthening or heightening stems without involving apical growth and the formation of more leaves. The mechanism is picturesquely revealed in striped bamboos; the yellow rows of cells without chlorophyll form vertical lines on the internode because they have been derived from the ring of dividing cells at the base some, only, of which are lacking in chlorophyll.

Now, where leaves are produced in large numbers, or in a high system of phyllotaxis, about an apical meristem, their bases and their vascular bundles overlap, and pieces of stem cannot be separated, as it were, for individual elongation. Hence arise the compact rosettes of leaves without internodes and, hence, in most cases the compact crown of palm-leaves. But where leaf-arrangement is simpler, stem-sections can be isolated. They become conspicuous in the pinnate-leafed palms with a lower order of leaf-arrangement and, especially, in the young actively growing stems. Thus the large fish-tail palms *Caryota* have internodes a foot or more long, which means that for every ten leaves their trunks can also mount ten feet higher, and this must be an advantage over the lusty *Borassus* or *Corypha* without conspicuous internodes. The greatest development of internodes is in the climbing palms where they may be six or seven feet long; it is their chief character. A good Malacca cane with curved handle is one internode of a *Calamus*, but a partridge cane is a stem with numerous internodes of the small-leafed fan-palm *Rhapis*. The rattan cabbages not only grow up but are thrust up, the action being enhanced by the relatively slight mass of their stems. They find their element in climbing because the very numerous fibrovascular bundles of the stems take up the bending, hanging, and twisting strain as well as, or better than, a rope. They make the most outrageous climbers in the forest and have pulled down many a tree in blind extravagance. We used, in the lazy days of sea-travel, to watch the liners come alongside, and I always admired the springy creaking of the great fenders made from entwined rattans, as they kept the grinding plates from the concrete. In olden oriental days and, even now, ships were rigged with rattans. No dicotyledonous climber excels them, and contrast the root-climbers which ascend like millipedes, forming short adherent roots at comparatively close nodes!

When erect palms lean, their crowns are kept upright, partly by the lengthening of the leaf-bases on the underside and partly by the lengthening of the short internodes on the underside. Thus the picturesque coconut, leaning over the strand as the shore is eroded, detects the inclination and rectifies it. The curve does not appear until the leaves have fallen from the matured and rigid part of the trunk. So, also, creeping and descending stems, which germinate into the ground, rectify the leaves.

A few palms have oddly swollen trunks. They are narrowly bottle-shaped or barrel-shaped, though the Cuban barrel palm *Colpothrinax* looks as if it were an anaconda with a meal inside. Examples are the Mascarene *Hyophorbe*, the Madagascan *Chrysalidocarpus decipiens*,

Figure 50. Bottle palms. Left, the Coryphoid *Colpothrinax wrightii* of Cuba; centre, the Cocoid *Acrocomia armentalis* of Cuba; right, the Mascarene Arecoid *Hyophorbe*; $\times \frac{1}{200}$.

the Hispaniolan *Coccothrinax spissa*, the Amazon *Iriartea ventricosa* and several species of *Acrocomia*, and according to Beccari the Bornean form of the fish-tail palm *Caryota rumphiana*. These swellings appear to be exaggerated delayed thickening occurring at the time when the palm is enjoying a maximum period of growth [95]. But not all variations in thickness along the palm trunk can have this explanation. It is well known to horticulturists that in lean years, caused by drought, or under adverse conditions for root-growth, such as heavy clay soil, palm trunks are lean, and that they fatten if good years succeed. The width of the trunk expresses the welfare of the palm apex, whereas dicotyledonous trees flatten out these irregularities with cambial activity. Perhaps this is the explanation of the swellings on the trunks of the African *Borassus aethiopum* which serve as one of the slight means to distinguish it from the Indian palmyra palm *B. flabellifer* [96].

Concerning the rates at which palms grow there is little information. The date-palm has numerous varieties some of which add ten inches and others up to twenty inches to the length of the stem each year. The palmyra palm adds twelve to fifteen inches per annum, and this seems to be a general rate for such massive palms as the coconut, but the oil palm achieves one to two feet per annum. The rate in the double coconut is said to be about seven inches per annum. Then *Caryota* and its ally *Arenga*, both with pronounced internodes, may add four feet per annum. The elongating rattans may exceed seven and eight feet per annum. These figures refer to the average rates during the period of maximum growth. Seedlings and saplings, of course, with fewer leaves establish themselves more slowly. Even after nine years the stem of the palmyra palm is merely four inches high and two inches wide [97].

The internal structure of palm trunks compared with their external variety, is comparatively uniform. A great many vascular bundles are dispersed through a mass of more or less thin-walled parenchymatous ground-tissue. The vascular bundles have, at least on their outer sides towards the stem-surface, a sheath of very thick-walled, hard, dark-brown or black fibres. Sectioning of stems for microscopic examination is, therefore, extremely difficult for it is like slicing splinters embedded in cheese; and for the same reason it is impossible to saw trunks, the stout fibres clogging the teeth. Lengthy and tedious methods have to be used to soften the fibres and it has even been found preferable to embed pieces of stem in hard material, such as canada-balsam, and grind thin sections as for petrified fossil material. One marvels at the unsurpassed drawings made by von Mohl in pioneering palm-anatomy. Even the great size of the material renders microscopic study laborious [98].

The vascular bundles vary in size, in the proportion of fibrous sheath to conducting tissue (phloem, xylem), and in their distribution through the stem. There are two extreme conditions, but with numerous intermediates. Either, in such as *Corypha* and *Mauritia* as the standard examples, the bundles are closely set towards the surface and are well-spaced in the central part of the trunk, or they are fairly uniformly distributed throughout, as in the coconut-palm. Then a *Corypha*-construction can be distinguished from that of *Mauritia*. In both, the fibrous sheaths of the outer bundles are many times larger than the conducting part. This proportion is maintained more or less in the inner bundles of *Corypha* but not in *Mauritia*, where the fibrous sheath becomes smaller than the conducting part. However, too few palms have had their trunks anatomized to draw general or detailed conclusions [99].

With these patterns in mind, it is necessary to consider how they have been formed and what they represent. Von Mohl discovered by gross dissection, in which he used rotted stems, and others have confirmed that the vascular bundles of the leaf-base pass obliquely downwards to the centre of the trunk and then, more gradually, towards the periphery again. In so doing the fibrous sheath becomes relatively more massive than the conducting part, but the whole bundle becomes smaller as it approaches the periphery far below the leaf-base. Hence arise the patterns of *Mauritia* and *Corypha*, with large and small, strongly sheathed and crowded outer bundles. During this passage there may be various interconnections between the bundles and their course may spiralize from the leaf-base so that their narrow parts end up at the periphery by joining vascular bundles on another side of the stem; such trunks are unusually difficult to split. In any case a sort of elongate network of thousands of strands is made which connects all the vascular bundles down the trunk to those of the roots.

But this is the wrong way of looking at the problem. The vascular bundles do not descend. They are produced upwards as the stem grows. This means that a small, very fibrous bundle developed near the outside of the stem gradually courses inwards and when it has nearly reached the centre below the site of a leaf-primordium it is developed outwards into that primordium; during this time it has branched to establish contacts with other vascular bundles and has altered the proportions of fibrous and vascular elements. Now the distance traversed by such a bundle in the stem of a large palm is so great that many months, if not several years, must elapse before it enters a leaf. In other words, there is a remarkable predestination in the laying down of the long intricate network. In the trunk of an adult coconut palm, one foot in diameter, there are about eighteen thousand vascular bundles as seen in cross-section. So complicated a system can be worked out only by following its build-up from the comparatively simple state of the seedling. And it must be observed that, inasmuch as palm anatomy is far from understood, so that of lesser and reduced monocotyledons is insecure [100].

Palm-leaflets contain a large number of more or less parallel, longitudinal vascular bundles with fibrous sheaths, and between them are various cross-connections; moreover some of these bundles unite towards the base of the leaflet. The larger, or groups of larger ones, make the more prominant veins. All are collected into the rachis, which is thickened downwards, and then they spread out in the leaf-base so that a shower of hundreds or thousands of bundles seem to enter the stem. It may be that all the stem-bundles are also leaf-bundles, though it is possible that some are confined to the stem.

As for the leaves themselves, they generally have differently organized upper and lower surfaces with the stomata on the lower surface. Some fan-palms which hold the leaves upright for a long while, such as *Corypha* and *Washingtonia*, have stomata on both working surfaces. It is the case also with the induplicate leaves of *Phoenix*, commonly held in a variety of directions and so requiring all-round activity. There is so much variation in detail that it is possible to identify the main groups of palms from the microscopic structure of the leaflet. The result is an important reconsideration of palm-alliances [101].

Phloem and xylem make the conducting part of the vascular bundles. The xylem varies in different palms and in different parts of the same long vascular bundle. There may be one or two large vessels, varying from 50 to 350μ wide in different palms, and several smaller ones. They are made up from longitudinal rows of short cells put into aqueous continuity by holes in the transverse walls. The total length of a vessel evidently varies, again, in different palms and is longest in the rattans where the superposed rows of cells developed in the long internodes facilitate the making of long vessels; rattan vessels are also the widest. Thus the construction automatically introduces the engineering requirement, and this is the mark of a successful organism.

It is well-known in rattan country that good drinking water can be obtained from the rattan-stems. If a piece about six to ten feet long, such as can be handled, is cut from a climbing stem and up-ended over a cup, it can be filled two or three times with cool, clear, if somewhat earthy-tasting, water. If the piece is cut in two, more water can be obtained from each half, and the process can be repeated, though the yield diminishes. The explanation is simple, as shown schematically in figure 51. Here nine vessels are represented to show the various positions in which they may end or start in the piece of stem. Firstly water will run out of vessels 1 and 9 because they traverse the whole length and have cut ends at top and bottom; as the water drops out, air can be drawn in at the top. Vessels 2–8 cannot be emptied because they act as sealed capillary tubes, no matter what the position in which the stem is held. If, now, the piece is cut across at A, the upper half *a* will drain vessels 2–5, not 6–8, and the lower half will drain vessels 6–8, not 2–5; vessels 1 and 9 have already been drained. If *aa* is cut across at B, it will drain vessels 2 and 3 in the upper half *b*, vessels 4 and 5 in the lower half *bb*. Similarly, if the upper part *a* is sectioned at C, its upper half *c* will drain vessels 6 and 7, its

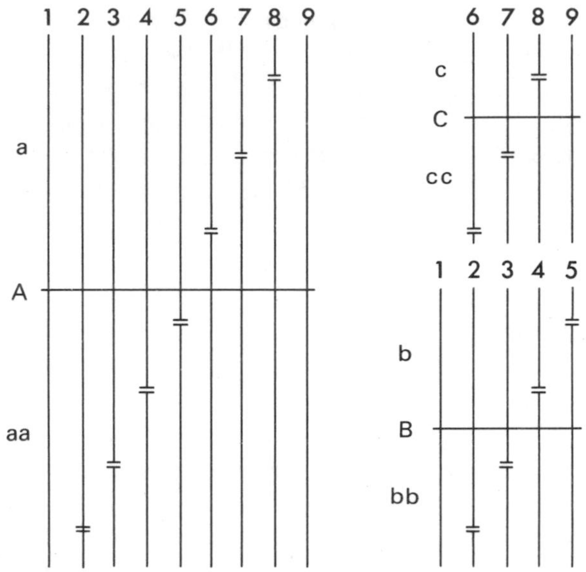

Figure 51. Diagram to show the effect of severing a rattan stem successively at levels A, B, and C. Xylem-vessels 1–9, the vessel-endings marked by transverse lines. *a*, *aa*, etc. refer to upper and lower stem-sections.

lower half vessel 8. If instead of nine vessels there are nine hundred, the effect is conspicuous. I have noticed, however, in many rattans that the lower half of a piece of stem, such as *aa*, *bb*, or *cc*, gives more water than the upper half; indeed, the upper half may give so little that the thirsty discard it. It is the enigma of the rattan. One learns, too, in the heat of the day how rapid is the transpiration stream. It is easy to cut a rattan stem near the base, but by the time the dangling stem has been caught and severed six or seven feet up, most of the water in it will have passed up the stem to the leaves. To slake the thirst, the stem must be cut as far away from the root as possible, and then severed into pieces. The experienced look for old stems coiled on the ground where they have sunken as their support has broken. A recent study finds the rate of flow in an Australian *Calamus* at $\frac{1}{3}$ litre per hour, which does not seem at all excessive [102].

Estimates for the coconut palm put the amount of water transpired from the crown at 28–75 litres in twenty-four hours. This flow occurs mostly in the daytime and is much quickened by full sunshine and wind. At night any water-deficiency in the plant, caused by excessive transpiration the day before, is made good. The water supply is diverted to the adult photosynthetic leaves during the day and becomes available for growth mainly during the night. Thus cells, stems, leaves, inflorescences, flowers, fruits, and seed grow principally at night; if they are parts which open, they do so usually in the early morning.

It is well known that cutting the stalk of a leaf in active transpiration will cause air to enter the cut vessels and that this air will block further entry of water if the stalk is then put in a vessel of water. Many palm leaves proceed to wilt, however, even though their stalks are cut under water to avoid this air-block. It is the difficulty also with cut pieces of bamboo. The means of water-supply to their leaves seems to differ from that in dicotyledons and to depend more on root-pressure; that is by the forcing of water into the stem by the absorbing roots rather than the drawing of it along the stem by the transpiring leaves. High root-pressures occur in a number of palms [103]. Pressures equivalent to a water-column 40–70 cm. high have been found in *Livistona* and *Caryota*, but as much as 5·5 m. in *Borassus* and *Areca*, 6·5 m. in *Roystonea* and *Ptychosperma*, and 12·5 m. in the coconut palm, cut leaves of which cannot be kept in a turgid but transpiring state [104]. The positive root-pressure in all these examples far exceeded the negative pressure or suction developed in the root by the transpiring leaves. Bamboos often exude drops of water from their leaf-tips in the early morning, just as lawn-grasses do, and this seems to be another expression of the high root pressure which injects the plant with water overnight. Palms do not show guttation, as the phenomenon is called, but the considerable power of exuding sugary sap that they possess may be a similar effect (p. 125). Nevertheless, the study of the Australian rattan *Calamus*, already mentioned, proved that its leaves developed a normal transpiration stream [105].

There occurred in India a wild date-palm *Phoenix sylvestris*, that became famous as 'the praying palm of Faridpore'. Through some misadventure its trunk had been turned nearly horizontal but it curved up at the end to carry the erect crown. Of an afternoon the leaves would begin to sag and by the hour of Muslim vespers not only the leaves were prostrate but all that end of the trunk to which they were attached. At night the palm recovered itself, the standing and the prostration continuing day after day, until its death. It was investigated by the unorthodox Indian physiologist Bose [106], but it has never been explained how the mature and woody leaf-bases allowed the whole crown to droop under loss of turgidity.

H

Except for the stout aerial roots of pandans, palm roots are the thickest and toughest primary roots (without secondary thickening) among all plants. They are also exceedingly numerous. It has been calculated that eight thousand roots, one centimetre thick, emerge from the base of a normal coconut or oil palm, and the number may be as high as thirteen thousand [107]. The seedling root, grown from the radicle of the embryo, is short-lived. Its place is soon taken by roots which break out from the base of the seedling stem. They branch in the soil, but their lives are limited, and they are replaced by more roots from the stem. Such are called adventitious roots because roots should normally arise by branching from other roots. Palms depend on this power to develop adventitious roots from the basal and oldest region of their stems.

Having no secondary thickening, the root remains cylindrical for long distances but, eventually, it tapers off to the root-tips one to four millimetres wide, which is covered with a stout root-cap. As this frays off by friction against the soil, bits of the cap may remain as collars round the root. There are seldom root-hairs, and water is absorbed in the short length of a few centimetres behind the root-cap. Further back the cortex of the root begins to develop under the epidermis, which also wears off, the strong, fibrous, lignified cylinder that makes the tough, rigid casing, and this gives to the root its great tensile strength. It is so hard that it may imprison lateral roots and prevent them from emerging until they have grown internally some distance towards the young and softer part of the parent root. The casing is more or less impervious to water and, while denying water-absorption to the greater part of the long root, it conserves that which is in transit to the stem.

Palm-roots are called polyarch, meaning with many beginnings. The word refers to the number of xylem-strands which alternate with the phloem strands. One of my earliest recollections of academic botany imposing its regulations was hearing students before an examination muttering diarch, triarch, and other shibboleths; thus we never forget these grand names. Small roots can accommodate little structure. They have few xylem-strands, generally two to five (diarch to pentarch), sometimes only one (monarch). In dicotyledons this small start is soon implemented by secondary xylem and phloem developed by the cambium, and the thickening root can accommodate the increasing water-flow as it branches. In monocotyledons, without cambium, the roots must remain small with little competence or they must be stouter to accommodate more conducting strands.

Palms and pandans have the most polyarch roots. Their stoutest roots, an inch or more wide, may have over a hundred xylem strands, puzzling the student for a Greek name. The coconut-root, barely half an inch wide, has about forty strands. Then, as these roots diminish in size towards the end of their growth the number drops to the more usual monocotyledon level of seven to twelve strands. At the base of the stem these xylem strands in palms and pandans make numerous deep connections with the vascular bundles; they may make as many separate connections as there are xylem-strands. Thus one stout root supplies many vascular bundles and these, interconnecting with others up the stem may supply a considerable part of one leaf or the flow may be distributed to parts of several leaves, these issues not having been found out. The massiveness of these roots is held to be exceptional, and so it is for it fits the exceptional character of these plants, excelling in primary massiveness. But the slender roots of herbaceous monocotyledons are the small neotenic effects of this massiveness.

The roots of the coconut-palm spread horizontally for twenty to thirty feet in the soil. They branch two to four times, more or less at right-angles and they diminish to rootlets one millimetre wide. They cover an area which exceeds the diameter of the crown, and they are so firmly intruded into the soil that nothing less than a hurricane may dislodge them. An uprooted palm is extremely rare. Undermining the soil, as on sea-coasts, causes the palm to lean and coconut trunks seventy feet and more long may incline horizontally over the shelving beach, but the roots do not break in spite of the enormous strain.

The coconut-palm also produces special breathing roots (pneumathodes). They are very short, spiky rootlets three to six millimetres long, grown on all sides of the more superficial roots. They do not breath but the loose texture of their cortical cells, which swell up and flare out like the powdery tissue of lenticels in tree-trunks, allows the ready diffusion of oxygen into the rootlet and of carbon-dioxide out. The spiky tip is the dried and hardened root-cap. Other palms such as *Elaeis*, *Oncosperma*, *Phoenix*, and *Raphia* have pneumathodes, especially in water-logged soils, yet the swamp palm *par excellence*, the nipa palm, seems without them. Large air-cavities traverse the cortex of its roots, connecting with the large air-cavities in its bouyant leaf-bases, and the rise and fall of tide may with slow strokes pump the air around.

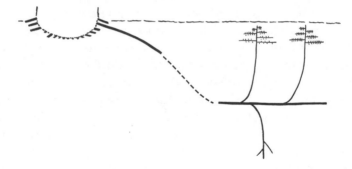

Figure 52. Diagram of the root-system of the oil palm *Elaeis*, the base of the trunk on the left; the primary root descending and travelling horizontally; a few deeply descending secondary roots and numerous ascending secondaries, the short tertiary and quaternary rootlets serving as the feeding roots; $\times \frac{1}{20}$.

The root system of the African oil palm, *Elaeis guineensis*, has been studied carefully [108]. The main roots descend steeply from the base of the trunk. At depths of fifty centimetres or more, they become horizontal and continue for some thirteen metres at a constant diameter of five millimetres (figure 52). They are the main anchorage roots. The secondaries arise from them at an angle of 45°, mostly from the upper sides, fewer from the lower sides, and none from the flanks. The lower descend to undetermined depths and branch occasionally. The upper ascend and on nearing the surface of the soil produce the short, narrow, tertiary roots, up to ten centimetres long, at right angles. These are the main absorbing roots and they often produce very short, five millimetre long, quaternary rootlets, at right angles; and these apparently become the pneumathodes. As with most plants of tropical forest, the feeding roots are more or less superficial. Plantations of oil-palm can, therefore, be manured with top-dressings and there is no need to plough in. Ploughing, in fact, would cut off many feeding and breathing rootlets. Thus from plantation practice, botanical knowledge grows. The oil-palm suggests that the root-system of palms may in general be as precise as their aerial construction.

Short spiky rootlets and pneumathodes lead to another modification. The trunk of the Central American palm *Cryosophila* (formerly known as *Acanthorrhiza* because of the spiny roots) are covered with straight or curved thorns up to several inches long. Some, in the lower part of the trunk where conditions are damper, lengthen into roots. All, in fact, are variously stunted adventitious roots, spiked with their

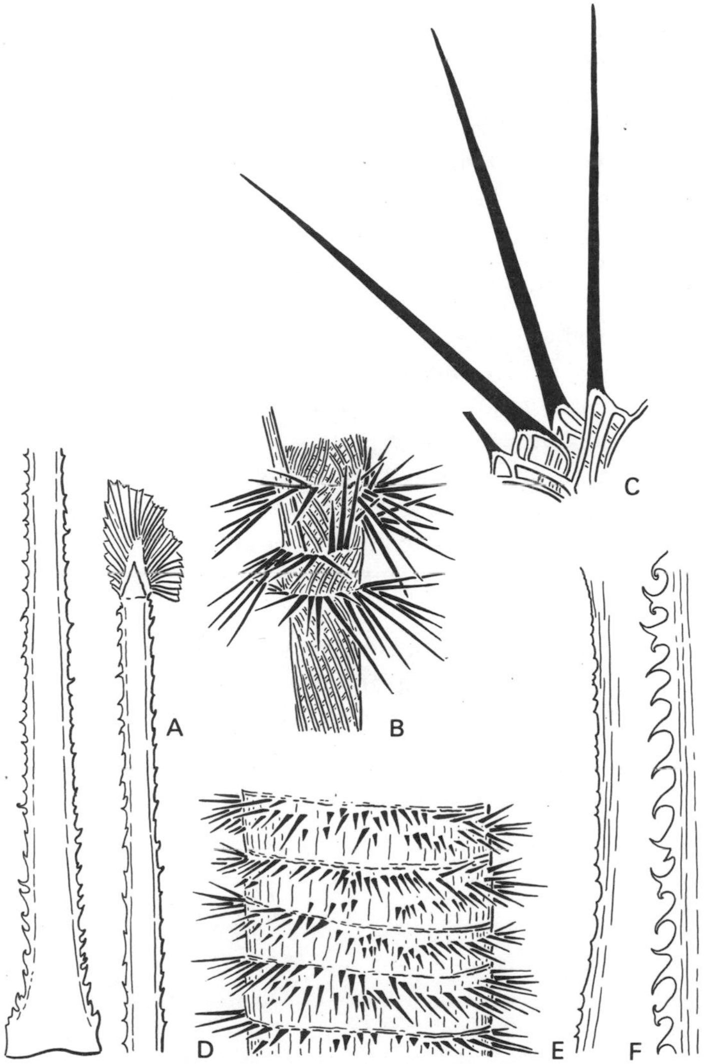

Figure 53. Spines. A, the spines on the sides of the stalk of the *Washingtonia* leaf, typical of many Coryphoid and Borassoid palms, the curvature of the spine tips possibly caused by the sliding growth over adjacent leaves in the bud; × $\frac{1}{20}$ (after Bailey, 1936). B, the leaf-sheath spines of the Coryphoid *Zombia*, caused by the separation and recurving of the fibro-vascular bundles of the sheath; × $\frac{1}{4}$ (after Bailey, 1939). C, similar fibre-thorns of the leaf-sheath of the Coryphoid *Trithrinax*; × $\frac{1}{2}$ (after Barbosa Rodriguez, 1903). D, the spinous trunk of the Cocoid *Acrocomia*; × $\frac{1}{6}$ (after Bailey, 1941); E, the spinous edges of the leaf-stalks of *Corypha umbraculifera* and F of *C. elata*; × $\frac{1}{10}$ (after Douglas and Bimantoro, 1957).

hardened root-caps. There are similar root-thorns on the trunks of the Amazon *Mauritia aculeata* and *M. armata*, and the aerial stilt-roots of the Amazon *Iriartea* are also thorny with abortive rootlets; the hard root-cap in their case may be needed to pierce the hard sheath of the root to let the rootlet out. Similar thorny trunks and roots are developed by the pandans.

Root-thorns return us to the subject of palm-thorns in general. There are many thornless palms. Others have thorny trunks, leaf-sheaths, stalks, leaflets, inflorescences and, even, fruits. Not a few bristle with needles, spikes, and lances up to a foot long. The American alliance of *Acrocomia, Astrocaryum, Aiphanes, Bactris,* and the climbing *Desmoncus* is so spiny that the plants often cannot be approached and handled without gloves. In *Acrocomia* the spines pass by gradual transitions into fine, stiff pungent hairs over the whole epidermis. In tropical Asia the Arecoid alliance of *Oncosperma,* developed so strangely in the Seychelles of the Indian Ocean, and the Lepidocaryoid rattans with their allies *Metroxylon* and *Salacca* are the chief offenders.

All these spines are epidermal outgrowths, developed from a group of cells on the immature and embryonic epidermis. The groups have their special places and form a pattern which can be seen on the adult

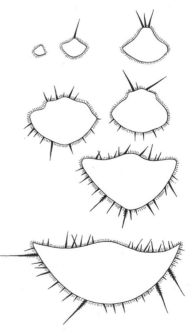

Figure 54. Cross-sections of the leaf-axis of the Cocoid *Acrocomia eriocantha* from below upwards, showing the stout spines (the larger of which are bristly themselves) and the bristly hairs; × ½ (after Barbosa Rodriguez, 1903).

parts, but the reason for this is not known and, certainly, in most cases, not every cell contributes to a spine or hair. The outgrowths become flattened because they must fit the compressed chinks in the palm bud; yet they are vigorous and, on lignifying, they imprint their outline in bas-relief on the surface which bears them. The larger develop vascular bundles, though they come to little as the spines dry off. They grow basally, as all aerial structures of palms, and they harden and change colour from yellow through pink and red to brown and black from the tip to the base. These beautiful patterns, worked on the creamy surface of young leaves, caught the eye of the early craftsmen in vegetable-ware, particularly in the villages of the rattan-pullers, and they were transferred from baskets, no doubt, and bamboo utensils to pottery and various ornamentation [109].

When the sword-leaf begins to expose its spines, they still have their soft creamy bases and each is supplied with a pulvinus the swelling of which pushes the spine outwards and sets it at the characteristic angle; spine-base and pulvinus then lignify into fixtures [110]. The spines, as well as the leaflets, are actively displayed. In the more elaborate instances there are combs or whorls of spines, some still upwardly pointing, others strongly deflexed between them, and there may be a multitude of lesser spines and needles set at various angles around them to make the surface unassailable to large creatures, yet protective for the small. Various grasshoppers and crickets lurk among them and imitate them with an unbelievable spininess of their own, so intricate that they cannot be extricated and are with difficulty detected.

Figure 55. The dwarf Cocoid *Bactris trailiana* of Brazil with spinous unsplit leaves; × $\frac{1}{25}$ (after Barbosa Rodriguez, 1903).

Figure 56. Seedling of the Cocoid *Astrocaryum* with spiny sheaths and frond from the outset; $\times \frac{1}{2}$ (after Barbosa Rodriguez, 1903).

Another way of making spines is possessed by various fan-palms of the Coryphoid alliance, such as the American *Trithrinax* and *Zombia*; it happens also in the African oil palm. Here there are no epidermal spines but the leaf-sheath on weathering away reveals its skeleton of fibrovascular bundles. The larger of these, chiefly near the upper edge of the sheath, dry up and reflex into vicious lances [111]. Yet another method converts the lower leaflets on the leaf-axes into spines. The whole leaflet turns into a thorn in *Phoenix* as a distinctive character of the genus. In the oil palm *Elaeis* the lower leaflets lose their slight lamina and the midrib persists as the spine.

There are so many glabrous land plants, especially monocotyledons, that glabrousness is often assumed to be their original and primitive state. Noting could be further from the truth, as Griffith might have exclaimed. Systematic study, which is the phyletic comparison of plants, shows clearly that glabrousness is incidental in most genera through loss of hairs. The conclusion must be that the

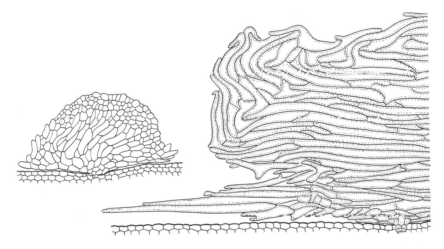

Figure 57. Small scales from the midrib of the leaflet of *Pinanga kuhlii*, one in the young state before cell-elongation; showing the derivation of the scale from a 4-celled gland hair (as in Fig. 58) followed by filamentous (pseudoparenchymatous) construction in one plane; × 50.

smooth epidermis has been derived from the hairy or that beset with outgrowths. Palms, besides displaying spinous outgrowths in the strongest and most varied way of any plants, possess a great variety of peculiar and elaborate hairs (Figs 57, 58). They occur mainly on the leaf-axis, leaflets, and inflorescences because the leaf-sheaths are usually pressed too closely together in the bud for epidermal excursions to take place; similarly they press too tightly on the stem and, by the time that the surfaces are freed, they have matured beyond the stage of forming hairs. Some of these secrete a mucilage in the seaweed way; others dry up and detach as smooth, microscopic rolling pins. They assist the growth of the young leaves in the tube of older leaf-bases by lubricating their passage. They dry

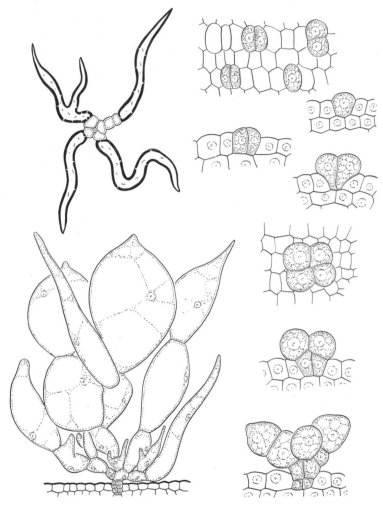

Figure 58. Hairs of *Pinanga furfuracea*. A thick-walled stellate hair from the leaf-sheath and a branching vesicular hair from the leaf-axis; × 100. Right, a series of stages in the development of a mucilage gland-hair with a head of four cells, this gland-hair being the initial stage of most of the larger and more complicated hairs; × 350.

up on the exposed surfaces as thin felt, fur, wool, or scurfiness, and even this detail has not escaped the notice of the palm-dweller. The fine dry chaff from the young leaves of coconut, *Arenga*, and other palms is used as tinder to catch the spark of flint or the heat of rubbing sticks. The palm epidermis, thickly invested and glabrous, primitive and advanced, is one of the most interesting among land-plants.

The larger voracious animals, against which a toughened epidermis is insufficient defence, are prevented from climbing palms or jumping on to them by the formidable thorns. They cannot take the bud, young leaf, inflorescence, or flower, and they must wait until the fruit falls. The harvest is bountiful, but it may not be attacked prematurely. Nowadays apes, monkeys, squirrels, rats, sloths, bats, tree-marsupials, bears, pigs, antelopes, giraffe, rhinoceros, tapir, and elephants are the chief assailants, but what were they? Palms have witnessed the coming of these modern creatures as they have witnessed the going of their ancestors. They have endured since the Mesozoic era and have taken part in, suffered, and survived the evolution of the great herbivorous reptiles, the giant marsupials, sloths, and other mammalian monsters. The armour of spines is the defence of a hundred million years. Yet, it has been discarded. Increasing massiveness and lignification may have rendered spines unnecessary; chemical warfare with poisonous or unpalatable tissues may have taken over. But where and what could have been the circumstances of the unarmed palm? The elaborate inheritance of living organisms deteriorates when the environment no longer provokes them. Perhaps the outer isles were the places, where there is little animal adversity and thornless palms abound. Madagascar, New Caledonia, and most of the lesser islands of the Pacific have thornless palms, whereas the armoured are chiefly continental. By the rivers, where the spiniest occur, they would have faced the tide of mammalian advance as they withstood the rise of dicotyledonous forest. In its interior the very multiplicity of trunks may have concealed the loss of the thorns; it may have prevented the ingress of the bulky animals, and when the intelligent came long after, the palm and the forest were evolved. The diversity of palms provoked the intelligence of primitive man into the employment of them for nearly every need of his simple existence; it may have provoked the intelligence of the incipient mammal, which eliminated the unprotected. Thus we can be sure that the unarmed and edible coconut palm, vulnerable in many ways and everywhere tended in civilization, of unknown origin, did not evolve on the progressive continents.

## Chapter 5

# Inflorescence

THE VEGETATIVE part of a flowering plant consists of leaf, stem, and root. The reproductive and flowering part is the inflorescence; its fruiting state is called the infructescence. Palm flowers are generally small and unpretentious. They work by massed effect on large, stout, and often highly branched inflorescences, and these structures must project out from the large leaf-bases, through the thicket of long leaf-stalks, even beyond, above or below, the crown of leaves. As branching frameworks bearing hundreds and thousands of flower buds, they are the antithesis of the palm trunk with its one head of giant leaves. If we assume that the first palms had unbranched or dichotomously branched trunks, we have to assume also that they could burst forth in the flowering time into a very elaborate and modern method of axillary branching to end in spikes or racemes of fruits. Here is a very difficult problem; yet it is no other than that of the cabbage when left to flower next spring. A talipot palm *Corypha* is an enormous cabbage which flowers after some thirty or forty years and from its heart comes a panicle twenty feet high with branches ten and fifteen feet long, while the leaves drop off the trunk and there stands a seventy-foot pole ripening half a million fruits like green marbles in termination of the giant. What the gardener scarcely notices makes the palm botanist thunderstruck. We enter that valley of botany most in need of exploration and we can only speculate for the guide to the history of the inflorescence has not been found. What is certain is that the slender unbranched fruiting spikes of small forest palms are simplifications befitting their neotenic habit. Before we can theorize, a botanical Hercules will have to grapple with the largest, most detailed, toughest, and most unyielding inflorescences in the plant world.

The inflorescence is organized as a spirally constructed shoot, the reduced leaves on which become spaced by internodes, while the ends of the branches bear the flowers which are congested through little or no internodal separation. Thus there are stalks, bracts and flowering spikes. The main stalk continues through the branching system as the axis of the inflorescence; its branches are the primary branches which continue as axes through the system of secondary branches which they bear; and there can be tertiary and quaternary branchings. At whatever degree the branching stops, the last set of branches become the flowering spikes. If these spikes were extended and the flowers set on pedicels, they would be racemes; the whole inflorescence would then be a branched raceme or, as sometimes called, a panicle. But the final branches are much condensed, so that the palm inflorescence is a panicle of spikes.

Because these spikes are thick and often succulent as well as tough, each is called a spadix (plural spadices) like the fleshy spadix, or axis, of the aroid inflorescence. In small palms the inflorescence may be a single spadix, terminal on the one elongate stalk. Hence the panicle of the larger palms is often thought of as a branched spadix but this is incorrect, for a branched spadix must be a branched spike and there are certainly no branched spikes of this magnitude. The whole terminology of the spadix is then extended to the palms and the bracts are called spathes; the smaller bracts higher up the axis or along the branches are called spathels as a diminutive, and the terms bract and bracteole are reserved for the very reduced leaves which subtend the flowers on the spike. This spike is sometimes called a rachilla or, even, spikelet when the term spadix is used for the whole inflorescence, but these are very small diminutives applicable, no doubt, to grasses but not suitable for the thick structures of palms which may be several feet long. It is simpler to speak of the inflorescence, its branches, and its spikes (meaning the parts which bear the flowers); the words spathe and spathel are convenient because they refer to much larger structures which do not subtend flowers like the small bracts. If the word spikelet is to be used, it must refer to the small clusters of flowers which substitute the single flower on the spike, as happens with *Borassus*, numerous Arecoid and Cocoid palms, and most, if not all, Lepidocaryoid genera.

The passage from palm trunk to inflorescence is abrupt. There are no intermediate structures between leaf and spathe as there may be between spathe and spathel, or this and bract; in some inflorescences, indeed, there is a gradual transition in form, size, and function right along from spathe to minute bract. The inflorescence never appears, therefore, as a vegetative branch that gradually transforms,

Figure 59. Terminal palm inflorescences, much reduced. A, the sago palm *Metroxylon*. B, the highly branched panicle of *Corypha*. C, a branch of the *Corypha* panicle showing the spathes and ultimate spikes of flowers.

and the inflorescence never continues into vegetative growth as may happen in various dicotylednous trees [112]. The growing point which is to form an inflorescence is physiologically altered from the vegetative growing point. Its spathes and bracts correspond with reduced, neotenic leaves but there is not the growth substance to develop

116

them into vegetative leaves. Spathe and bract stop their leaf-development before the stage of forming folds; hence, on expansion, they are hood-like or boat-shaped with more or less of a sheathing base, but without leaflets or marginal strips. Higher up the inflorescence these structures become more neotenic as crescentic leaf-primordia, enlarged and encircling the bud, but not or rarely hooded; this, too, is the form of the sepals and petals. Every branch of the inflorescence develops from the bud in the axil of a spathe or spathel and every flower develops from the axil of a bract.

Nevertheless, as usual with living things, there are exceptions. The terminal inflorescenes of some stout palms, such as *Corypha* and *Metroxylon*, may have reduced leaves at the base and they may show how the vegetative leaf is transformed into a spathe. Among the rattans there are some, as *Korthalsia* and *Plectocomia*, in which the lower spathes have the form of reduced pinnate leaves. Then, as a most unusual instance, the slender inflorescence which develops from the base of the small stemless palm *Salacca flabellata* and grows along the ground to produce axillary spikes, may root at the end and turn up into a new leafy plant. It is a trick found in several flowering plants with this geocarpic habit of flowering (figure 67). The peculiarity is not so much an inflorescence becoming a vegetative shoot, as a vegetative runner becoming fertile.

The inflorescences of most palms are lateral and axillary. They come from the buds in the axils of the foliage leaves and these buds are given over entirely to reproduction. The young inflorescences are extruded by basal growth of their internodes along the upperside of the leaf-stalk until they project into the gaps between the fronds or, indeed, far beyond them. This is the habit of many fan-palms, such as *Erythea*, *Livistona*, *Pritchardia*, *Sabal*, and *Washingtonia* [112a]; the magnificent and much branched sprays, six to twelve feet long, then turn into fruiting sprays which sag under their burden. At the other extreme there are the relatively short and upright inflorescences in the smaller palms and these may be highly branched or variously reduced with few branches to the ultimate unbranched condition. Nevertheless there are Arecoid palms of considerable size which have very long unbranched inflorescences consisting of a spike several feet long, for instance *Calyptrocalyx* of the Moluccas, *Howeia* of the Lord Howe Isle, and *Linospadix* of New Guinea and Australia [113]. The length, angle, outline, branching, density and, in fact, the whole display of the inflorescence is specific to every kind of palm.

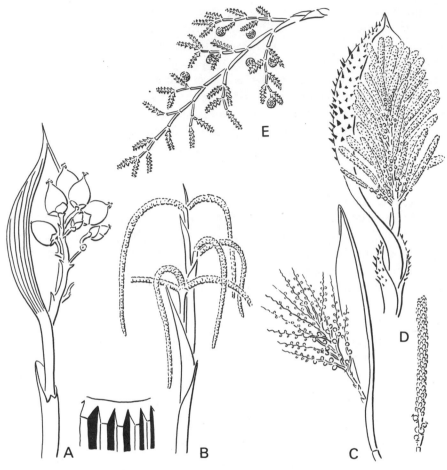

Figure 60. Lateral inflorescences. A, the Cocoid *Attalea* setting fruit, with the large fissured spathe (a portion enlarged at the bottom right); × $\frac{1}{6}$. B, the female inflorescence of the Borassoid *Medemia*; × $\frac{1}{8}$. C, *Cocos* with female flowers at the base of the branches; × $\frac{1}{8}$. D, the Cocoid *Acrocomia* with thorny spathes and (lower right) a spike or spadix enlarged to show the basal female flowers; × $\frac{1}{6}$. E, the Lepidocaryoid *Calamus* with tubular spathes and distichous bracts; × $\frac{1}{4}$. (A, C, D, after Barbosa Rodriguez, 1903; B, after Jumelle, 1945).

The eye can master the character quickly, but the understanding calls for pages of explanation.

In palms with strong tubular leaf-sheaths, the young inflorescence cannot escape until the tube is split and the leaf is ready to be pushed off. So, in the many Arecoid palms, the inflorescences appear not among the leaves but at the top of the stem immediately below the

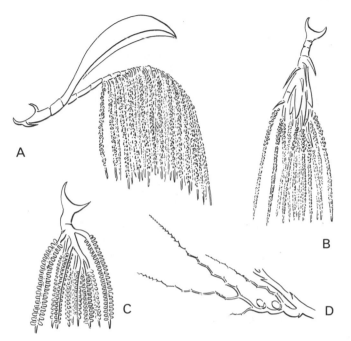

Figure 61. Arecoid inflorescences, much reduced. A, *Oncosperma* with large spathe and the flowers in triads. B, *Kentia* with female flowers in the basal half of the spikes. C, *Pinanga* with the flowers in two rows. D, a branch of the *Areca* inflorescence with female flowers at the base, the distal solitary male flowers fallen.

crown, and they open several weeks or months after the leaf which bore them has fallen; this interval of time in *Actinorhytis* is fifty to sixty days. They are generally shorter and more compact, befitting their inclusion within the leaf-sheath until that leaf has finished its life. This habit is called infrafoliar flowering in contrast to the inter-foliar; it is an advance towards that of cauliflory, or stem-flowering, which occurs in many dicotyledonous trees, but it is not developed further in palms except in the very special way of Caryotoid palms; for most palms the trunk below the leaves becomes a conducting pole rather than a food store. Infrafoliar flowering expresses the refinement of the palm trunk into the terminal crown, compacted by the crown-shaft, and the subterminal flowering-fruiting zone; the first gives place to the second as the stem heightens. The arrangement may help in supplying an umbrella to the opening flowers and setting fruits. A peculiar and unexplained example of this habit is the Andean *Catoblastus* which bears several inflorescences from the

Figure 62. The arecoid *Calyptrocalyx* of the Molucca Islands with long unbranched inflorescence; $\times \frac{1}{100}$. (after Blume, 1841).

axil of one leaf: the stem below the crown appears ringed with a whorl of inflorescences at each leaf-scar.

There are still other ways of extricating the axillary inflorescence. It may push through the triangular gap created by the splitting of the leaf-base, as in *Lodoicea* (figure 127). In *Bactris, Salacca* and its rattan ally *Korthalsia*, the young inflorescence actively pierces through the thick base of the leaf-sheath in the side of the frond. In the rattans *Calamus* and *Daemonorops* the bud, from which the inflorescence is developed, is carried up by some peculiar intercalary growth so that it is placed on the outside of the leaf-sheath above that to which it was axillary; hence their inflorescences appear to sprout from a leaf-sheath on one side of its leaf-stalk and somewhat below it (figure 63). By this means the advanced, yet spiny *Calamus* at once brings its inflorescences, three to twenty feet long, into play to participate in the entangling and climbing life of the forest. The spathes are armed with recurved spines or claws and the extremity of the inflorescence may run out into a long whip armed with clusters of grapnel-like hooks, just as on the end of the climbing leaves. In

Figure 63. Part of a flowering system of the rattan *Calamus* to show the attachment of the inflorescence to the side of the leaf-sheath; the inflorescence ending in a flagellum; × $\frac{1}{8}$.

many species of the genus, too, the lower leaf-sheaths bear sterile inflorescences in the form of long, unbranched, and barbed whips which aid in the general catching and scrambling; no other genus of palms has such specially modified, immature and sterile inflorescences. Indeed, these species of *Calamus* are the biggest and most specialized climbers. They build the immense rattan thickets which festoon the trees from ground-level and are rendered impenetrable by the tough, springy, lengthy, and barbed leaf-sheaths, leaf-whips, and inflorescence whips. Who is caught among them must retreat and unhook and, in doing so, must take care lest he becomes inextricably hooked. The allied *Daemonorops*, though with the same extra-axillary inflorescences, has not evolved the inflorescence whips and its relatively short inflorescences take no part in the upward struggle.

The alternative to the axillary inflorescence is the terminal. It alters entirely the life of the plant, and occurs in so few genera that they are noted for this peculiarity. *Corypha* and its humble ally *Nannorrhops* are the two fan-palms in the Coryphoid subfamily. The pinnate-leafed are seven Lepidocaryoid genera, *Eugeissona*, *Metroxylon*, the

Figure 64. *Corypha elata* in full growth (right) and fruiting with a terminal panicle at the end of its life; the trunk with slight spiral fluting; × $\frac{1}{200}$.

eastern rattans *Korthalsia*, *Myrialepis*, *Plectocomia*, and *Plecto-comiopsis*, and the African rattan *Ancistrophyllum*. The inflorescence is not produced until the trunk has completed its vegetative growth and the terminal bud has changed into the reproductive. When it has flowered and fruited, that trunk is exhausted and dies. As a tiny weed may exhaust itself in producing a little flower or spike, the palms exhaust years of massive development in a final outburst. The greatest is that of the spectacular *Corypha* whose giant corpses slowly crumble and topple in decay [114]. The Indian talipot *C. umbraculifera* requires forty to seventy years to reach the flowering stage, by which time the trunk is about seventy feet high; the Malaysian *C. elata* requires thirty to forty years [115]. The rattans develop stems one to two hundred feet in length before flowering. *Corypha* and the rattan *Plectocomia* die completely after the final effort; they are un-

Figure 65. *Nannorrhops*, the dwarf ally of *Corypha*, with terminal panicle but branching after fruiting. Left, *N. ritchieana* of India (after Aitchison, 1882); right, the stemless, tufted *N. arabica* (after Burret, 1944); × $\frac{1}{100}$.

branched palms in the sense that they develop the single trunk. The other genera provide, as it were, for their vegetative continuation by developing suckers from the base which grow up and in their turn flower and die, one by one for each clump of palm.

This is the hapaxanthic mode of life, perfected in *Corypha* and *Plectocomia*, as it is in hapaxanthic bamboos which gather the whole clump into premonitory flowering [116]. It depends on the build-up of enormous food-supplies. The excess from the working life of the leaf is stored in the trunk and what is not needed to make roots, leaves, and new sections of trunk is stored as starch and protein in the ground tissue until there comes the order to mobilize this capital and export it as seeds. All palms undergo a preliminary vegetative period before flowering and every kind seems to build up to its specific capital. In the pleonanthic palms with continual axillary flowering, the new order effects the axillary buds; in the hapaxanthic it is the terminal bud and this, as the largest, needs the biggest effort in conversion [117]. The pleonanthic have a lower threshold-value which can be maintained leaf by leaf and, except for *Nannorrhops* and one or two species of *Eugeissona*, all small palms are pleonanthic. What physiological factor determines the order for flowering is not known. It cannot be the mere accumulation of immobile starch and protein. It may reside in the build-up of growth-substances under the influence of light-duration rather than light-intensity, in the manner that day-length affects the flowering of herbaceous plants [118]. In any case, hapaxanthy is the expression of the capitalistic life of plants, admired by all and sundry. It is that which makes trees. Man is trying, nevertheless, to force the vegetable kingdom into his concept of community by promoting annual crops, as the least capitalistic and degrading. Concerning the ability of palms to develop and provide where there is no opportunity for the cheap forms of life, Bondar has observed:

In the granite formation of Bahia, subject to long periods of drought, and without any agricultural soil . . . there are palms which grow on the solid granite stream banks covering great extensions of territory. They sustain domestic animals and thus enable man to survive there. Thousands of pigs, sheep, chickens, and cattle are exported annually from Santa Terezinha, these animals being fed chiefly on palms. The pigs never smell one root of cassava or one kernel of maize. [119]

It is no surprise to learn, therefore, that the chief sago-producing palms are the hapaxanthic *Eugeissona* and *Metroxylon*, which raise their fantastic inflorescences like palaeozoic attempts at forest making. The sago-folk have discovered when to cut down the trunk, chop out its interior, and pound up the fragments to extract the starch-grains with water, at its maximum storage just before flowering begins and before the food reserves have been mobilized to make the inflorescence. The Bornean *Eugeissona* is ready for this operation in five or six years from seed. The Moluccan *Metroxylon* requires two or three times as long. *Corypha* is usually too massive to be worth the effort at handling, particularly since the cheap and easy cassava or tapioca plant *Manihot* was spread by the Portuguese through the tropics from Brazil. But those trunks are the biggest storage-organs in the plant-kingdom. The dicotyledonous tree, which fills up with secondary xylem, has scaffolding but comparatively little storage capacity.

We may interpolate another instance of the massive functioning of the palm. Man has discovered other means of broaching the reserves in its trunk. He taps it to drain off the flow of sweet sap which results from the conversion of the starch reserves into sugar for the growth of the stem-apex or the inflorescences. There are several ways but the commoner consist in excavating a cavity in the stem-apex, after cutting off the leaves, or decapitating the inflorescence; in either case a receiving vessel, gourd or bamboo, is attached where the sap will flow and, usually, some stimulus must be applied to the injured surface in order to commence or to maintain the flow. The young inflorescence, spike-like and wrapped in its spathe, needs pommelling for several days with a wooden mallet before tapping; the epidermis is not broken but the inner tissue is bruised and induced to respond by organizing the flow. The date-palm, apparently, exudes the sap directly into the cavity made at the stem-apex when the leaves have been cut off, but other palms whose trunks are thus drastically destroyed for this purpose must be maltreated. The Mexican wine palm or coyol, the Cocoid *Acrocomia mexicana*, is felled and excavated in several places in order to obtain the sap [120]. The Chilean wine palm *Jubaea spectabilis*, also a Cocoid palm, is cut down, preferably so that the trunk is inclined up hill, and then the stem is sliced at intervals from the apex over a period of six to eight weeks, during which seventy-five to a hundred gallons of sap may be obtained from this eradicated trunk deprived of any external supply of liquid [121]; the thirst for this *miel de palma* has depleted that country of most of its one indigenous palm. The Amazonian fan-palm *Mauritia flexuosa* needs not only to be felled and defoliated, but scorched with fire to stimulate the flow of sap from its inflorescence stalks [122]. The sap, thus withdrawn, is drunk as such or is fermented into palm-wine (toddy), that may be distilled into palm-alcohol (arrack), or converted into vinegar, and it may be evaporated into brown molasses-like palm-sugar (jaggery). The outflow is astonishing and ranges from four to twenty litres per twenty-four hours from a single palm which has been left intact except for the tapping of its inflorescences, and this rate may be continued for two or three months. The sugar content of the sap varies from ten per cent in *Borassus* to seventeen per cent in the nipa palm. For details, I refer to the notes in chapters 12–14 under *Borassus, Caryota, Nipa, Phoenix,* and *Raphia.*

The mechanism of the flow is not understood. It was studied in some detail by the Indian plant-phsyiologist Bose, but his interest has never been extended into rigorous plant physiology [123]; it has become the custom, after repeating the statements of botanists of last century, to ignore them. Yet, as so many plants are simplifications and reductions from massive ancestry, it must follow that their functions have also been attenuated. Palms show the transport of large quantities of food material inside them, and nowhere better than in the development of the inflorescence. That the transpiration stream is, at most, incidental to this flow is proved by the fact that it continues in defoliated trunks and felled trunks; moreover, it reaches a maximum about 2 a.m. when transpiration is minimal, if it has not stopped, and a minimum about 1–2 p.m. when transpiration is maximal. From a cut inflorescence of the wild date palm *Phoenix sylvestris,* Bose found the rate of flow to be 32 cc. per hour at 1 p.m. rising to 112 cc. per hour at 6 p.m., 212 cc. at 2 a.m., 142 cc. at 6 a.m. and then falling gradually to 1 p.m. When the leaves were cut off this palm, the flow was increased by twenty-five per cent but continued with the same rhythm. In a palmyra palm, *Borassus flabellifer,* he observed a similar, but less marked, rhythm with a rate of 40 cc. per hour at 1 p.m. rising to 119 cc. per hour at 3 a.m. He considered that palms had no root-pressure, which is clearly untrue in the light of Davis's work (p. 103), and assumed that the flow was due to active secretion by the living cells which had been stimulated to glandular activity by the essential preliminary pummelling. Thus, after cutting down the palmyra palm which he had studied, he found that the sap-flow stopped but could be renewed when the tissue was further sliced, though the trunk had now, of course, no external supply of water. He found also that the explanation of the fact that palm inflorescences are tapped usually on the east or west side of the trunk lies in the heating effect of the oblique rays of the rising or setting sun, as they strike the tapped surface and stimulate the flow. It would seem that both root-pressure in the intact plant and secretory activity on the bruised and cut surface are responsible. Thus, broken branches of inflorescences on wild palms exude, if slowly, a sugary sap, which must be that which is normally passed to the developing structures. On these natural exudations wild yeasts grow and ferment, and monkeys lick the drops with relish. So man may have derived even his taste for alcohol from nature's sinless ways.

The question arises whether the terminal inflorescences, present in so few genera, are advanced on the lateral inflorescences of most palms, or primitive to them. Those of *Corypha* and *Metroxylon* appear to be so extraordinary that the first impression is to consider them as derived; on reflection, with growing familiarity, the strangeness disappears. Every plant, as every animal, goes through a growing, vegetative or developing stage before entering the reproductive, and the production of a flowering panicle from a terminal bud may not be so extraordinary; the bigger the vegetative trunk and bud, by so much the panicle will be enlarged. It is the way of many common herbs, though they may be so small that their lives are completed in a few weeks. It is the way of all grasses and bamboos; it is the chief way of the banana-order Scitamineae, of the terrestrial orchids and their less specialized allies Apostasiaceae, of the lilies, rushes, sedges, bromeliads, pandans, aroids, and dracaenas. In fact, among monocotyledons, the lateral inflorescence is the exception. Thus, Solomon's seal *Polygonatum* and the aloes are exceptional in the lily-order, the Traveller's Palm and *Strelitzia* in the Scitamineae, and various epiphytic genera of the orchids. The lateral inflorescence appears as the exception that has evolved in parallel in the different groups of monocotyledons, and has come to predominate among the palms [124].

The terminal inflorescence often transforms into lateral inflorescences among the dicotyledons. The terminal structure is produced first and stops the further vegetative growth of the stem; then lateral buds are set in motion from above downwards to form lateral inflorescences until the whole plant is exhausted. This is the method in many composites and umbellifers, in *Verbascum* and *Campanula*, as well as in many grasses and bamboos, and with single flowers in place of inflorescences in the buttercups and poppies. It is the method characteristic of the Caryotoid palms, which in grand manner show how terminal hapaxanthic flowering transforms into the pleonanthic and axillary; but it occurs also in the dwarf *Nannorrhops*.

This genus consists of a few species restricted to the north and west of the distribution of its ally *Corypha*. They form low swards by means of suckers in the dry, open, stony or saline regions of the

Punjab to Afghanistan and south Arabia. The commonest, *N. ritcheana*, can grow erect trunks to twenty feet high when the terminal inflorescence is produced, smaller and more delicate than in *Corypha*. It is followed by terminal panicles developed on axillary branches from the trunk and, apparently, in order from above down towards the base. It seems, however, that they may also develop from below upwards; if so, and if they were limited to the extent of forming only inflorescences, there would be the pleonanthic habit of the other Coryphoid palms. In *N. naudeniana* the inflorescences are said to appear at the end only of sucker shoots from the rhizome. Unfortunately, too little is known about this genus [125].

Figure 66. The Lepidocaryoid *Raphia ruffia*, leafless and flowering (? hapaxanthic); (after Jumelle, 1945).

A tall fish-tail palm, such as *Caryota urens* or *C. rumphiana*, builds a massive trunk fifty to one hundred feet high, and during these many years it has been sterile. Then an inflorescence appears at the top, to be followed by others developed from axillary buds in succession from above downwards, so that the uppermost will be fruiting, the next below flowering, the next in young growth with small flower buds until the base of the trunk is nearly or quite reached (figure 10). The process continues over five to seven years, meanwhile the leaves die and break off. Eventually the whole trunk dies, being truly hapaxanthic as *Corypha* but in descending manner. This is the habit of the sugar-palm *Arenga pinnata* and its ally *Wallichia*; and in all of these genera there are smaller species which develop suckers from the base of the trunk and so perpetuate a cluster of palms in the soboliferous manner of *Metroxylon*. In these cases the first, uppermost inflorescence is, or seems to be, axillary to the uppermost leaf; it is doubtful if the terminal bud is converted into an inflorescence, though this has not been explored anatomically. It seems to be the explanation in *Metroxylon*, also, that the true apical bud aborts while a lateral in the axil of a reduced leaf in the terminal bud forms the inflorescence [125a]. The same may hold for the hapaxanthic rattans [126], though it would hardly apply to *Corypha*.

Now the most primitive rattan, so far as its bisexual flowers indicate, is the hapaxanthic *Korthalsia*, and the less advanced, dioecious rattans are the hapaxanthic *Plectocomia* and *Plectocomiopsis* (see chapter 9). Thus, it seems that in this oriental group pleonanthy is the advanced state fitting the most advanced *Calamus*. *Metroxylon* with pinnate leaves and bisexual (or male) flowers occupies a similar primitive position in the non-climbing Lepidocaryoid palms, but it has one species *M. amicorum* of Micronesia which is peculiar in being a solitary pleonanthic palm flowering in the ordinary way with axillary inflorescences developed from below upwards: it is a species which should test the hypothesis that the terminal inflorescence is the primitive state. The anomalous Lepidocaryoid *Eugeissona* supports the hypothesis in its possession of so many primitive marks (p. 180).

A detail, that may be significant, is the primitive monopodial construction of the terminal inflorescences. It persists in many lateral inflorescences, such as the long structures of Coryphoid palms, but in general there is a tendency to develop the branches in the basipetal or cymose manner at the expense of the main axis. The extreme is found in the advanced nipa palm where the construction is essentially sympodial; the inflorescence is axillary and its main axis is terminated by the head of female flowers, around which male branches then proliferate.

Modifications of the inflorescence are many and they have occurred in different ways in the various alliances of palms. All need to be worked out in detail, particularly in regard to the manner of development, but they fall under six general headings. Firstly the whole inflorescence becomes more slender, fitting the stems of the smaller and more slender species, such as many large genera have evolved. Secondly the amount of branching may be reduced until there may be a single unbranched axis with one stalked flowering spike. While this distinguishes more particularly the lesser undergrowth palms as *Chamaedorea*, *Geonoma*, and *Iguanura*, it may occur, as already mentioned, in fairly massive palms such as *Howeia* and, even, the South American *Cocos*. Thirdly, the radial (spiral) arrangement of the branches may become more or less flattened into one plane until there are merely two rows of branches in the distichous manner. It is the trend in single genera, such as *Areca* and *Pinanga*, and it is the

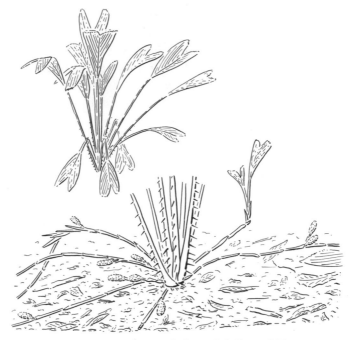

Figure 67. The stemless Lepidocaryoid *Salacca flabellata* of Trengganu; upper figure, showing habit with simple leaves, × $\frac{1}{50}$; lower figure showing the flowering geocarpic runners issuing through the leaf-sheaths, the humus cleared away to expose them; × $\frac{1}{16}$.

trend both in the Lepidocaryoid rattans, where *Calamus* has distichous inflorescences, and in the fan-leafed Lepidocaryoid palms of America, *Lepidocaryum* itself being distichous. However the genera with distichous leaves (p. 48) do not possess this arrangement in the inflorescence, nor *vice versa*. They represent independent trends in vegetative and reproductive parts, exemplifying the universal trend to distichous arrangement in all advancing land-plants.

Fourthly, the internodes may shorten. The result is the compact inflorescence, predominant in the pleonanthic palms, where it is often accompanied by the great enlargement of the lower few spathes

Figure 68. The apex of the male inflorescence of *Borassus* opening one flower at a time from each bract, × $\frac{1}{6}$; a section through a bract to show the cluster of male flowers, × $\frac{1}{2}$, (after Baillon, 1895).

as the prime cover for the whole inflorescence. These enlarged spathes may persist and shelter not only the flowering but the fruiting inflorescence. In various Cocoid palms of South America they may be massive cylindric structures several feet long, and furrowed longitudinally as if they have retained a tendency to form leaflets, though they never split into such. The compact and specialized habit, enclosing the sympodially amplified inflorescence, contrasts so strongly with the slow, multibracteate, and primitively monopodial emergence of the terminal inflorescence that it is not easy, at first, to discover the homologies.

Fifthly, the flowering spike may shorten from a length of several feet to compactly cylindric bodies of a few inches. The process has been carried to the extreme of a rounded head in the case of the female inflorescences of nipa and the ivory-nut palm *Phytelephas*. By this feature they are distinguished from all other palms; yet it does not ally them for they differ between themselves in so many respects that the resemblance must be regarded as another instance of parallel evolution. *Phytelephas*, of Andean America, has male and female plants, the male inflorescence being an unbranched spike, sometimes of fantastic length (figure 11). *Nipa* is monoecious and

Figure 69. The axillary inflorescence of *Nipa* with many spathes, a central head of female flowers surrounded by branches with short spikes of male flowers, $\times \frac{1}{16}$; left, a fruit-head, $\times \frac{1}{12}$, (after Loomis, 1956).

has the female head surrounded by short male spikes in the same inflorescence. It is the only palm inflorescence to have the female flowers above, or distal to, the male, but not the only monocotyledon for this arrangement is repeated in a slender way among the sedges *Carex*.

The last point about the inflorescence is made evident by the sexuality of these two genera, and concerns the distribution of male and female flowers in the inflorescence. The palms show every stage in the separation of the sexes better than any other family of flowering plants, though a great deal is paralleled in that diverse and instructive dicotyledonous family *Euphorbiaceae*. Palms, indeed, become strongly sexed and some of the dioecious kinds with male and female trees, such as the date palms *Phoenix* and the palmyra *Borassus*, have sex-chromosomes. In genetical notation the male plant has an XY pair of chromosomes, with the X-chromosome as the larger, and the female has an XX pair. There is something odd about this, however, because these two palms have a haploid chromosome number of eighteen, and they are considered to be tetraploids produced by the doubling of a haploid number of nine. If this ancestral state had had a pair of sex-chromosomes, then the present palms should have two pairs instead of the one. Sarkar, who discovered these facts, suggested that the sex-distinction arose after the doubling of the chromosomes, and affected the single pair, and the ancestors of *Phoenix* and *Borassus* must accordingly have been monoecious palms $(n=9)$ without sex-chromosomes [127]. Both genera have a sterile ovary in the male flower and sterile stamens in the female. This is a common occurrence in the unisexual flowers of palms, as of other plants, and is always taken to imply that, primitively, the flowers were bisexual. The genetical discovery corroborates the morphological conclusion which goes on to argue that the monoecious state with male and female flowers on the same plant, or in the same inflorescence, precedes the dioecious with separate male and female plants. There is the sequence from bisexual flowers to unisexual but monoecious and, finally, dioecious, comparable with the animal and evinced, also, in chromosome equipment.

Bisexual flowers occur in most Coryphoid fan-palms and in merely four other genera of pinnate-leafed palms, all of which are Lepido-caryoid, namely *Ancistrophyllum*, *Eugeissona*, *Korthalsia*, and *Metroxylon*. These four have terminal inflorescences like the bisexual *Corypha* and the possession of the primitive flower-type supports the contention that this is the primitive inflorescence. In fact, as the inflorescences have specialized, so very largely the sexuality of the flowers has evolved. There are four Coryphoid genera with uni-

sexual flowers and they are all subtropical or temperate and, therefore, more derived outliers of the group; thus *Chamaerops* (Mediterranean), *Rhapis* and *Trachycarpus* (Sinohimalayan), and *Rhapidophyllum* (subtropical North America).

The bisexual flower becomes a male flower with sterile ovary
(pistillode) and female flower with sterile stamens (staminodes), and
then these sterile structures may disappear. However, the sterile
ovary generally secretes the nectar for the pollinating insects and is
more often retained than the apparently functionless staminodes.
But even this fairly sharp distinction is gradually bridged, as usual
in plant evolution. There is the intermediate 'polygamous' condition
with bisexual flowers and male flowers in the same inflorescence and
set, commonly, side by side. One or more male flowers surround the
bisexual flower in a small cluster on the spike, and the bisexual flower
opens last as the most basal flower in this basipetally developed
cluster; by virtue of its position, the developing fruit is seated nearest
to the axis which must supply the food for its growth. Many Coryphoid palms with bisexual flowers are really polygamous and have
the tendency, that becomes more and more pronounced in other
palms, to produce the male flowers first in the apical or distal part
of the basipetally developed spike and the bisexual flowers towards
its base. *Metroxylon*, however, has a male flower beside a bisexual
flower all along the spikes of its enormous inflorescence. The complete separation of male and female flowers then leaves the inflorescence with many male flowers distal on the spikes and few female
flowers basal or proximal. The exception is the nipa palm.

A common intermediate arrangement for the unisexual flower in
Cocoid and Arecoid palms is the triad which has a central female
flower and two flanking male flowers. The female flower opens last,
often several days or, even, weeks after its attendant males have
opened, and fallen. The arrangement is not the same, therefore, as
may occur in dicotyledons where the central flower opens before the
lateral, in cymose construction. A few Arecoid genera (*Hyophorbe*,
*Mascarena*, and *Synechanthus*) show how the condition has arisen in
the palms. They produce in the axil of every bract on the spike four
or five flowers of which the lower one or two are female, and these
flowers open in succession from above down to the female flowers,
thereby indicating the order in which they were developed. There is,
in effect, a raceme or spikelet that develops basipetally in the axil of
the bract. If this were restricted to three flowers, the result would be

the triad in which, as a matter of fact, the male flowers of a pair commonly open on different days to show that their development has been successive and not simultaneous. *Borassus* explains the derivation more clearly because it has seven or eight flowers in the male cluster which open in basipetal succession with one flower every day (figure 68).

The construction of the palm spike is shown in figures 70 and 71, where from a spike branched into spikelets the simpler arrangements of the triad, diad, and even the solitary unisexual flower can be derived. The scheme has still to be tested by research into all the groups of palms, but it emphasizes the fact that the apparently simple inflorescences are the outcome of reduction, just as with the

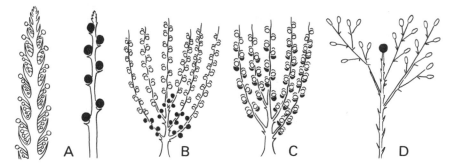

Figure 70. Diagram of palm inflorescences, the female flowers as black circles. A, *Borassus* with male (left) and female (right). B, the Cocoid inflorescence with paired male flowers and basal female flowers. C, the Arecoid inflorescence with triads of flowers (the central being female). D, *Nipa* with central head of female flowers surrounded by spikes of male flowers.

Figure 71. Diagram to show the reduction of a branch of a panicle of bisexual flowers (circles with dots) to a spike with spikelets of sessile male flowers (empty circles) and female (black circles); the end being either the triad of flowers with basal and, apparently, central female or the dioecious with paired male flowers and a female paired with a sterile male (as in *Calamus*).

134

simpler leaves. Often the question is raised empirically why modern plants should be treated as reductions from a more complicated or more highly branched ancestral state, and the reply is that living plants carry proof of this in their vestigial structures; the theory of reduction-simplification is derived from the facts of palm construction and is not just applied as a theoretical exercise.

When the flowers become unisexual, the inflorescence becomes protandrous; that is, its male flowers open first and a male phase is followed by a female phase. When the flowers are in triads, the inflorescence may appear entirely male for two or three weeks because there is no sign as yet of the female flowers which are hidden as rudiments between the pairs of males; then, after several days, the females open and, as each female flower lasts for several days, instead of falling off in a few hours as the males did, the inflorescence appears entirely female. Collectors, arriving at any moment, may gain a false idea of the sexuality of the inflorescence. There are species with perfect triads throughout most of the inflorescence; others with the distal flowers merely as diads of males and the proximal as triads; and the most thoroughly evolved cases, such as the coconut itself, has the female flowers restricted to the base of the inflorescence branches which distally have pairs of male flowers or solitary male flowers. The spikes of the *Raphia* inflorescence have the female flowers in the proximal part and the male flowers in the distal, as a separation of the sexes more complete than in the allied *Metroxylon*. The consequence of this separation of the flowers in time and, maybe, also in space is to reduce the possibility of self-pollination inasmuch as only one inflorescence will be opening flowers at a time in any one palm crown.

The complete separation of the sexes on to different plants, rendering the species dioecious, has occurred in several different groups of palms. Thus *Phoenix, Phytelephas* and all the Borassoid genera are dioecious. It is the case with the tropical American Cocoid complex of *Attalea, Maximiliana, Orbignya*, and *Scheelea*, and of certain Arecoid palms as *Wettinia* and *Catoblastus*, in the alliance of *Iriartea* and *Chamaedorea*, and it occurs in the advanced genus *Calamus*. That is, the final dioecious state distinguishes genera which are pleonanthic with axillary inflorescences in the advanced degree of evolution [128].

The African oil palm, *Elaeis guineensis*, is peculiar in having separate male and female inflorescences on the same individual. They are borne in succession in the leaf axils in such a way that a palm has a male phase of three to six months, during which successive leaves carry male inflorescences, and then follows a female phase of like duration or longer. Different palms in the same area will be in different stages at the same time; the functioning of a male inflorescence seldom overlaps on one plant with that of the female; freak plants occur which may be entirely male or entirely female, in which case the female are said to be sterile [129]. The cause of this differentiation is unknown but it seems to indicate the evolution of the dioecious habit. A similar, but phyletically unrelated, case is that of the sugar palm *Arenga pinnata* in which the female inflorescences give little or no yield of sugary sap on tapping (p. 288).

The flowering of the oil palm is not seasonal but dry weather may delay its general growth; it affects, therefore, the succession of inflorescences developed automatically in the leaf-axils. Probably this is the usual climatic effect on most palms which in their distribution impinge on the monsoon areas bordering the tropics. Where temperature and rainfall are constantly high, flowering proceeds without environmental restraint at the palm's own internal rhythm, which is not necessarily day by day but leaf by leaf or trunk by trunk. As palms approach more seasonal climates they must either conform in order to proceed or they are stopped. There must be many interesting facts awaiting discovery and investigation along these climatic fronts. In India, with cool dry winter and hot wet summer, palms might be expected to flower between May and August and to fruit in the winter; yet the converse is true. The flowering season is November to March. Such typical Indian genera as *Phoenix, Borassus, Hyphaene*, and *Nannorrhops* appear therefore to differ physiologically from the Malaysian which would be impeded in their flowering during these months, and there is a front passing, roughly, from Chittagong to Assam that separates the Afro-Indian palms from the Indo-Malaysian.

This general sketch serves as an introduction to the palm inflorescence. The only way to sort out its evolutionary history is to follow the steps systematically in the various parallel groups of the family. There are great difficulties because these immense structures cannot be collected satisfactorily and transferred to European and North American laboratories where so much research into plant-structure has been undertaken. They must be studied where the palms grow in abundance and there is plentiful material. Since Martius, von Mohl,

Eichler, and Drude wrestled with these problems, progress has been desultory. For this I blame the camera, the facile click of which is no substitute for drawing out in detail in order to understand.

Coryphoid palms are a contrast in vegetative evolution and inflorescence standstill. The palmate leaf is the advance on the pinnate, but the Coryphoid inflorescence is the much branched, unspecialized, monopodial, and primitive panicle so far as palms are concerned. The bisexual flowers are solitary or in twos and threes, in which case the extra flowers are usually sterilized into males. Whether these small flower clusters represent spikelets or whether the whole flowering spike at the end of each branchlet represents a spikelet of the Arecoid, Coccoid, or Lepidocaryoid inflorescence is undecided. Combinations of an alpha and an omega of evolution are not infrequent. *Magnolia* has a primitive flower, *Durio* a primitive fruit, yet both are advanced as small-leafed, lofty trees. That well known pair, the human hand and brain, are the ultimate example.

*Phoenix* supplies much evidence of affinity with the Coryphoid palms, being apparently an offshoot of the pinnate-leafed ancestry. In inflorescence, however, it is fully advanced to the dioecious state; the axillary inflorescence has the much enlarged basal spathe, and the inflorescence axis is short while the branches are basipetally lengthened. The Borassoid palms, also dioecious, retain the many spathes in evidence of monopodial development of the inflorescence, but its branching is restricted and the massive spikes retain in their male state the evidence of simplification. *Borassus* and *Lodoicea* have numerous male flowers in the short spikelets hidden under large bracts, but the number is reduced to one, occasionally two or three, in other genera such as *Hyphaene*. The difference in size between male and female flowers, such as occurs also in *Cocos*, is evident in several Borassoid genera and finds its extreme in *Borassus* and *Lodoicea* (figure 127). Their enormous female flowers are usually regarded as exceptional results of late evolution, but it is necessary to bear in mind that the flower has simplified in its early course of evolution from a massive state. The female flower of *Lodoicea* is one of the most massive flowers of all and it may owe this size to its primitive nature, similar to the big flowers of the dicotyledonous *Dillenia*.

The Lepidocaryoid palms, distinguished by the scaly armour of their fruits, show a great range of inflorescence from the terminal, much branched panicle of *Metroxylon* to axillary and supra-axillary distichous inflorescences, such as those of the dioecious *Calamus*; its ally *Daemonorops* adds, with contraction of the inflorescence, the enlarged lower spathes. In this subfamily the advanced fan-palms *Mauritia* and its allies are dioecious, unlike those of the Coryphoid subfamily. The spike in nearly all the Lepidocaryoid palms shows its compound nature with axillary spikelets of two or more flowers. The inflorescences which need much fuller investigation are those of *Eugeissona* as the most central and perplexing genus (p. 180).

Cocoid and Arecoid palms, specializing in the axillary inflorescence, tend to the condensation of this inflorescence with basipetally prolonged branches enclosed in the bud by one or two very large spathes. They have evolved in many genera small undergrowth palms the inflorescences of which are variously simplified to unbranched spikes. The general arrangement of the flowers in both groups seems to be based on the contracted spikelet of three flowers (two male and a central female). It diverges into the dioecious state in some Cocoid palms and into the monoecious with basal female flowers and distal male flowers, of which the coconut and betel palms are the familiar examples in each group. Then, in the Arecoid palms, infrafoliar flowering becomes a common feature with the development of the crown shaft. These subfamilies, with advanced inflorescences, have retained consistently the pinnate leaf.

## Chapter 6

# Flower

PALM TRUNK, leaf, and inflorescence are immense structures. Their fruit is copious. The flower is the meanest bud that can be made. As vegetative structures palms contend with trees in the forest; fruiting, they summon bird and mammal; by flower they communicate through small insects and the wind. There is a similarity with the catkin-bearing trees of northern climates, such as the oak, beech, and hazel, but palms show how these things have come about through exploitation of tropical existence. The big seed, which palms possess, is the prime forest factor establishing the seedling in the shade and in the midst of root competition within the forest. Massive seeding means massive vegetating. The flower is the mediator which transfers the products of growth to the offspring, and palms have discovered how this may succeed with the smallest instruments at their disposal. In a system without secondary thickening, ramification tapers to small branches. These have small apices which make small leaves and small buds; and being small, they can be numerous. The leaves on the palm inflorescences are reduced to spathes and bracts; they are neotenic and display the simple rounded contours of the embryonic leaves. This is the simplicity of the palm flower for which in the variety of surviving palms there are many vestiges of reduction from a larger and more complicated state. The power of these reduced, effective, and efficient structures lies now in the fruit which they form (figure 72).

Male flowers are so cheap that they are discarded in enormous numbers to make a mulch round the base of the trunk. Some twelve thousand fall from every male inflorescence of the date-palm, having sprinkled into the air thirty to sixty million pollen-grains of which, perhaps, merely a few hundred help to set fruit. The date has, as palms go, rather small inflorescences. Yet the profligacy of palms may be connected with a hereditary defect; there is a high degree of sterility among the pollen-grains many of which are rendered

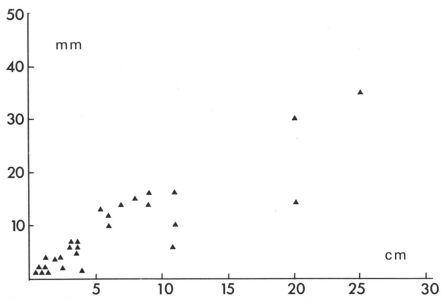

Figure 72. Graph relating ovary size and fruit size from the very small fruits of *Rhapis* to the largest in *Borassus*, *Cocos*, and *Lodoicea*. Ovary size represented by ovary length (excluding the style) in mm., fruit size by fruit width in cm.

ineffective through irregularities during meiosis [130]. The palm expends its large capital in farthing male flowers, its fruits and seeds – for most fruits are one-seeded–as pound notes and even fifty pound notes. The contrast is the orchid which with few, select, well-directed, and expensive flowers distributes the chaffiest seeds. It is as well to have these perspectives because, on turning to books, overmuch emphasis may be laid on the flower which is so easily encapsuled on a herbarium sheet. The balance between vigorous leafing, flowering, fruiting, and seeding seems to have been most evenly struck by the Caesalpinioid trees. Thus the pendulum swings in the lives of tropical plants, and it will be an exciting day when biochemistry explains the molecular configurations which ordain these botanical careers.

As a matter of fact, very little is known how wild palms are pollinated. They have lived so long that they have discovered how to use the myriad little incidents of the forest life which has evolved around them, none of which is striking enough to arrest our senses during our brief visits to the scenes of their activity. Beetles, flies, and bees visit the flowers for nectar and pollen, and pollen can be shaken readily from some inflorescences. Bees hum among the male flowers and crawl over the female for the nectar-drops exuded from the base of the ovary and from the stigma. Tropical honey is very largely palm honey, sweet and insipid, as palm wine is fiery and flavourless. *Phoenix*, the northerly *Chamaerops*, and the South American species of *Cocos* are said to be wind-pollinated [131]; yet the male flowers of *Phoenix* have a sweet scent, while the female seem to be scentless.

By these abundant small means, palms are unobtrusively pollinated. The large inflorescences supply thousands of small flowers, even more than half a million from the terminal panicles of *Corypha* and *Metroxylon*, such as these small agents require, and as the flowers open in gradual daily succession from apex to base of the spikes and spikelets, so the flowering period is extended over weeks. There will be many opportunities for the pollen to drift by wind and insect from flower to flower or palm to palm through the forest. The slow randomness will be assisted by the random flowering, since most palms in the equatorial belt flower continually, inflorescence by inflorescence as leaf succeeds leaf. Nevertheless there must be some direction for the pollinating insects, whether visual and occasioned by the creamy yellow colour of the inflorescence against the foliage, or by scent. Many inflorescences have a fresh farinaceous odour on opening, and there must be minor scents as the flower buds expand. Some, as *Washingtonia*, have a fragrance of orange blossom. *Lodoicea* has the aroma of honey. *Phytelephas* is said to emit a penetrating, almost almond-like smell [132]. The flowers of *Corypha* have the odour of sour milk [133]; it is the character of many nocturnal bat-flowers and suggests that bats may assemble during its giant flowering just as they assemble to eat the green fruits. There is no positive evidence, however, that palm flowers are nocturnal. In most common palms the male flowers open shortly after dawn and fall off in a few hours. The female, which are often larger, notably in *Cocos*, *Borassus*, and *Lodoicea*, remain receptive for several days but all that they may evince of this state is a drop of nectar at dawn, which is renewed daily, and protruding stigmas, for the sepals and petals remain compressed about the ovary.

The compact arrangement of the flowers is caused by the decreasing elongation of the internodes from the lower part of the inflorescence. There are usually no internodes in the spike and, as the flowers are sessile in most palms, they add to the squat effect. Similarly, as in most flowers, no internodes separate the parts. A tight perianth of three sepals and three alternating petals encloses the stamens in two alternating whorls of three each, and in the centre there are either three carpels or an ovary with three cavities; in each carpel or cavity there is one ovule. This is the typical trimerous flower of the monocotyledon, radially constructed and condensed without any flaring of petals.

The arrangement in threes corresponds with the one-third system of leaf-arrangement in phyllotaxis, in which the leaves are produced singly round a stem-apex at a divergence of 120° from each other.

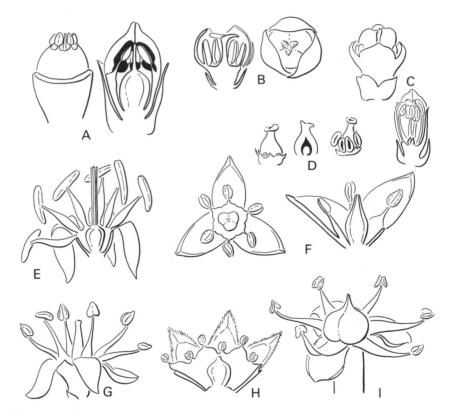

Figure 73. Coryphoid flowers, bisexual except in *Chamaerops* (B) and *Rhapis* (C). A, *Licuala*, the left flower with calyx and corolla removed; × 6 (after Furtado, 1939). B, *Chamaerops*, male and female; × 4 (after Baillon, 1895). C, *Rhapis*, male and female; × 3 (after Beccari, 1931). D, *Hemithrinax* with very short perianth, the left flower with the anthers removed, the central figure showing the ovary in section; × 8. E, *Washingtonia*; × 5 (after Bailey, 1936). F, *Brahea*; × 5 (after Bailey, 1943). G, *Sabal*; × 5 (after Bailey, 1944). H, *Copernicia*; × 3 (after Beccari, 1931). I, *Corypha*; × 6 (after Douglas and Bimantoro, 1957).

During the interval between each leaf-initiation the stem-apex grows upwards and every leaf is placed higher on the stem. Thus, the fourth leaf in this arrangement stands over the first, the fifth over the second, the sixth over the third and so on. But in the flower the successive sets of three are not superposed. They alternate because the three leaf-primordia are initiated more or less simultaneously at one level round the stem-apex which then bulges towards the intervals between these three and forms the next set above and alternating with them. This is the whorled construction into which the flower-bud is compacted. In dicotyledons the whorls consist generally of five leaf-primordia, representing the two-fifths leaf-arrangement, or a set of five leaves the succession of which goes twice round the stem-apex before the sixth leaf comes over the first; the divergence between the two successive leaves is then $\frac{2 \times 360°}{5}$. The arrangement in some dicotyledons may also drop to threes, and in both dicotyledons and monocotyledons it may drop to twos, when the leaves are set opposite each other at 180° divergence. The arrangement of the flower parts in twos is rarer among palms than the distichous leaf-arrangement to which it corresponds; for instance in the perianth of *Chelyocarpus* and some species of *Orbignya*. Now, these ratios are connected with the relative sizes of the stem-apex and the leaf-primordium which it produces, as one expression of the unsolved problem how the stem-apex works. There are, however, no observations on these matters in palms and very few, indeed, even on the initiation and early development of palm-flower which is so basic to the understanding of it.

The sepals and petals are short, thick, rounded structures like bud-scales and their function seems mainly to be protective, firstly to the young flower and secondly to the enlarging fruit. They always persist in the bisexual and female flowers which set fruit, though they fall with the stamens in the case of the male flowers and in the unpollinated bisexual flowers. Their shape is that of the very young, crescentic leaf-primordium before the apical hood or tubular sheath has been developed. They are, thus, extremely neotenic leaf-primordia. The sepals may overlap each other, as an expression of their incipient extension round the stem-apex, and this suggests that they had not been formed exactly simultaneously; a slight interval of time would enable the first sepal to grow over the other two, and the second over one side of the third. This is the imbricate or over-lapping arrangement, as in the coconut, in contrast to the valvate in

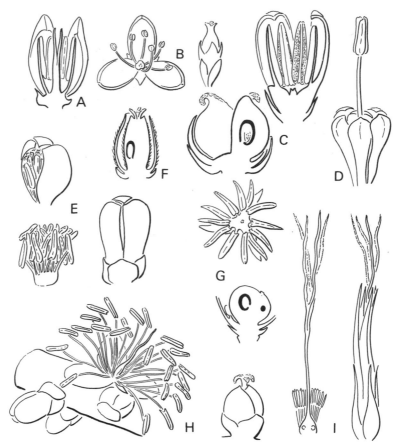

Figure 74. Palm flowers. A, *Areca*, male flower bud with pistillode; × 2. B, the Arecoid *Podococcus*, the male flower with pistillode, and the female flower; × 3. C, *Phoenix*, male and female flowers in section; × 2. D, *Nipa*, the male flower with three anthers on a column, × 2. E, the Arecoid *Manicaria* with many stamens; three male flowers, one with the petals removed; × 2. F, the Cocoid *Bactris*, female flower in section; × $1\frac{1}{2}$. G, the Arecoid *Ceroxylon*, the male flower with twelve stamens in three groups of three alternating with single stamens, the female flower in section, × 1. H, the Arecoid *Ptychosperma*, male with many stamens and pistillode, and the female flower; × $1\frac{1}{2}$. I, *Phytelephas microcarpa*, female flowers with long sepals and petals, staminodes, and forked style; × $\frac{1}{2}$. (A, B, C, D, F, after Baillon, 1895; E, after Drude, 1881; G, I, after Karsten, 1858; H, after Martius, 1823).

which the sepals and petals fit neatly edge to edge. The valvate signifies practically simultaneous origin of the members of the whorl; and there are, of course, intermediates in which the sepals or petals are imbricate at their bases and valvate at their apices. These distinctions are much used in the separation of palm genera, particularly in regard to the petals, and it is well to realize that it may refer only to slight differences in time and extent of development. Quantitative distinctions, such as this, are always subject to variation. Special names are given to the apparently qualitative differences and special generic names assigned to the palms possessing them, so that the mind is overcome with the amount of new wording, but to the untramelled that thinks in terms of development the distinctions are not great. Indeed, it is hard to visualize what it should matter to a

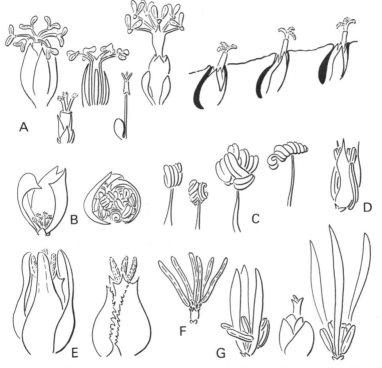

Figure 75. Palm flowers. A (upper row), male and female flowers of the Arecoid *Geonoma*, produced in sockets of the spike (as the female flowers on the right), the stamens joined in a tube with divergent anther-lobes; × 3. B, the Cocoid *Orbignya*, male flowers with two large petals and convolute anthers; the flower bud on the right × 2. C, the stamens of *Orbignya*; × 7. D, the Cocoid *Attalea*, male flower with stamens about as long as the petals; × 1½. E, female flowers of *Orbignya*, the right flower with the sepals removed; × ½. F, the Cocoid *Maximiliana*, male flower with very short petals; × 1½. G, the Cocoid *Scheelea*, two male flowers with the petals much longer than the stamens, × 1½; and a female flower, × ½. (After Drude, 1881; Barbosa Rodriguez, 1903, and Bailey, 1933, 1947).

145

palm if its corolla were imbricate or valvate, and why genera should be founded on such trifles. Unfortunately, the classification of most genera is beset with these seemingly insignificant details, without any relation to the main life of the palm, for the flowers are its briefest phase, and that is why so many genera need what may be called a sensible overhaul.

The perianth is green, whitish or, in the ephemeral male flowers, creamy yellow. So are the spathes, bracts, and inflorescence stalks. Brighter colours are few. There may be tinges of pink and red, but the Arecoid palm *Loxococcus*, with one species in Ceylon, has a dull red perianth and inflorescence, and the Arecoid *Rhopalostylis sapida* in New Zealand has a purplish lilac flower. Greens, whites, yellows, and browns predominate in all parts of the palm plant; thus the petiole may be striped, and these colours are blackened in the spines. A few palms have bronzed young leaves, and they are said to be crimson in the New Caledonian genera *Actinokentia* and *Chambeyronia*. Orange sheaths occur in the stilted *Areca langloisiana* of Celebes, and an orange rim elegantly tops the sheath in a Malayan species of rattan

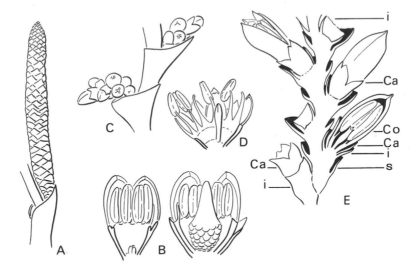

Figure 76. Lepidocaryoid inflorescences and flowers. A, a spike of the inflorescence of *Salacca*, the bracts spirally arranged, × ½. B, *Metroxylon*, bisexual flower with scaly ovary and male flower with pistillode; × 2. C, the rattan *Plectocomiopsis*, two spathels (diminutive spathes) on a branch of the inflorescence, each with a spikelet of several flowers; × 1. D, *Calamus*, part of the complicated male spike in section to show the involucre *i* as a cup between the spathel *s* and calyx *ca*, the corolla *co*; × 3. (After Beccari, 1908, 1918).

*Plectocomiopsis* [134]. The finest colouration occurs in the Malaysian sealing-wax palm *Cyrtostachys lakka*, which has scarlet leaf-sheaths and stalks; the colour is in the epidermis and renders this the most ornamental of palms. But it is not until the fruits ripen that palms begin to colour.

A number of palms have more than six stamens in the flower. There may be 9, 12, 15, 20, 24, 30 up to 90 and 120; and some species of *Phytelephas* have more than a thousand. In contrast the advanced Arecoid genus *Dypsis* of Madagascar has merely three fertile stamens and the nipa palm has but three anthers elevated on a common stalk. Such a range in other families represents the evolutionary reduction from the state with many stamens (multistaminate) to that with few stamens (paucistaminate) and it implies restricted growth and neotenic evolution of the flower bud. Thus the flower of *Magnolia* may simplify to a state with few stamens and the Annonaceous flower may reduce to six [135]. The many stamens, over five hundred, of some Mimosaceae reduce to ten $(5+5)$ of most Leguminosae, or $4+4$. Similarly the multistaminate flower of some bamboos reduces to the customary three stamens of the grass. It is a general thesis of floral theory that the state with many stamens is the primitive, yet this theory has not been applied to palms. The multistaminate flowers occurs in very few families of monocotyledons, most of which have six or fewer stamens. In the palms, it occurs in all the subfamilies except that of *Phoenix*, the Coryphoid palms, and *Nipa*. Thus we find palms not possessed of, but arriving at, the monocotyledonous flower; and the tendency is found not just as a single occurrence in the subfamilies but repeatedly in several of their genera.

The most striking instance is *Phytelephas*; some of its species have over a thousand stamens, others one hundred to one hundred and fifty, and a few merely thirty-six. In the Cocoid group *Polyandrococos* of Brazil has over one hundred stamens and the number is reduced in the allied *Jubaea* and *Jubaeopsis* to six in *Cocos*. In the *Iriartea* group of the Arecoid palms *Metasocratea* has over one hundred stamens, *Socratea* twenty to twenty-five, *Iriartea* nine to twenty, and others, as *Catoblastus* and *Wettinia*, have the typical six. Other genera with many stamens are *Latania* and *Lodoicea* among Borassoid palms, *Eugeissona* and *Raphia* among Lepidocaryoid palms, *Arenga* and *Caryota* among the Caryotoid, *Attalea* and *Orbignya* among the Cocoid, *Drymophloeus*, *Howeia*, *Manicaria*, *Nephrosperma*, *Reinhardtia*, and *Sclerosperma* among the Arecoid in as many separate tribes of this subfamily.

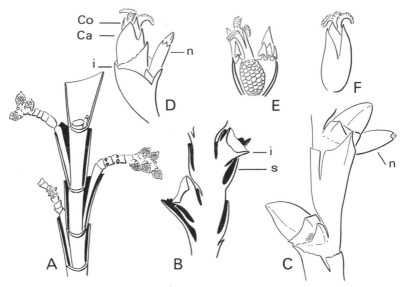

Figure 77. *Calamus*, female inflorescence and flowers. A, part of an inflorescence branch with the tubular spathels cut open to show the spikes; × 1. B, part of a spike in section to show the involucre *i* (as in Fig. 75 D) with an additional involucre below it, and the spathel *s* (the female flower detached); × 6. C, part of a spike to show the female flower paired with a neuter flower *n* (fallen from the lower female flower and leaving a scar); × 6. D, a pair of female and neuter (*n*) flowers; *co* the corolla, *ca* the calyx, *i* the lower involucre; × 6. E, the female flower cut open to show the scaly ovary and the staminodes; × 6. F, the female flower, × 6. (After Beccari, 1908.)

There can be no mistake that the primitive palm flower was multi-staminate.

In individual genera *Areca* has species with twenty-four, six and three stamens; *Bactris* twelve, nine, and six stamens; *Pinanga* many to six; *Reinhardtia* forty to nine. In these genera the more reduced species, which live as undershrubs in the forest, have the smaller number; it is the habit of *Dypsis* with three stamens. Thus, the stouter species of *Reinhardtia* with stems up to twenty feet high and fully split leaves have twenty to forty stamens; those with eight to ten stamens have slender stems two to four feet high and more or less undivided leaves [136]. The most typical undergrowth genera as *Chamaedorea*, *Geonoma*, *Iguanura*, and *Licuala* have six stamens; and so have the advanced climbers *Desmoncus* and the eastern rattans. It seems clear that, as the palm reduced in size through diminution of its stem-apex and shortened its life, so the inflorescence and the flower became smaller and assumed the monocotyledonous character.

The range in stamen-number suggests multiples of three, as if the multistaminate flower had many whorls of three stamens intercalated between the three petals and the three carpels. However there appears to be no investigation into the development of these flowers. Comparison with dicotyledons would indicate that the higher numbers had been obtained through the more primitive method of spiral phyllotaxis, as happens in Magnoliaceae, Annonaceae, and Mimosaceae. The exceptional subfamilies without multistaminate flowers are those of *Nipa*, *Phoenix*, and the Coryphoid palms; yet the Coryphoid *Thrinax* is said to have six to twelve stamens. Now Coryphoid palms have mostly bisexual flowers and a late evolutionary tendency to develop males in the polygamous condition. It seems, therefore, that in the neotenic simplification of the palm flower the multistaminate condition has been retained in those subfamilies which had early evolved unisexual flowers. The reduced bisexual flower seems unable to cope with both many stamens and an ovary, which the larger, primitive, and now extinct palm flower could have done. The relic is *Eugeissona*, which so intrigued Beccari.

When, in its evolutionary progress, the flower bud has been strongly checked, new methods of basal growth may be intercalated. Thus, a growth ring may be developed at the base of the petals to lift them up on a petal-tube (corolla-tube). Similarly stamens may be lifted on a staminal tube and this may be joined with that of the petals into a tube common to both. These constructions are met with in varying degrees in palm flowers and are also made the basis of general differences, but they do not carry much weight for the student of development.

The stamens have filaments and anthers, the relative lengths of which may also be used as generic criteria. There are filaments and anthers of different shapes, but they are the outcome of variations in growth fitting the cavities in the flower bud. All these points need evaluation through studies in development before one can be persuaded that the mature form expresses a qualitative, rather than a quantitative, difference. One of the more striking instances is the curious stamen of *Orbignya*, the pollen-sacs of which become intricately twisted in the manner of Cucurbitaceous stamens. The fact is that genera have been defined too often on superficial differences without any profound enquiry into their botanical significance. The broad recognition of a genus such as *Ficus*, *Solanum*,

*Bauhinia,* or *Cassia* is almost entirely lacking in the modern classifica-tion of palms, to the detriment of their appreciation. The exception is *Calamus* and it stands out not so much as the largest genus of palms, but that replete with palm-botany. Its spines have warded off the splitters who negate scientific synthesis.

In most palms the ovary is standardized to the number of three

Figure 78. *Phytelephas macrocarpa.* The base of the cylindrical male inflorescence emerging from the spathe (upper left), $\times \frac{1}{2}$; the head of female flowers in section, $\times \frac{1}{2}$; details of the female flowers with staminodes, $\times 2$; two seeds, one in section, $\times \frac{1}{2}$; (after Hooker, 1856).

parts, each with one ovule. There is no evidence in any palm that there was ever more than one ovule; yet this possibility must be argued when the palm fruit is considered. The three parts of the ovary may reduce to one and thus give to the female flower the limiting state of one ovule and one seed. The opposite extreme, corresponding with the multistaminate flower, is revealed to us by the genus *Phytelephas* of tropical America. As an ordinary, pinnate-leafed, and thornless palm, it would pass for a member of the Arecoid subfamily. It is distinguished by the cylindrical male inflorescences, the head of female flowers, the much reduced perianth, the large number of stamens, and the peculiarity that the ovary has five to ten cavities, each again with one ovule. This structure develops into a remarkable fruit with as many seeds; yet it is indehiscent. The numbers suggest six, nine, and twelve as primitive states of the trilocular palm ovary, just as with the multiples of stamen number.

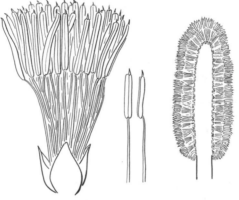

Figure 79. *Phytelephas ruizii*, male spike in section, male flower and stamens, magnified. (After Gaudichaud, 1840).

The ovary of *Phytelephas* is syncarpous. It consists, that is, not of separate carpels but of an ovary-box or carpellary tube, on which the primordia of the separate carpels are raised on a style to form its five to ten branches or stigmata; into the box the ovules have been transferred. How this is done is not known; indeed, the development of the common syncarpous ovary has not been adequately explained in any plant [137]. The syncarpous condition predominates in most palms as a limiting case of reduction to three parts; the three styles or stigmas stand over the cavities and alternate with the inner whorl of three stamens or staminodes. This condition may, also, reduce to the unilocular state in different palm alliances. The unilocular ovary occurs in *Nipa*, Coryphoid palms as *Thrinax*, and various Arecoid palms as *Areca*, *Geonoma*, and *Rhopalostylis*. In these cases the ovary has three stigmas, which show its derivation, but only one section of it develops normally and contains an ovule. The style, or stigmas, may be terminal as in *Areca* or variously subterminal to lateral until in *Geonoma* it arises from the base of the ovary. In this case three carpel primordia are formed in the developing flower, to be carried up on the style as an intercalated column of tissue, but only one sector of the ovary-box develops; and this it does asymmetrically to one side of the originally central style. Here is, virtually, the reversion of the syncarpous ovary to the apocarpous condition with one carpel-analogue, but the style has three stigmas.

The primitive apocarpous state of the ovary with separate carpels, each possessed of a single style and stigma, occurs in *Phoenix*, as the surviving representative of the proto-Coryphoid palms, and in a number of Coryphoid genera; perhaps it occurs also in the little known Arecoid palm *Pelagodoxa* (p. 178). However, among these Coryphoid palms, there are extraordinary gradations to the syn-carpous state and it is impossible to decide where the one ends and the other begins. In those genera which form a northern tropical and subtropical alliance in Asia and North America impinging on the territory of *Phoenix*, namely *Chamaerops*, *Trachycarpus*, *Rhapis*, *Liberbaileya*, *Maxburretia*, and *Rhapidophyllum*, the ovary is apo-carpous. In *Licuala* and its allies, the three styles only are joined. In *Pritchardia* and *Washingtonia* the carpels are more or less joined. Then in *Corypha* and *Sabal* the ovary is fully syncarpous and trimer-ous; yet, when it develops into the fruit, only one seed grows and its one section of the ovary develops into the fruit which has the style attached near the base as in *Geonoma*. These differences are used as generic but it is extremely difficult to understand where the line is to be drawn; the authorities differ, in fact, in ascribing the transitional states now to the apocarpous and then to the syncarpous. It is a tantalizingly interesting series in need of developmental investigation.

The Cocoid ovary is typically trimerous and syncarpous but there are not infrequent examples of ovaries with four, five and six cavities, reminiscent of the multilocular ovary of *Phytelephas*; for instance, they occur as variations in several species of *Attalea*, *Cocos*, and *Orbignya* (figure 84). The fruit, however, is usually one-seeded. The other ovules or incipient seeds are squashed out of existence, but there remain at the base or on the sides of the nut the three pores so characteristic of the subfamily: they mark the points of entry of the vascular supply into the three sections of the ovary. This is the nature of the one-seeded coconut; its three basal pores create the 'monkey-face' after which the Portuguese sailors who reached India at the end of the fifteenth century named it *coco* or ape [138]. Nevertheless it is reported that one in a thousand coconuts may have two seeds, and one in forty thousand may have three seeds as a reversion to the original state [139].

The Arecoid ovary seems also to be based on the same trimerous and syncarpous state but, again, there are all degrees of abortion to that with one cavity and one ovule. *Manicaria* develops one, two, or three one-seeded stones in its fruit in the manner of *Borassus* (figure 86). In most genera the fruit becomes one-seeded by abortion, but it does not have the stone and pores of the Cocoid. In *Chamaedorea* the two undeveloped sections can be found at the base of the fruit, simulating the apocarpous condition. The appearance is even more

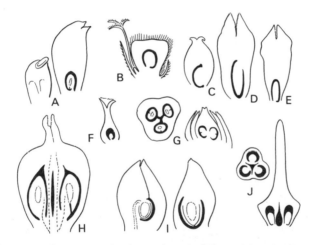

Figure 80. Palm ovaries and ovules in section. A, *Nipa*, with a single ovule; × 2. B, the Arecoid *Wettinia* with basal style; magnified. C, the Arecoid *Gulubia* with laterally attached ovule, × : D, the Arecoid *Leptophoenix* with apically attached ovule, × 6. E, the Arecoid *Gigliolia* with basally attached ovule, × 3. F, the Cocoid *Thrinax* with single ovule, × 1½. G, the Arecoid *Iriartea* with straight ovules, × 5; ovary section, × 10. H, the Coryphoid *Copernicia* with joined styles, × 15. I, the Arecoid *Rhopalostylis*, × 5. J, the Coryphoid *Pritchardia* with joined styles and partly free carpels, × 3. (A, after Griffith, 1851; B, after Gaudichaud, 1840; C–E after Beccari and Pichi-Sermolli, 1955; G, H, after Drude, 1881; I, after Wendland and Drude 1875; J, after Beccari, 1886).
(Compare *Licuala* in Fig. 81 I and *Rhapis* in Fig. 82 C with *Pritchardia*; also *Catoblastus* in Fig. 83 E with its ally *Iriartea*).

Figure 81. Palm ovaries and ovules. A, the Arecoid *Chrysalidocarpus lutescens* with asymmetric ovary, × 4. B, the Cocoid *Attalea*, showing the ovule in its cavity and its vascular bundle, × 15. C, the Lepidocaryoid *Calamus* with scaly ovary, × 12. D, *Borassus*, the ovary in cross-section with minute straight ovules surrounded by their incipient stones, × 1. E, *Areca catechu* with single ovule, × 5. F, the Caryotoid *Arenga*, ovary in cross-section, × 1½. G, *Phoenix*, female flower in section, × 5; cross-sections of fruiting carpels in two stages of growth to show the inner layer of the fruit-wall separating on to the seed, × 8. H, the Cocoid *Aiphanes* with straight ovules as in *Borassus* and *Iriartea* (Fig. 80 G), × 30. I, the Coryphoid *Licuala*. (A, after Venkata Rau, 1955; B–I, after Drude, 1877).

154

realistic in *Catoblastus* where the three sections diverge after pollination though only one develops fully. In many genera the fruit becomes lop-sided in the way of *Sabal* and cants the style variously on to the side or base; such small points are again used in so-called generic diagnoses. In *Areca* and *Dypsis* the ovary is already partly sterilized before pollination and when the flower opens there are the merest traces of two undeveloped sections. The palm ovary, thus, demonstrates the neotenic trend observed in all flowering plants [140]. Two sections abort after pollination. Then the two sections abort before pollination. There is the hereditary effort to make a trimerous fruit, but it fails through lack of growth substances, the action of inhibitors, or some such physiological cause; and through a precocious effect, this inhibition enters before pollination. The neotenic effect can be seen, also, in palm ovules; normally curved (anatropous), they become less and less developed until they function in the rudimentary uncurved or straight (orthotropous) form, for instance in *Aiphanes* and *Borassus* (figure 81). Whether there is a palm with a completely unilocular, yet syncarpous, ovary, such as occurs in various dicotyledons, remains to be discovered. Possibly this is the condition in *Eugeissona* (p. 180).

From these points of flower structure, all of which need further investigation, some important conclusions can be drawn. The great alliance of palms shows better than any other group of monocotyledons the derivation of the simple, trimerous flower from the multistaminate and multicarpellary condition. It shows in greater diversity than any family of flowering plants the transition from the apocarpous to the syncarpous ovary and the conversion of this into the unitary state. These are the experiments of a primitive kind of flower revealed to us now by the parallel consequences among the survivors in the various subfamilies, all approaching the standard monocotyledonous arrangement. This primitive flower must have been much larger than the modern neotenic palm flowers and, surely, produced in fewer numbers on the inflorescence. The trend has been to many small unisexual flowers of simple construction. Therefore, of all monocotyledonous groups, the palms indicate in their floral ancestry the nearest approach to the dicotyledonous parallel of *Magnolia*; both have the perianth in sets of three parts, followed by many stamens, and many carpels.

To consider the palms to have been derived from the essentially trimerous and syncarpous order Liliales, as is often done, is entirely erroneous. They stand out as the predecessors of the normal run of monocotyledonous floral types and show how the Liliales may have materialized. Theirs is a variation at an unusually primitive level, made possible, perhaps, by the early advancement to the state of one ovule in each carpel. The pre-palm flower was that with many ovules. For a hybrid between *Phytelephas* and *Michelia*, a medal should indeed be given.

In two common ways of advance palms have never succeeded. The ovary has never become inferior. In some genera the flowers are sunk more or less in pockets in the tissue of the spike, for instance in the advanced *Geonoma*, but the ovary itself never comes to be embedded beneath the perianth. It is certainly a protection and, possibly, the thick tough persistent perianth of the palm prevented this advance, but it should be looked for in the search for palm derivatives among the remainder of the monocotyledons (p. 267). The other way is that of the bilaterally symmetrical flower, with petals attractive to birds and large insects. But palm-flowers do not call for this attention. They evolved, certainly, before there were birds and, perhaps, before there were *Lepidoptera* and *Hymenoptera*. As they did without them, they have continued; their flowers had dwindled before the modern pollinators arrived.

## Chapter 7

# Fruit

THE DIFFERENCES between a coconut and a date are numerous
enough for a discourse in itself. Yet they are the extreme of one
diameter of the variety of palm fruits. Many temperate families of
plants specialize in one sort of fruit, particularly if they are herbaceous
families. So the labiates, composites, crucifers, umbellifers, grasses,
sedges, and rushes offer merely details in their generic and specific
characters. The larger families of tropical trees and woody climbers
introduce a diversity in the form, structure, and manner of distribution of the fruit or its seeds which is so great that doubts arise if the
term family, as a rank of classification, has any comparative value at
all. This is the situation with the palms. Their leaves and flowers have
a common aspect sufficient to associate them into one family, but
their fruits seem to offer far too many differences. Presented merely
with the fruit of the date palm, the coconut, a Lepidocaryoid fruit
such as that of the sago palm, an Arecoid plum, and the huge warty
structure of *Phytelephas*, no one would like to state dogmatically
that they belonged to a single family.

Palm fruits, nevertheless, have three features in common. They
are fairly large. They contain usually one large seed. And they do not
dehisce. They function, therefore, as if they were seeds and they are,
in this respect, an end of fruit evolution. They are called variously
drupes, berries, and nuts but many of them do not fall into these
particular categories because their massiveness does not lend itself to
precise definition. A succulent berry to an elephant is a nut for a
smaller animal; the date has a stone like a drupe but this stone is the
seed, not the woody inner layer of the fruit-wall. A berry should have
many seeds, but palm berries are one-seeded. Then a drupe from an
apocarpous ovary, as in the date-palm, is not homologous with a drupe
from a syncarpous ovary. Undoubtedly special terms are needed to
describe accurately palm fruits and, therefore, to bring their great
differences into line with the scientific classification of fruits; a big

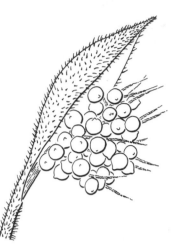

Fig. 82. The Cocoid *Bactris minor*, a bunch of plums covered by the spinous spathe; × $\frac{1}{3}$ (after Bailey, 1943).

vocabulary, however, is commonly a hindrance, and it is sufficient to refer to the differences by the subfamily name.

Most palm fruits develop a pulpy wall at maturity. The pulpiness varies from the softness of the date and the oily sliminess of the oil palm to the fibrous farinaceous texture of the palmyra and the gingerbread consistency and taste of the doum palm *Hyphaene*. Though many are green, yellowish-brown, or blackish, others pass through a spectrum of colours as they ripen to white, red, purple, and black; and, as the panicles or spikes mature the fruits in succession, the effect can be the gayest in the forest. Undershrubs like *Iguanura* and *Pinanga* enliven the shade as *Livistona* the canopy.

The simplest, but not necessarily a primitive form, is the pulpy fruit which is without a stone. It may be apocarpous as in *Phoenix* and several Coryphoid genera, or syncarpous as in other Coryphoid genera and most Arecoid genera. In many genera this is converted into the drupe by lignification of the inner part, or endocarp, of the fruit-wall. The result is the hard woody stone within the pulpy tissue and containing in it the large seed. It is the character of the apocarpous drupes of the Coryphoid *Rhapidophyllum* and of many syncarpous Coryphoid fruits as those of *Licuala*, *Livistona*, *Pritchardia*, and *Washingtonia*. It is pre-eminently the character of the Cocoid palms, the endocarp nut of which has the three distinctive pores, but it occurs in some Arecoid genera, and in *Arenga* which is close to the stoneless *Caryota*. Thus it is clear that this character has evolved independently in various groups of palms from the state with the fruit-wall entirely pulpy. Comparative microscopic studies are needed to explain the phyletic differences, but this is more easily said than done on account of the extreme hardness of the stone. It is composed of heavily lignified cells compacted into very dense tissue (figure 87); that of the coconut shell is about the densest of all botanical matter and for this

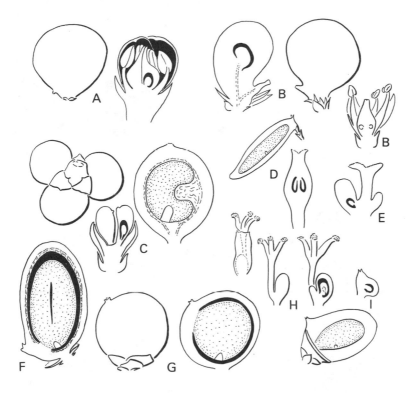

Figure 83. Coryphoid and Arecoid fruits, mostly asymmetric through the development of one seed from the ovary with three ovules. A, *Corypha*, fruit with basal style, × ½; flower-bud in section, × 7. B, the Coryphoid *Sabal*, two immature fruits with basal style × 2; flower in section × 4. C, the Coryphoid *Rhapis*, the apocarpous fruit with three drupes, × 2; one drupe in section, × 3; female flower in section, × 3 (compare *Phoenix*, Fig. 81 G). D, the Arecoid *Podococcus*, fruit × 1; flower, × 3. E, the Arecoid *Catoblastus*, young fruiting ovary developing asymmetrically, × 4. F, the Arecoid *Brongniartikentia* with basal style and fibrous woody stone, × 1½. G, the Arecoid *Lepidorachis* with slightly asymmetric fruit, × 1½. H, the Arecoid *Geonoma*, female flowers beginning to set the asymmetric fruit, × 7. I, the Arecoid *Chrysalidocarpus*, young and mature fruits in section, × ⅔. (E, H, after Drude, 1881; D, after Baillon, 1895; A–C, after Beccari, 1931; F, G, after Beccari and Pichi-Sermolli, 1955; I, after Venkata Rau, 1955).

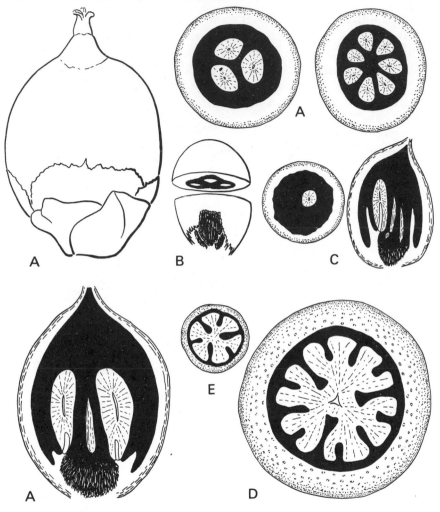

Figure 84. Fruits of Cocoid palms (A–C) and of *Eugeissona* (D, E); the fruit wall with fibrous outer layer and dense woody stone (in black); the endosperm hatched; × ½. A, *Orbignya speciosa*, entire fruit, in longitudinal section, and in cross-section (3- and 6-seeded), with basal germ-pores. B, C, *Scheelea*. D, *Eugeissona macrocarpa* and E, *E. tristis* in cross-section to show the 12 and 6 incomplete partitions of the stone. (A, C, after Barbosa Rodriguez, 1903; B, after Karsten, 1858; D, E, after Beccari, 1918).

reason makes the best medicinal charcoal. It is not usually realized that a great deal of our knowledge of the microscopic structure of fruits and seeds, as well as of flowers and leaves, comes from the pages

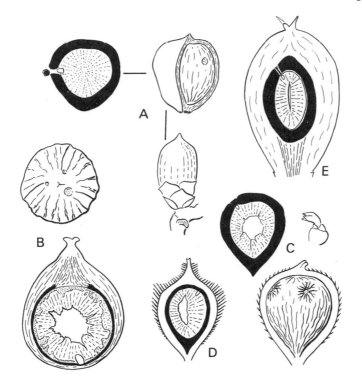

Figure 85. Cocoid fruits. A, *Jubaeopsis*, the stone with more or less equatorial germ-pores, × ⅔. B, *Cocos (Barbosa) pseudococos* with fibrous husk, ruminate endosperm, and basal germ-pores, × ½. C, *Astrocaryum farinosum*, fruit with the husk removed to show the star-shaped fibres radiating from the subapical germ-pores; a stone in section; a female flower, × ½. D, *Astrocaryum murumuru*, the fruit covered with short spines, × ½. E, the oil palm *Elaeis guineensis* with pulpy fruit wall round the stone with subapical germ-pores, × 1. (A, after Barry, 1957; B–D, after Barbosa Rodriguez, 1903; E, after Surre et Ziller, 1963).

of applied botany concerned with the verification of marketable plant-products and their adulteration. Thus, after describing the structure of the coconut shell, Winton wrote:

Powdered cocoanut shells appear to be a distinctively American adulterant. The leading treatises on the microscopy of foods in the German, French, and English languages, even those of recent publication, make no mention of it, and a number of prominent European food chemists and microscopists have declared to the writer that they had never heard of its use. On the other hand, cocoanut cake (the residue from the oil presses), which in Europe is commonly employed, both as a cattle food and as an adulterant of human foods, is almost unknown in America [141].

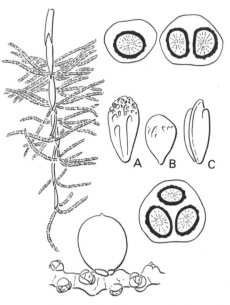

Figure 86. The Borassoid *Latania*;
male inflorescence, × $\frac{1}{20}$; fruit on a
piece of the female spike, × $\frac{1}{3}$; fruits
in section with 1, 2, and 3 seeds,
each with their own stones,
A, the stone of *L. loddigesii* of
Mauritius, B, of *L. borbonica* of
Réunion, C, of *L. verschaffeltii* of
Rodriguez, × $\frac{1}{2}$. (after Bailey, 1942).

Three Borassoid palms, *Borassus*, *Borassodendron*, and *Latania*,
illustrate the parallel trend in an instructive way. Instead of one stone
for each fruit, and that stone representing the endocarp of the fruit
wall round all the cavities of the developing ovary, each cavity
develops its own stone and there are three stones per fruit (figure 86).
The result is the elephantine berry. The construction is paralleled in
the American Arecoid palm *Manicaria*. It is far from clear, however,
in the published descriptions of the drupes in most genera whether
the stone is compound and includes the three original cavities of the
ovary, or whether it represents the endocarp only of the cavity which
contains the developing seed.

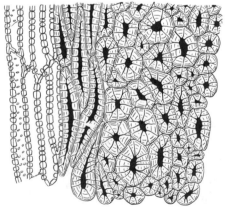

Figure 87. The tissue of the stone
(shell) of the coconut showing the
very thick-walled cells and the
fibrous cells of the sheath of a
vascular bundle (on the left); × 300
(after Winton, 1901).

162

The final progress of the drupe is that which converts it into the dry inedible nut. The lignification of the endocarp extends variously into the ground tissue of the outer fruit wall which dries up at maturity into a tough fibrous husk. This is the nature of the coconut, and its allies in South America possessed of drupes show how the process has taken place. The dry nut distinguishes also the Borassoid double coconut *Lodoicea*, the Arecoid *Manicaria* with its one, two, or three stones, and the nipa palm. The betel nut, *Areca catechu*, has almost arrived at this state but its fruit wall is bright orange red and thinly farinaceous between the fibres of the husk.

In contrast to these fruits, there is the Lepidocaryoid distinguished by the hard, shiny, yellow or brown scales which completely cover it. The scales point backwards to the base of the fruit and overlap into a hard armour within which there is a pulpy or a fibrous layer round the seed, according as this armoured or loricate fruit is a drupe without a stone or has advanced to the state of a nut. The scales vary from a millimetre or two in width to as much as a centimetre, but in some species of *Salacca* and in *Myrialepis* they point outwards as a fuzzy, prickly coating. At maturity the scales may separate individually from the edible layer, as in the Amazonian buriti or miriti palm *Mauritia*; in the muddy flats and lowlands of this vast region, the

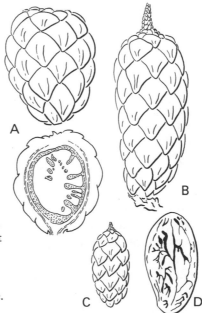

Figure 88. Fruits of the Lepidocaryoid *Raphia*, × ½. A, *R. ruffia*, with the fruit in section to show the ruminate endosperm. B, *R. longirostris*. C, *R. wendlandii*. D, the seed of *R. manii* to show the ruminations on the surface. (After Beccari, 1910).

enormous quantity of these fruits make an important item in the food supply whether of the Indian or of the mammals in the forest [142]. In other genera, such as the eastern rattans, the scales hang together and must be torn or peeled off in a thin rind. This is the construction of *Salacca edulis*, which is one of the few palms cultivated, like the date palm, for the edible fruit. It is commonly seen in the markets of Indonesia, where the genus is indigenous. The firm astringent flesh ripens to a yellowish sour-sweet pulp the flavour and texture of which

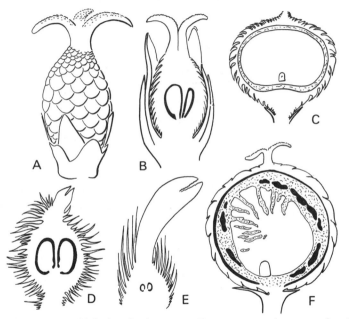

Figure 89. Lepidocaryoid fruits. A, the rattan *Daemonorops*, the ovary shortly after fertilization, and B, the flower in section; × 3. C, the rattan *Plectocomiopsis*, the fresh fruit in section to show the pulp (? aril) round the endosperm, D, *Salacca vermicularis* and E, *S. secunda*, the young fruits with spinous, rather than scaly ovaries, × 3. F, the dried fruit of *Daemonorops* with ruminate endosperm, × 2. (A, B, D-F, after Beccari, 1911, 1918).

recalls the jack fruit *Artocarpus*, but there are better, if smaller, fruits to be gathered from the wild rattans, too intractable for cultivation. In other genera, such as *Raphia* and *Metroxylon* the pulpy layer is pervaded with heavily lignified fibres and dries up to make a large round or oblong armoured nut; like the nuts of other palms, they can be floated by streams and floods which serve for dispersal. The question arises how these beautiful structures, more elegant than any toy-maker has achieved, are made by unimaginative nature.

The scales are arranged in oblique spirals. A set of spirals to the left crosses another to the right. There are the same number of spirals in each set, the number being about 8, 12, 16, 20, 24, or 27 according to the species, and they ascend the fruit with the same inclination. The scales are smaller towards top and bottom of the fruit. The spirals correspond with those seen on a pineapple or an unopened pine-cone where they are the consequence of the way in which the bracts or cone-scales have been formed in spiral sequence of phyllotaxis at the growing point of the pineapple inflorescence or the pine cone. In these examples, however, the number of spirals in one set is always less than that in the other, and the set that ascends more steeply has the greater number. This is the outcome of forming the bracts or cone-scales one at a time in the usual manner of leaf-formation, and the spirals can be detected in any compact leafy plant, even in the arrangement of leaf-scars or leaf-bases on the palm-trunks. Thus, two patterns result from the process of phyllotaxis, though both are merely the consequence of developing leaves or appendages at a constant angle of divergence round the lengthening stem-apex. There is the series of vertical or longitudinal lines, called orthostichies, which can be drawn through more or less superposed leaves, and there is the more accurate series of oblique lines, called parastichies, which can be drawn as spirals through leaves in oblique contact. When the number of intersecting parastichies to the left and to the right are equal, this is the expression of the whorled arrangement of leaves or appendages; it is the consequence of developing a set of appendages simultaneously, not one at a time, at the growing apex. Thus we learn that the armour on the palm-fruit is formed in whorls of eight to twenty-seven scales, according to the species, in the same manner as the whorls of flower parts were developed at the stem-apex. The scale-arrangement must be the consequence of regularly apportioning certain regions of the ovary to scale-formation. We turn to the flower and find minute scales as a tesselation of the same intricacy on the surface of the small ovary, but the ovary has no growing apex like that of a stem; it is terminated by three styles. We must consider how an intercalary structure can simulate phyllotaxis at a stem-apex.

The styles represent the primordia of three carpels at the stem apex. The ovary is the box or tube intercalated below them and on which they are raised up by the growth of the ovary-tube at its base.

As this tube forms, the outgrowths which will become the first scales, are equally spaced around it; there follow more and more sets of outgrowths in alternating whorls downwards towards the base of the ovary. As the ovary is pushed up by its basal growth within the surrounding parts of the flower bud, these outgrowths flatten and are rubbed or deflected downwards to form the overlapping down-pointing scales similar to the downpointing hooks of the rattan leaves whereby they act as grapnels. The ovary, as any plant-organ, under-goes a grand period of growth whereby its initial expansion rises to a maximum and falls away to zero. At the base of the styles the expan-sion is small, and the scales are small. In the middle region of the ovary, which accommodate the ovules, expansion of the tissue is greatest and the scales are largest. At the base of the ovary, where the scales are forming, expansion is arrested as the ovary is completed, and the scales are, again, small. The scale itself, has the same period. Its tip stops growing; its median part dilates; its base continues growth as the plastic attachment.

When the ovary is pollinated, it resumes growth. It enlarges to accommodate the growing seeds, and the scales enlarge, without increasing their number, to maintain the close armour. The base of the ovary enlarges to accommodate the vascular bundles needed to supply the fruit and seeds with water and food. It not only enlarges but it resumes its basal growth and more scales are formed, the tips of which are also deflexed because they are pushed up within the persistent perianth which presses the more tightly as the fruit swells. Given these plastic outgrowths which are equivalent to the out-growths that will form leaf-spines, and their whorled arrangement on the ovary, which is no more recondite than the whorled arrangement of the parts of the flower, however recondite that be, the basal growth of the flower cannot but produce the Lepidocaryoid armour. Its perfection helps one to assess the significance of basal growth to palms and other monocotyledons.

We can appreciate now the function of the thick, unspectacular perianth of the palm flower, protective rather than attractive. It persists after pollination and embraces the base of the ovary so as to conceal the pale tender growing region; it lasts throughout the growing period of weeks, months and even years, and parts company with the fruit only when this falls off at maturity. Normally, as the base of the young fruit enlarges, the perianth keeps in step with it; the surface exposed beyond the perianth is already hardened and adult. If the processes get out of step, as happens in some strains of palms, the still tender surface may be exposed and, then, it may be attacked by a variety of insects among which the plant-bugs Hemiptera are the most injurious. They pierce the tissue, suck out the sugary sap, inject toxins which may kill the tissue, and can cause so much damage that the fruit falls prematurely.

The coconut suffers in this way. It has been the subject of a fascinating study in natural history in the Solomon Islands, and the practical problem of the coconut estate has added considerably to our knowledge of the palms [143]. *Amblypelta* is the bug which attacks the coconut and causes premature nut-fall. It can pierce the mature green surface of the coconut but most damage is done when it gets at the 'Achilles heel' under the perianth or exposed just beyond it. It was found that the nut grows in length from the base at a rate of 1·5 mm. a day (figure 90), but it also widens particularly in the middle region where the seed is forming. The bug pierces to a depth of 4·5 mm. and its saliva kills the surrounding tissue of the green husk. Wounds at the base of the nut dilate and gape, as they are raised into the region of

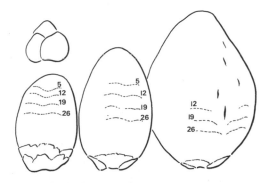

Figure 90. Coconuts marked with pencil lines along the top of the perianth during successive weeks August 5th, 12th, 19th, and 26th, to show the basal growth of the nut, × 1/6. Top left, a young nut just emerging from the perianth. Right, a nut with necrotic injuries caused by the bug *Amblypelta*. (After Leach, 1948).

widening, and here they become seats of secondary infection. Now coconut palms have a friend in the ant *Oecophylla* which drives off the bug. The ant usually nests in small undergrowth trees or bushes, but it also uses the trunks of coconuts for the same purpose, so where *Oecophylla* occurs there is little or no disease. Unfortunately two other kinds of ant are hostile to *Oecophylla*, and where either occurs *Oecophylla* is driven off and the bug returns. One of these ants,

M

*Pheidole*, nests in the exposed roots at the base of the palm-trunk and its presence is favoured by 'clean cultivation' of the plantation; when undergrowth is restored, this ant disappears and *Oecophylla* can return to the bug's disadvantage and the coconut's advantage. The other ant, *Iridomyrmex*, nests all over the palm on which it builds covered runways, and there seems no natural means of getting rid of it. Thus palm fruiting may be bound up with ants; palm-anatomy discovers weak points; and, though the conditions of coconut-plantation are highly unnatural, the diseases which they engender lead to a wider grasp of the problems encountered by the palm. It is so often the case in biology that exceptional phenomena reveal the general and unsuspected.

With regard to the time required for palm fruits to develop, there is surprisingly little information for the wild species, but the following facts give a fair indication of what may be expected. The measure refers to the width of the ripe fruit.

| | | | |
|---|---|---|---|
| *Lodoicea* | $12-14$ | inches | 6 years |
| Coconut | $8-10$ | inches | 9–10 months |
| Palmyra | $6-8$ | inches | 4 months |
| Nipa | $4-5$ | inches | 3 months |
| *Actinorhytis* | 2 | inches | 11 months |
| Oil palm | $1\frac{1}{2}$ | inches | 5–6 months |
| Betel palm | $1\frac{1}{4}$ | inches | 8 months |
| *Corypha* | $1\frac{1}{2}$ | inches | 9–13 months (according to the species) |
| *Coccothrinax* | $\frac{1}{2}-\frac{3}{4}$ | inch | 6 months |
| Date palm | $\frac{3}{4}$ | inch | 6 months |
| *Sabal* | $\frac{1}{3}-\frac{1}{2}$ | inch | 4–5 months |
| *Washingtonia* | $\frac{1}{3}$ | inch | 4–5 months |
| *Ptychosperma* | $\frac{1}{2}$ | inch | 3 months |

That most palm fruits are eaten is so obvious that there is remarkably little information about their detailed dispersal. What there is comes mainly from reports on the habits of particular animals. It is probable, however, that the dissemination of any large palm involves so many animals, diurnal and nocturnal, that it is generally beyond the powers of the botanist to cope with the situation. We are indebted to the great naturalist of this century Henry Nicholas Ridley (1855–1956) who, after a long life in the Malayan region and many years of retirement among the collections at Kew, brought together a mine of information on the dispersal of plants [144]. Ridley drew very greatly on the writings of the early naturalists, not simply because they were recording for the first time in vigorous language things so novel from the tropical world, but – sadly to say – because the wild life is receding and there is less opportunity to make these fundamental observations now on the natural interplay of plants and animals.

There are little fruits for little creatures, big fruits for the big creatures, and more than enough to be rotted away by the organisms of the soil. Birds flit in and breakfast early on the ripenings of last night; these are pigeons, starlings, minahs, bulbuls, finches, crows, barbets, orioles, and, even, woodpeckers and babblers. Squirrels and monkeys search the day long; rats, civets, and bats come after dark. There are fruits in the canopy and fruits at all levels down to the undergrowth as the animals are inclined. So many small fruits are produced that even the grounded pigs, deer, cattle, rhinoceros, tapir, and cassowary may fatten on the fallen.

Bigger fruits need bigger mouths, or hands and feet that can grasp them. Parrots, toucans, hornbills, bears, monkeys, apes, and the larger pigeons have, as it were, this extra course, and there are big fruits at ground level for the four-footed; for instance, the large clusters of the *Salacca* palms in Asia, and of the more or less stemless species of *Acrocomia*, *Astrocaryum*, *Bactris*, *Attalea*, *Scheelea*, and *Orbignya* of tropical America. The largest succulent palm fruit is that of the palmyra palms *Borassus*, which is six to eight inches in diameter and contains three large seeds, each in its very hard stone. It is the elephant fruit which from Africa to Malaya coincides with the range of living elephants. They may spit out the seeds, which are too hard for them to crush, or swallow them, and lines of *Borassus* palms in East Africa mark the trails of the African elephant.

David Livingstone (in his *Missionary Travels*, 1847) says also that the elephant shakes the Palmyra Palm (*Borassus*) for the fruits, which it picks up and eats, and this is confirmed by D. D. Garnett (in *Country Life*, 21 October 1927, p. 446), who, writing of the Semliki plains in Uganda, says that the elephants are passionately fond of the fruit of the Borassus palm, and their tracks are often to be seen converging to an isolated tree, around whose base the ground is trodden down hard, and littered with the fibrous kernels of the fruit which had been rejected. [145]

Elephants eat also the smaller doum fruits of *Hyphaene* and those of the wild dates *Phoenix reclinata* (figure 130).

The fruits of fishtail palms *Caryota* are eaten by birds, squirrels, civets, and jackals, in spite of the microscopic bundles of needle-crystals in the pulp which irritate the human mucosa almost beyond endurance. The fruits of the allied genus *Arenga*, also with these crystals, are especially attractive to the civets and this has lead to a popular belief that the seeds which they scatter germinate with greatest vigour [146]. The fruits of *Chamaedorea* contain these crystals, too, but they seem to be absent from the rest of the plant, unlike *Arenga* and *Caryota*; the young inflorescences of *Chamaedorea*, still enwrapped in their large spathes, are sold abundantly in the markets of Central America where they make a raw vegetable like celery or they are cooked like asparagus [147]. My first botanical monkey died from collecting specimens of *Caryota* in the Malayan mountains, but the lower animals seem unharmed by the crystals; they occur also in many wild grapes *Vitis* or *Cissus* which pigeons, at any rate, are able to relish.

The civets introduce a nocturnal element. Little is known about this in regard to the palms, which are certainly visited by fruit-bats. They prefer sour, bitter, and astringent fruits or oily fruits, the colours of which are usually sombre green, brown, or black. The *Corypha* palms, some species of *Livistona*, the Arecoid *Onocosperma*, and, perhaps, some species of *Arenga* are specialized this way. Bats, also, may get at the rattan fruits which hang among the thorny leaves and inflorescences. The oily fruits of the Andean palm *Jessenia* have been observed as a main source of food for the nocturnal cave-bird *Steatornis* in Peru, but the seeds fall into the darkness of the cave unsuited for plant growth [148]; at other times this bird takes oily Lauraceous fruits.

The bright colours of many palm fruits, which are yellow, pink, orange, red, and purple, or as in *Chamaedorea* and *Pinanga* black against the red fruiting sprays, seem adapted to the colour vision of birds and primates [149]. These highly evolved creatures, however, had ancestors and, seeing that some fish have colour vision, I am persuaded that the prototypes of modern fruit-eating birds and primates were as well-endowed, though the survivors of these more primitive kinds have been driven from the daylight to nocturnal existence and twilight vision. Botanists know that modern fruits existed in the Cretaceous period and were, presumably, as colourful as nowadays; they demand appreciative animals contemporary. Not only the giant sloth, but the ancestors of the giant sloth, shook the palms of the Brazilian shield with a vigour, sight, and taste that their poor survivors lack. Palms have helped to feed not only the modern birds and mammals but their ancestors way back to reptilian stirrings. That is why, as a botanist, I do not believe the blithe histories read from bones; the mystery of the origin of the flowering plant is the mystery of the origin of fruiting plant and fruiting palm, and of all the creatures that lived in their shade. What is significant is a statement such as this: 'A spadix of Pupunha (*Gulielma gasipaes*), laden with ripe fruit, is one of the most beautiful sights the vegetable world can show; the fruits are of the deepest scarlet in the upper half, passing below into yellow and at the very base to green' [150]: it implies Cretaceous natural history.

Concerning the tastes of palm fruits there is much to be learnt in regard to the animals which have acquired them. The cultivated date is by far the sweetest; the wild dates have sour, astringent, or dry fruits. In *Calamus* there are sweet, sour, watery, and astringent fruits, some with an aromatic flavour like that of the cultivated *Salacca*. The Amazonian asai *Euterpe oleracea*, the juice of which is made into drinks and ices and used to flavour all manner of sweetmeats, resembles a mixture of blackberry and raspberry with an earthy nutty undertone which grows upon the palate [151]. The dark violet fruits of the Amazon *Oenocarpus baccaba* have an oily flavour of 'filberts and cream' [152]. The fruits of the American pupunha *Gulielma gasipaes*, the beauty of which was extolled by Humboldt and Spruce, are not eaten raw but roasted, when they resemble Spanish chestnuts *Castanea* [153]. The Amazon species of *Leopoldinia*, *L. major* and *L. pulchra*, have very bitter fruits, but the Indians extract a salt-substitute from those of *L. major* [154]. The red or yellow fruits of *Iriartea* are so excessively bitter as to seem inedible, though Wallace records that birds may eat them. It is interesting to note the varied contribution made by edible palm fruits in tropical America, where primate activity has advanced but little, compared with tropical Asia. There is, however, much more to be learnt about the fruit ripening. In *Ptychosperma* the fruits turn yellow for a week, then deep red during the next week, but they are not eaten by birds until three or four weeks later they have become dull crimson.

The effect of all this eating is to drop, tumble, or scatter palm seeds in the immediate neighbourhood of the parent tree, to trample them in the ground, and to carry them off to various distances, according as they are stored in the nests of rodents, retained in pouches, flown off by smaller bats to be dehusked in adjacent trees, or swallowed and subsequently voided. A hornbill that Ridley fed with a betel fruit, two

inches long, swallowed it and soon disgorged the seed. A nutmeg-
eating pigeon *Myristicivora*, to which he gave Pinanga fruits at
8.30 a.m., passed the seeds at intervals from 10 a.m. to 4 p.m., in which
time the bird might have flown from one island to another. Pigeons
seem to be the most able long-distance distributors of palm seeds.
They have been thought responsible for the presence of *Pritchardia*
in Hawaii by bringing them from Fiji, though the opposite might be
true, and for the wide distribution of *Areca* and *Kentia* in the South
Pacific [155]. In Brazil, various rodents bury the nuts of *Attalea* and
*Orbignya* in their underground nests, where their germination is
stimulated by the heat generated in the annual burning of the savanna
vegetation; the young seedlings sprout through the blackened heath
[156]. Cattle eat the fruits of an Amazonian *Astrocaryum* and the
seedlings which sprout from their droppings are widely scattered
over the artificial pasture land. So, presumably, most of the larger
omnivorous mammals may convey the seeds. A smooth trunked palm
in full fruit must be a satisfactory shake for an elephant.

Now distant dispersal is more theoretical than practical for forest
plants. Their problem is to establish the next generation in the same
soil under the same conditions. It is a matter of time rather than space.
The seeds will sprout but they will not grow up unless there is an
opening to admit sufficient light and rain. Fruiting over many years,
as the usual way of palms, increases the opportunities. Short distance
scattering will improve the chances by reducing the congestion and
competition between seedlings without removing them from the
suitable environment, which long distance dispersal might do. The
big seed, travelling a short way, and supplied with a big food-store to
prolong the seedling life, is the palm's way of progressing through
time over the earth. That the fruit should be eaten first seems
unnecessary and some palms, as we have seen, have evolved the
inedible fibrous nut which is carried by inanimate forces. It may roll,
and the bigger the nut, the heavier its fall and the better its bound, as
happens with the giant double coconut (p. 311). It may fly off in a
gale; it may be gathered gently in the seeping waters of a flood and
drifted over the forest floor; it may be swept away in a torrent and
float down river to be stranded on an island, or taken out to sea and
cast up on the shore. A great many palms are spread by flood-waters,
whether their fruits are edible or not. They are no exception in the
riverside and swampy forests, where many trees and climbers are
distributed in this way. I have seen shoals of fruits drifting through the

forest. Even wild figs, sodden and swollen, are conveyed by rivers.

It seems, however, that only two kinds of palm are habitually and, therefore, satisfactorily conveyed by water. Firstly the nipa palm, which lives on the mud-banks of brackish tidal rivers from Ceylon to the Solomon Islands, bears a head of hard nuts, and these dry up on the head before dropping into the water or on to the mud from which the tide floats them off. And they may float for several months during which time the seedling is slowly sprouting. If stranded in a suitable place, the seedling quickly secures itself on the mud and develops a new plant which can begin to fruit in three or four years. So strict is its habitat on inundated mud-banks beside deep channels that the nipa palm has no other choice of dispersal. As Ridley remarks of Malaya, nipa fruits with a short plumule and root are common objects floating in the sea off the low-lying shores of tropical Asia. The fossil record reveals that nipa, which is a very advanced palm, already had this manner of existence by the Eocene period, if not earlier.

The second example is the coconut *Cocos nucifera*. It is a strand plant, but its home is unknown for it occurs within human record only in cultivation. It appears to be of insular Pacific origin (p. 293). Its fruit is the most admirably adapted to long flotation during several months at sea. The large nut dries up on the palm before falling. It is buoyant because of the air entangled in the brown dry tissue between the fibres of the husk, which is covered by the waterproof cuticle on the firm smooth epidermis, and because of the air inside the large stone, or coconut proper of commerce. It very slowly becomes waterlogged. It undoubtedly continues to grow while floating, but its plumule and root cannot endure the salt water as readily as those of the nipa palm; sprouted coconuts, therefore, do not float round the shores, though unsprouted ones are more conspicuous than nipa fruits. Stranded it can also establish itself, but it meets adverse conditions for root growth if too near the salt water and it meets many enemies among which crabs may be the most destructive for the larger like to chew up the plumule [157]. Hence the records of the successful natural establishment of this best known of all palms, which may travel successfully the longest distances, are few though undeniable. It has achieved a mechanism for long distance dispersal, yet it is nowhere wild! Every coconut palm that has been seen by man has been derived from a planted one. The history of this palm becomes one of the intriguing problems of botany (p. 291).

At the mouth of a large palm river, such as the Amazon, vast numbers of many kinds of palm seeds can be found on and under the accumulation of tree-trunks thrown up on the shore. They appear to be water distributed but in fact they are practically all dead. They are seeds that have been floated downstream because they are dead, having dried up before being carried off by the flood, or they are derived from fruits that have fallen into the water and decayed there, probably dehusked by nibbling fish as well as by friction. As a rule palm seeds sink in water and soon die from lack of oxygen when the gases of decomposition begin to float them. Thus, it happens that palm seeds are often stranded on sea coasts and give the appearance of being water distributed. There are records of *Acrocomia*, *Astrocaryum* and *Phytelephas* in the sea-drift on American coasts, but the most spectacular is that of *Manicaria saccifera*. Its seeds are common objects of the shores of the Caribbean islands, where it does not grow except on Trinidad, and they have been found on the west coast of Scotland. It is a native of the Amazon valley and the north coast of South America, with the possibility of long distance dispersal which its embryo cannot tolerate. The structural means may be there, but not the viability. So palms fail, in general, with long distance dispersal.

We have spent a great deal of this and preceding chapters on describing the structure and anatomy of palms. It is necessary for the subject of natural history because the existence of a plant is to occupy and use a portion of space, and to reach for such gaps when it reproduces. Its character depends on its powers of construction, and the study of this structure is the clearest way to understand the life of the plant. Whichever came first, or whether they proceed together, function is rendered apparent by structure. Botanists are at a disadvantage because plants lack the elaborate body of animals, but the flower and the fruit have a considerable amount of hereditary detail and, of all plant organs, show best the course of evolution. Both, we have learnt, in palms have undergone reduction, the one to monocotyledonous trimery and the other to the one-seeded indehiscent drupe or nut. These end-products now supply an immense quantity of food to animal life. Palms give freely of their great capital for animal sustenance; in return they are pollinated and dispersed. There is no other family of plants that provides so consistently among its species, so universally throughout its tropical territory, so bounteously, so lusciously, and so continuously for mammals and birds. Throughout their concourse palms dump daily thousands of tons of fruit. They have been doing this for millions of years which stretch back into the Cretaceous period and surely much earlier, for there are also the palm ancestors to be considered whose fruit must have been available long before there were hogs or elephants, monkeys, bats or pigeons, or any of the creatures that now attend the repast. Here is a beneficence that must have been a potent factor in the evolving hub of natural history. No one interested in the origin of the higher forms of life can overlook the antiquity of palms. Their modern way, since the Mesozoic era, is to ward off the larger animals until the fruiting time. What preceded this? How came palms to pursue this role? Their fruit must be studied more thoroughly to see if it comes into line with what is known about the evolution of the fruit in general.

The line to which I refer is that of the durian theory [158]. This theory has found few supporters for the simple reason that very few biologists are sufficiently acquainted with tropical life and the supply of tropical fruits. The supporters are those who have lived in the tropics and endeavoured to discover how the extraordinary creations about them have come into existence. The theory deals with big things and big operations, exactly as the study of palms requires. No explanation has yet been advanced for the existence of palms which is in any way realistic. They require the massive approach and, as I have written elsewhere, botany has been fed on the tit-bits of plant-life without thinking of the joint [159]. The durian theory postulates for the primitive fruit, whether apocarpous or syncarpous, a spiny, red dehiscent structure enclosing black seeds covered with red or yellow arils. It was mechanically protected and supplied with food for animals about the seeds. It was massive and required a massive stem, itself spiny, with compound pinnate leaves to produce it. It has given place very largely in the course of evolution to smooth indehiscent fruits, as drupes, or nuts with their diminutives. This sequence can be followed in a large number of families of tropical dicotyledons and to a great extent in the banana-order *Scitamineae*. Is there any evidence among the palms?

In the first place there is the spininess of the palm in general for the primitive nature of which we have given the evidence (p. 113). In the second place there is the massive construction of the palm with its great leaves compound in the monocotyledonous style. In the third place there are the Lepidocaryoid fruits which are no other than spiny fruits with the spines deflexed by the nature of the palm perianth. We look in vain for any explanation of this fruit in the books on theoretical botany. The imperfectly recurved spines of *Salacca* bridge the transition to the durian form. In the fourth place, there are a number of Cocoid drupes which are thickly spinous with erect thorns and needles, for instance species of *Acanthococos*, *Aiphanes*, *Astrocaryum*, and *Bactris*; they retain the spines on the fruit, as their vegetative parts do, whereas other palms have gone on to the unarmed stem, leaf, and fruit [160]. In the fifth place, the pericarp or fruit-wall of *Astrocaryum* actually dehisces; the soft, orange-coloured and sweet-tasting pericarp splits into six lobes that spread back in star-form to expose the nut which finally drops out [161]. In the sixth place, there are eight or nine genera of palm the fruits of which differ from all other palm fruits in having pyramidal warts over the outside as a mechanical protection exactly like the durian fruits, yet they are indehiscent, and without aril. These fruits have to be explained, and the only explanation that can be given on the background of tropical botany where they operate is that they are the relics of the dehiscent, arillate fruit of the palm-ancestor.

The eight genera are *Phytelephas*, to which we have continually referred, the Arecoid *Manicaria*, *Pelagodoxa*, and *Sommiera*, and the Coryphoid *Chelyocarpus*, *Haitiella*, *Pholidocarpus*, and *Teysmannia*. The warts on their fruits are not flattened as the Lepidocaryoid scales, but pyramidal and rather blunt; the form suggests that they have been developed in and over a perianth less tightly fitting than usual, and there is some indication that they may have a whorled arrangement as a result of basal growth of the ovary. However, none of these fruits has been studied in detail; in fact most of these genera are inadequately known. They raise many problems in the classification of palms because they do not fit well into the general scheme, and this is what is to be expected if they are relics.

*Pholidocarpus* has five species in western Malaysia. They are big palms, easily mistaken for *Livistona* until the fruits are seen. Whereas *Livistona* has smooth pulpy drupes, the big fruit of *Pholidocarpus* has a rather thick and dry wall covered with low flat warts. It is usually related with this genus, as the least problematic of palms with warted fruits, but is has also been placed nearer to *Teysmannia* [162].

*Teysmannia*, with a single species *T. latifrons*, also in western Malaysia, is a stemless palm with an enormous undivided diamond-shaped leaf. It is classed as a Coryphoid palm because it has the typical bisexual flower, but the leaf is not so much fan-shaped as

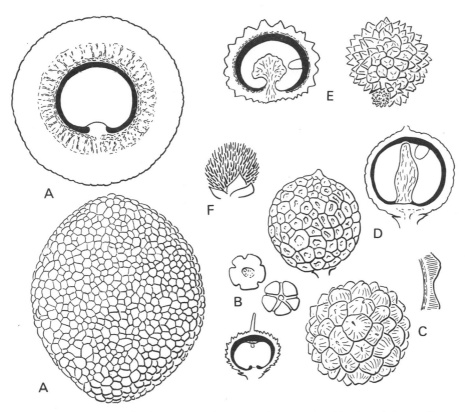

Figure 91. Warted palm fruits, the hollow between the dried husk and the seed in black. A, the Coryphoid *Pholidocarpus macrocarpa*, × ½ (after Beccari, 1886). B, the Coryphoid *Haitiella ekmanii*, × 1½ (after Burret, 1929). C, the Arecoid *Pelagodoxa mesocarpa*, × ½ (after Burret, 1927). D, the Coryphoid *Thrinax tesselata*, × 3 (after Beccari, 1931). E, the Coryphoid *Teysmannia altifrons*, (after Miquel, 1868). F, the spinous Cocoid *Aiphanes echinocarpa* × ½ (after Dugand, 1944).

pinnately folded and unsplit. The stiff blade, four to eight feet long, is supported throughout its length by a strong midrib, which is not the character of a palmate leaf, and there is no ligule at the junction of blade and stalk such as usually distinguishes the palmate leaf.

The leaf-stalk, however, is thorny as in many Coryphoid leaves. The folds are very oblique, but distributed along the midrib in the manner of the full-grown, but unruptured, pinnate-leaf. I have often slept under these fronds, so convenient for quick thatching, and used them as umbrellas, but it never occurred to me that they were not pinnate leaves until I consulted the books. A more intermediate

177

construction between the palmate and the pinnate could hardly be devised. The genus could pass as a relic of pre-Coryphoid palms in leaf and fruit, and it may already possess the habit of *Sabal* in which the seedling stem descends into the ground. Unfortunately, because of the use made of the leaves by woodcutters for the quick erection of shelters, one must now travel far into the forest to meet large, unspoiled plants, and in those gloomy depths, where the camera is tardy, one of the vast leaves is always swaying in a slight convection current [163].

Manicaria, *Pelagodoxa*, and *Sommiera* are pinnate-leafed Arecoid palms. *Manicaria* has two or three species in tropical America [164]. *Pelagodoxa* has one species in the Marquesas Islands of Polynesia and a second which may have come from New Caledonia [165]. *Sommiera* has three species in New Guinea [166]. Burret classified them together, in spite of the big gap in geographical distribution. They are monoecious palms with unisexual flowers, as usual in the Arecoid palms, yet they seem to link in many respects with *Teysmannia*. They have the same prominently warted dry fruits with a thinly woody endocarp enclosing the same kind of seed (basal embryo in non-ruminate endosperm), and their pinnately formed leaves also tend to be undivided. The oblong blade of *Manicaria saccifera*, reaching to thirty feet, is the largest of all unsplit palm fronds and, indeed, the largest entire leaf-blade of any plant, but it becomes tattered in age and shredded by the wind into leaflets in the manner of the banana-leaf. The leaves of the other species *M. plukenetii* are completely split into leaflets. Those of *Pelagodoxa* are shorter and resemble *Teysmannia*-leaves; unsplit on opening, they become divided nevertheless with age. The leaves of *Sommieria* are either unsplit or divided into few compound leaflets. The agreement in fruit-characters seems to point undoubtedly to a common ancestry. The resemblances in leaf may be convergent as the blade becomes undivided. The flowers of the four genera, however, show so many differences that any near affinity must be ruled out. *Teysmannia* has the bisexual Coryphoid flower. *Manicaria* has the Cocoid arrangement with female flowers at the base of the branches, and the male flowers set distally with twenty to thirty stamens each. *Pelagodoxa* and *Sommieria* have the Arecoid triads and six stamens in the male flower, but the female flower of *Pelagodoxa* appears to be uniquely apocarpous among Arecoid palms.

The pinnate-leafed *Phytelephas*, with several species in tropical

America, chiefly Andean, is for most palm-systematists an anomalous genus that does not fit any subfamily. The dioecious habit, the capitate female inflorescence, the cylindric male inflorescence, the multilocular ovary, the very large number of stamens, and the numerous seeds in the fruit make an exceptional combination. Yet the fruit is studded with sharp durian-like spines and so much resembles that of *Pelagodoxa* that Burret has classified *Phytelephas* as an unarmed Arecoid palm and placed it with *Manicaria* (which may develop two to three seeds in the fruit), *Pelagodoxa*, and *Sommiera* [167]. It may be a highly modified relic of Arecoid durian ancestry: of the Brazilian *Phytelephas microcarpa*, Spruce wrote that its fruit was a big as a child's head, resembling a muricate *Annona*-fruit, 'reddish within and, although tough, may be eaten, having a flavour of melon or mouldy cheese' [168]. This most primitive syncarpous ovary in the palms develops a fruit so nearly that of the durian that, if it dehisced and had arillate seeds, it would exactly resemble the durian. These, as we know, are relatively minor deficiencies, turning up in many series of durian analogues in the

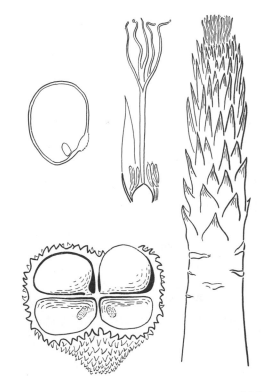

Figure 92. *Phytelephas pavonii*, seed and fruit, × ½. *P. ruizii*, female head with emergent styles at the top, and female flower with staminodes (mag.) (after Gaudichaud, 1840).

families of flowering plants. But how sad that nothing more can be added to Spruce's exciting observation!

Concerning *Chelyocarpus*, all that can be said is that here is an Andean Coryphoid genus of two or three little known species with a warted fruit [169]. *Haitiella*, with one species in Haiti, is another Coryphoid palm allied with the Caribbean complex of *Thrinax*, *Coccothrinax*, and *Colpothrinax*; their palms dot the old landscapes of Cuba. *H. ekmanii*, the gouane palm, grows on limestone rocks and forms strongly warted fruits on which the warts are set in whorls like Lepidocaryoid scales [170]. Perhaps, in this durian complex, there should be added *Thrinax tesselatus* of Jamaica, the fruits of which appear to have small flattened warts as in *Pholidocarpus* [171].

We find, therefore, in the Arecoid and Coryphoid palms of Malaysia and America, in the Cocoid palms of America, and in the pantropic Lepidocaryoid palms relics of durian ancestry mostly firmly brought out in *Phytelephas*. We must revert to *Eugeissona*. In suggesting that it was wrongly placed in the Lepidocaryoid palms, Beccari wrote:

The Eugeissonas are more closely related to the Cocoineae than to any other group of palms. In fact, with the exception of the scaly pericarp, the Eugeissonas have no other character in common with the Lepidocaryeae, as no other genus of this tribe has such inflorescence and flowers, and especially a fruit with woody endocarp pervious at its base. I think therefore that the Eugeissonas constitute an isolated group of palms, intermediate between the Lepidocaryeae and the Cocoineae and that in any case they represent a subtribe of the latter [172].

Here is a genus of six species living in the dense forests of the Sunda shelf under conditions which must still approximate to those of the early Cretaceous period, and with a challenging character. It has the primitive terminal flowering, though the individuals persist by suckering and build tufts. Its habit with ungainly roots is not modernized into the customary form distinguished at ground-level into underground root-system and aerial stem. The much branched inflorescence of spiral construction, the flowers set singly along its axis (not in spikelets), and the spikes ending in sterile pointed tips are Cocoid features rather than Lepidocaryoid; the monopodial form of the inflorescence, however, is primitive, and Cocoid inflorescences have all advanced to the axillary position. The flowers, unusually long and tough, are bisexual and multistaminate. The ovary has indications of a primitive multilocular state with six or twelve incomplete partitions, though their development seems mainly to occur after pollination (figure 84). This genus appears to have more primi- tive vestiges than any Cocoid or Lepidocaryoid palm, and it combines the two subfamilies by having the hard stone or endocarp of the first and the scaly fruit-armour of the second. Beccari pursued this last point and found evidence, which should be followed, that certain Cocoid palms as *Orbignya* and *Scheelea* have microscopic traces of scale-formation on the ovary, just as in the Lepidocaryoid palms. As a relic of palm evolution, *Eugeissona* almost balances *Phytelephas* on the other side of the world. The point is that both genera are picked up at once on the durian theory as relics of palm ancestry. Geographically they fit with the other genera possessed of durian characters, and this wide distribution bespeaks the antiquity of the warted fruit. Africa, be it noted, does not enter.

The evidence from the palms is, then, that their ancestors had durian-like fruits from which primitive mammals or birds, or pro- gressive reptiles, ate the arillate seeds. But the restriction of the palm ovary to one ovule in each compartment and the tendency to develop only one compartment into the fruit, rendered this indehiscent; and

Figure 93. *Eugeissona tristis* (left) of Malaya, tufted, stemless, and the foresters' weed. Right, a species of *Eugeissona* (? *E. insignis*) from Brunei, with stout wide-spreading roots, growing on a rock in the forest; $\times \frac{1}{200}$.

as the aril became functionless, so it disappeared. Whether any palm retains an aril inside its fruit seems unlikely, but it has been suggested, without demonstration, that the firm flesh round the seed of *Calamus* is an aril, and a figure of the ovule of *Salacca* also suggests such a structure [173]. Presumably pre-birds and pre-mammals were evolving about the pre-palms, and this piece of ancient natural history has been carried on into modern times in modern dress. No one doubts the antiquity of palms (chapter 11); what is curious is that, as a family of great diversity, they should still be working on the ancient precept. The cry of the tree-lizard, so reminiscent of the squawk of birds and the chatter of squirrels, can yet be heard in the palm crown.

1. (top) the coconut palm *Cocos nucifera*, the central trunk with a gourd tied to a cut inflorescence-stalk for collecting toddy; (bottom) the talipot *Corypha umbraculifera* beginning to form the immense terminal inflorescence which ends the life of this palm; from Rheede's *Hortus Malabaricus*.

2. (top) the male palmyra *Borassus flabellifer* with sparingly branched inflorescence; (bottom) the female palmyra with unbranched inflorescence and with three seeds in each fruit; from Rheede's *Hortus Malabaricus*.

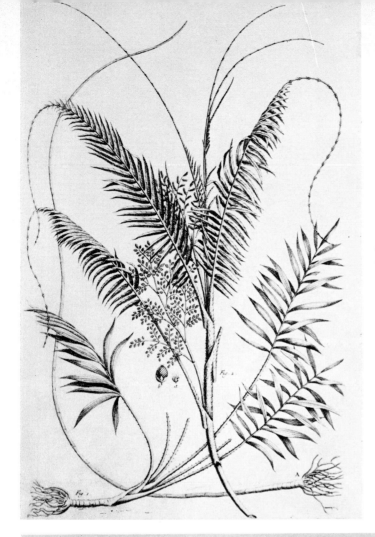

3. (top) the rattan *Calamus viminalis* showing a young plant with a rosette of non-climbing leaves which lack whips, the base of a climbing stem from which the leaves have been shed, and the fruiting top of a climbing stem the leaves of which bear whips, from Rumphius' *Herbarium Amboinense;* (bottom) von Mohl's drawing of the apex of the stem of the date palm *Phoenix daetylifera* in longitudinal and somewhat oblique section (without the true growing point), showing the youngest central leaves and the young vascular bundles in the stem and bases of older leaves, from Martius' *Historia Naturalis Palmarum.*

Tab. Z.VI

4. (top) 'Fontes fluvii Paraguay' with *Mauritia* palms; (bottom) 'Palmetum Mauritiae flexuosae' by the Amazon; from Martius' *Flora Brasiliensis, Tabulae Physiognomicae.*

5. A young coconut palm, a young banana plant, and across the stream a clump of *Pandanus aurantiacus*, in south Johore. Note the sinuous leaf-scars on the coconut trunk.

6. (top left) the sugar palm *Arenga pinnata* flowering and fruiting from the top of the trunk downwards, the leaves dying, with coconut palms in Negri Sembilan; (top right) a freak coconut palm in the Solomon Islands, the trunk curling from right to left in the direction in which the leaves have developed along it; (bottom left) the coastal screwpine *Pandanus tectorius* in North Borneo.

7. The Coryphoid *Teysmannia altifrons;* (top right) a young palm in lowland forest, Sarawak; (bottom right) old palms in the Waterfall Gardens, Penang.

8. The Coryphoid *Pholidocarpus maiadum* in the lowland forest of Sarawak.

9. The nipa palm in Johore; (top) inside a colony of palms the older leaves of which have been cut for thatching; (bottom) palms floating with buoyant leaf-stalks on the semi-liquid mud of a river at low tide, a palm on the left and two on the right subsiding into the river which will carry them out to sea, many of the old leaves cut for thatching.

10. (top) a dwarf rattan *Calamus*, not a climber, with a young plant of the Arecoid *Pinanga* with simple leaves on the right, in the lowland forest of Trengganu; (bottom) the foot of a clump of the Arecoid *Oncosperma*, developing new trunks from buds and suckers at the base of the old, with a young creeping fig *Ficus villosa* on the trunk in the right foreground.

11. (top) fish-tail palms *Caryota* with wild bananas and tree-ferns in the mountain forest of Pahang, the palm on the right beginning to flower from the top downwards and its leaves dying; (bottom) a stemless species of the Coryphoid *Licuala* in the lowland forest of Negri Sembilan, the palmate leaves with their characteristically wedge-shaped leaflets composed each of 3-11 folds.

12, 13. The Lepidocaryoid palm *Eugeissona minor* raised on stilt-roots in the lowland forest of Sarawak.

14. (top) the leaf-stalks of the stemless Lepidocaryoid *Salacca*, between which pigs search for the fruit-clusters at ground-level; (bottom) a clump of *Salacca* by a forest pool in Johore.

15. A flowering *Salacca* in the mountain forest of Kinabalu, North Borneo.

16. (top) a species of the Arecoid *Pinanga* forming part of the undergrowth in the lowland forest of Negri Sembilan, the tuft of stems developed by suckering from one seedling; (bottom) a colony of the stemless, geocarpic, Lepidocaryoid *Salacca flabellata* in the swampy rattan forest of Trengganu, the vegetation in the foreground cut away, the leaves of the *Salacca* split into two at the apex but otherwise undivided like those of many palm seedlings.

17. (top) the male inflorescences of the wild date palm *Phoenix humilis* with their persistent spathes, the leaf-stalks with the lower leaflets transformed into spikes, both features typical of the genus; (bottom) Solomon islanders carrying parts of the massive Arecoid *Cyrtostachys kisu*, peculiar to their islands, in order to make botanical specimens; the one on the left holding the stem-apex enclosed in the massive tubular leaf-sheaths from which the pinnate fronds, lying on the ground, have been cut; the other holding the inflorescence with young fruits, which opens below the crown-shaft of leaf-sheaths in the same manner as the Arecoid *Dictyosperma* in Plate 19; in palm collecting photographs, measurements and sketches must take the place, very largely, of herbarium specimens.

18. The African Lepidocaryoid *Raphia gigantea*, showing the growth of the inflorescence; (top left) a branch of a very young inflorescence removed to show the spathels and branchlets with bracts; (top right) part of the fruiting inflorescence; (bottom left) the young inflorescence with the spathes on its stem cut off to show the young fertile branch emerging from its tubular spathe; (bottom right) young inflorescences emerging through the split bases of reduced leaves at the top of the trunk.

19. (top left) inflorescences of the Arecoid *Dictyosperma album;* (top right) those of the Coryphoid *Cryosophila nana;* (middle) the inflorescence of the Arecoid *Pseudophoenix sargentii;* (bottom) that of the Cocoid *Attalea cohune.*

20. (top) stilt-roots of the Arecoid *Iriartea exorrhiza* of the Amazon, emerging through splits in the trunk and bearing on their aerial parts stunted rootlets the sharp caps of which make thorns; (bottom) Oriya script (a version of Bengali) written with a stylus on the dried leaflet of the palmyra *Borassus flabellifer*, the numerous small longitudinal veins of the leaf serving as ruled lines.

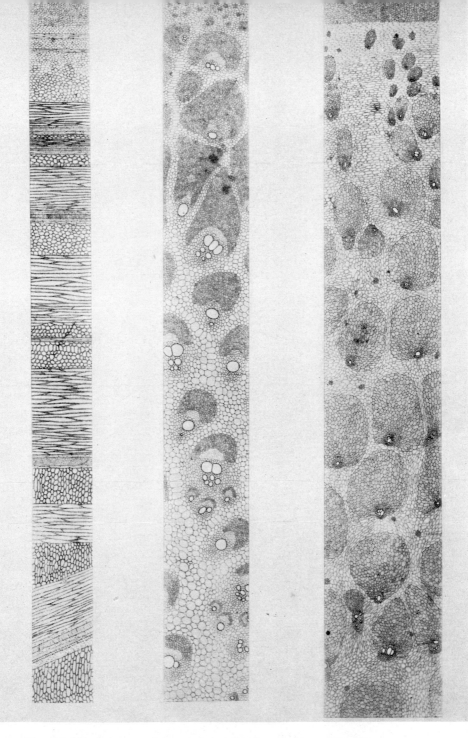

21. Von Mohl's drawings of the anatomy of palm trunks to show the arrangement of the vascular bundles (with large xylem vessels) and their sheaths of thick fibres, those on the right in transverse section, that on the left in longitudinal section; from Martius' *Historia Naturalis Palmarum*.

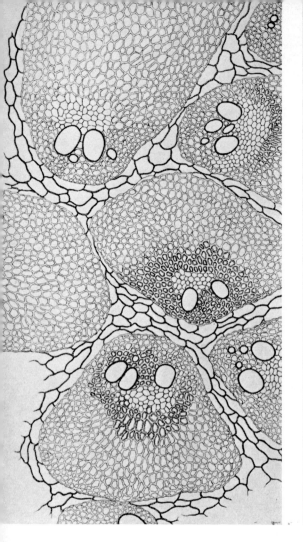

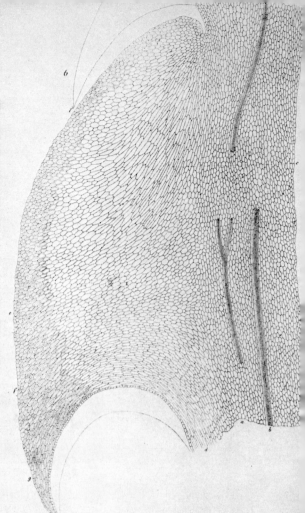

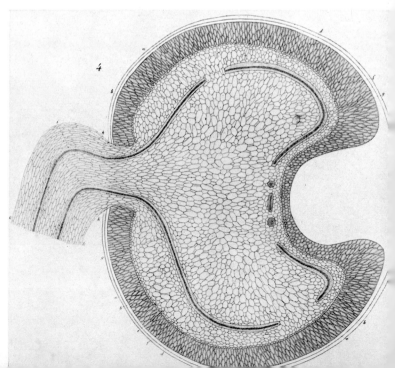

22. (top left) a fragment of a fossil palm trunk in cross-section showing the vascular bundles; (top right) von Mohl's drawing of the microscopic structure of a fruit-scale of the Lepidocaryoid *Raphia*, and (bottom) that of a germinating palm seed to show the thin-walled tissue of the cotyledon with vascular bundles invading the thick-walled endosperm; from Martius' *Historia Naturalis Palmarum*.

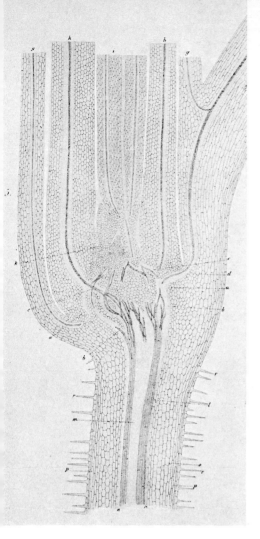

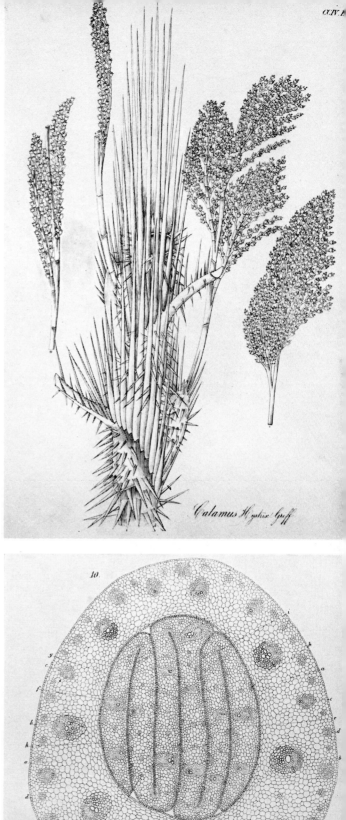

23. (top right) Griffith's drawing of the very spinous rattan *Calamus hystrix;* (top left) von Mohl's drawing of the structure of a palm seedling in longitudinal section, and (bottom) that of a cross-section of a young date palm leaf enclosed in the sheath of an older leaf; from Martius' *Historia Naturalis Palmarum.*

24. The rattan tree *Calamus arborescens*, from Griffith's *Palms of British East India*.

## Chapter 8

# Seed and Seedling

THE LARGE cavity of the palm fruit is filled by the seed. Its nature is to be plump, hard, dense, and solitary. The exceptions are few. *Phytelephas*, as we have noted, has regularly four to ten seeds in its fruit, and they are as large as most palm seeds. *Borassus* and its allies have normally three seeds; *Manicaria* has one to three seeds, and this happens abnormally in *Cocos* and its allies, some of which have occasionally four, five, and six seeds (figure 84). The smallest seeds, a quarter of an inch long, are found in small undergrowth palms, and the largest of all seeds, nearly a foot long, is that of the double coconut. Though generally rounded, they may be somewhat flattened, oblong, or even conical, and in a few species curved. They consist mainly of hard endosperm, which is the storage tissue, and on one side of this there is the small soft embryo. They are bounded by a thin, dry, brownish skin which is the remains of the seed-coat, derived from the wall of the ovule. Generally this skin is united more or less to the inner wall of the fruit, against which it was pressed and crushed during the swelling of the endosperm. It happens, therefore, that the objects which are called palm seeds are mostly the stones or cores of fruits enclosing the true seeds; thus the coconut and oil palm nut are endocarps of fruits, but for all practical purposes they are seeds. The exception is the date palm and its wild allies, *Phoenix*; the stone in their case is actually the endosperm of the seed, and the membranous pellicle that surrounds it is the thin inner layer of the fruit wall.

The seeds have little, if any, power of dormancy and they cannot withstand desiccation. Even incipient drying may impair germination. It is difficult, therefore, to believe the statement that nipa fruits remain for several years in a dried state on the fruit-head [174]. The seeds may appear to be dormant but, in fact, the embryo is slowly growing internally at the expense of the endosperm and it seems that the embryo never really ceases from growing at any time since its inception, even while the seed is being dispersed. Coconuts, still in

N

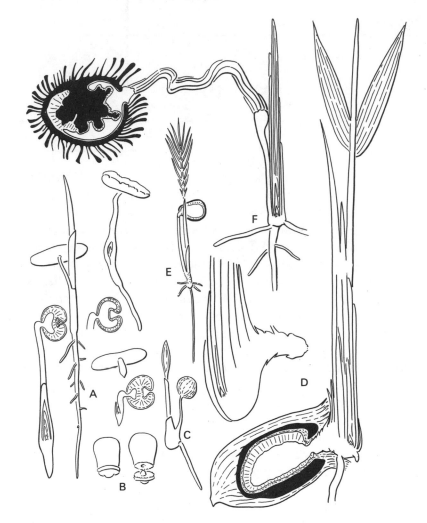

Figure 94. Seedlings. A, the date *Phoenix dactylifera* with one scale-leaf before the first foliage leaf, × 1; sections of the seed to show the enlargement of the cotyledon until it absorbs all the endosperm, × 2. B, *Phoenix* embryos to show the relatively large cotyledon enclosing the minute stem, and the minute radicle, × 5. C, *Sabal umbraculifera*, descending into the soil, × ⅔. D, *Nipa*, in section, the woody stone in black; 6–7 scale-leaves before the first foliage leaf (with prominent apical spine or flange), × ½; a section through the base or an older seedling with descending stem (after Griffith, 1851). E, *Phytelephas* with two scale-leaves and the first foliage leaf pinnate, × ½. F, *Pholidocarpus macrocarpus*, the woody stone, its fibres, and the rumination of the seed in black; planting the seedling at a distance; × ½. (A, B, after Baillon, 1895; C, after Gatin, 1906; E, after Karsten, 1858.)

their husks, can be hung up, and yet they will sprout; the embryo obtains water both from the endosperm and from the endosperm juice which still remains as the coconut water in the ripe fruit; and the roots of the seedling, growing into the husk, can absorb the rain which filters through it. Nevertheless, it has been found that the pulpy tissue of the fruit-wall does inhibit or delay the germination of the seeds of the fan-palm *Livistona* [175]. Palm seeds, however, are essentially massive structures which germinate without delay and establish on the forest floor by means of their large food-store massive seedlings. Their apparent slowness is a measure of their effective massiveness. A little seedling, which ups in a week, could not compete in the long run either with the debris or the intense root-competition of the forest floor. Thus palm seedlings can push out from incredible thickets and they can establish themselves even on rock-faces if they have lodged in a crevice or some adherent tangle of roots and twigs. Yet, there is no epiphytic palm; this mode of life requires root-properties of adherence and the ability to survive exposure and drying which palms evidently do not possess. It may be noted, too, that there are no parasitic palms. Mistletoes, with relatively large seeds, are epiphytic parasites, whereas ground-parasites have very small seeds with slight reserves, and this is not the direction of palms.

To make the seed, the minute ovule of the flower has to increase from a length of half a millimetre at the time of fertilization up to its final size, to develop the endosperm tissue and store within it the food reserves, and to develop the embryo. Thus, palm fruits take months to develop and the largest require several years (p. 168). That there is a relation between the age of the leaf, the age of the inflorescence, and the age of the fruit in a genus of palms, if not consistently throughout their subfamilies, seems clear from the manner in which these parts work in succession, but we are without the comparative information to establish the rhythm.

In the course of its development, the seed makes numerous structures which persist in its final state and are much employed in the classification of palms. The seeds are easily preserved, and every kind of palm seems to have its specific marks on its seeds; they are augmented when, to the seed proper, there are added the features of the stone or fibrous covering around it. Some of the points, such as the thickness and hardness of the stone and the provision of weak areas as germination-pores, play an obvious part in the life of the palm, but others such as the rumination of the endosperm and the vascular supply to the seed-coat are merely expressions of the inner working without contact with the external world. As such they are the more valuable in classification, even though nothing be understood of their causation, because they represent the intrinsic character of this most intimate part of the life-history. The value of a thick

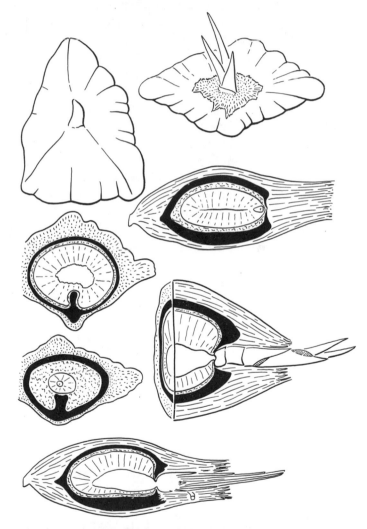

Figure 95. *Nipa*, fruits and seedlings, $\times \frac{1}{2}$. Left, the nut with fibrous husk, woody stone (in black), and a thin buoyant layer of loose corky tissue between the stone and the endosperm (hatched). Lower right, the seedling with six scale leaves, two showing incipient leaflet folds, and a prominent apex.

186

stone is at once obvious, because large animals may crack thin stones and digest both endosperm and embryo. A selective value can be attributed to tendencies to increase lignification, but this process is itself one of the intrinsic workings of the palm fruit. The elephant masters all but the palmyra and doum palms; yet it does not naturally encounter coconut and double coconut which might be equally defiant. Some other environmental factor may have elicited them.

The absence of a definite structure from the seed-coat is unfortunate for botany because the microscopic structure of the well-defined seed-coat is a valuable guide to the relationships of flowering plants. The seed-coat, which is derived from the one or two integuments of the ovule, retains its simple groundwork of parenchyma in the palm until it dries up at maturity of the fruit. This generalized structure

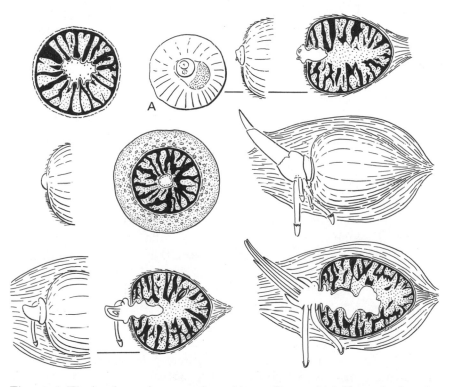

Figure 96. The betel nut *Areca catechu* and its seedling; a thick fibrous husk and a thinly fibrous shell round the ruminate endosperm, the ruminations in black, the endosperm stippled; the husk removed in most cases; × 1. A, the basal end of the nut showing the furry patch on one side of the issuing seedling. Sections to show the cotyledon growing into the endosperm between the ruminations.

implies continued growth so long as there is room to enlarge in the fruit. Where the seed-coat has a special structure, it differentiates at a fairly early stage of seed-growth and arrests it. Palm-seeds are, therefore, overgrown seeds which fit tightly the fruit-cavity. The outer integument, however, becomes fairly massive and forms in itself a system of vascular bundles which may be very numerous, having to irrigate the enlarging seed, and they form a pattern on the dried seed which may have a generic, if not specific, character.

The seed-coat gives rise to another feature, the so-called rumination of the endosperm. Many palm-seeds, when cut open, sawn or chopped across, have a homogenous hard white or yellowish endosperm. Such is the non-ruminate endosperm. Others show brown lines, wedges, or plates of tissue proceeding from the seed-coat into the endosperm for shorter or longer distances; these are the ruminations, so-called from their resemblance to the patterns on the teeth of ruminants. They are active ingrowths or folds of the young seed-coat into the soft jelly-like young endosperm. This tissue is the parenchymatous mass of triploid cells developed after pollination by the triple fusion of two embryo-sac cells of the ovule with a male nucleus from the pollen-tube. It develops much more rapidly than the embryo and forms at first a soft nourishing, semiliquid mass in which the embryo resides. When the growing seed has nearly reached its full size, the cells of the endosperm begin to harden from the outside next to the seed-coat inwards. The walls of the cells thicken with cellulose, or a modification called hemicellulose, until they occlude half or more of the cell-cavity. The cells then resemble those of the stony or hard endocarp of the fruit, the thick walls being pierced by the strands of cytoplasm which link with neighbouring cells, but these walls are not lignified as in the endocarp. Thus the mature endosperm has a hard horny or bony texture, not the brittleness of wood; the harder and larger kinds make the vegetable ivory of commerce, e.g. *Metroxylon*, *Phytelephas*. The wall-substance of the endosperm is, in fact, a form of carbohydrate storage for the embryo and it is dissolved again on germination of the seed.

When the endosperm is in its soft state, the ruminatory folds of the integument appear to bulge into it, and the endosperm returns the stimulus by expanding between the folds. At maturity, the folds dry up and become brown, for they are part of the now effete seed-coat, while the cells of the endosperm remain alive. Exactly how these folds arise and proceed has yet to be made out. It seems that, con-

Figure 97. Seedling betel
palms *Areca catechu*, with two
scale-leaves before the first
foliage leaf; the larger seedling
with the endosperm almost
completely absorbed; × ½.

trary to their appearance, they do not grow into the endosperm but
that they originate as lines of resistance to the expansion of the endosperm and that they are extended by intercalary growth into folds.
The patterns they make differ in longitudinal and transverse sections
of the seed, and these patterns are specific and generic.

It has become customary to distinguish genera according as the
endosperm is ruminate or not, but there is no reason why this striking

pattern should have this rank. Opinion is conflicting. In one group of palms the criterion is maintained. In another we find the large genus *Euterpe* with two sections based on the distinction [176]. Functionally the ruminations increase the area of contact between the endosperm and the integument from which it is deriving the material for its growth and storage, and the oxygen to maintain the respiration of the cells within the ovule. Some ruminations, indeed, develop about a vascular bundle in the integument and hold it in the expanding endosperm [177]. Rumination should, therefore, be an important item for classification. We find this argument negated, however, by the largest palm seeds which should have the greatest need of rumination; their endosperm is not ruminate, for instance *Cocos*, *Lodoicea*, and *Metroxylon*. Many small seeds, by contrast, are ruminate. In *Reinhardtia* there is the opposite trend; its small seeds are not ruminate, while its large seeds are [178].

When we try to discover, too, which state was the original, the ruminate or non-ruminate, the situation is equally confusing. *A priori* there can be no argument unless it is accepted that simplicity precedes complexity, and this is often fallacious. If we try to associate one or other state with a character that is held to be primitive, such as the multistaminate flower or the terminal position of the inflorescence, the issue seems always ambiguous. Thus all genera with terminal inflorescences have non-ruminate endosperm except *Korthalsia* which seems to be one of the primitive rattan genera. Certainly in the Lepidocaryoid palms such evidence, supplied by *Eugeissona* and *Metroxylon*, affirms the non-ruminate as the primitive state; it may also be the original condition in Cocoid palms where rumination occurs infrequently and mainly in the generic cluster round *Cocos*. If this is so, then the ruminate endosperm must be another instance of parallel evolution in the various subfamilies and there may well be details in the mode of development of the ruminations and their structure to indicate the divers trends.

The palm ovule is anatropous. That is, in its development, the knob-like growth which becomes the ovule curves by one-sided growth until the original tip is turned down towards the stalk (figures 80 and 81). During this process the integuments have grown round the apex and produced the fine canal known as the micropyle, through which the pollen tube will enter the ovule. As with all features in palms, there are many variations on this fundamental plan which is generally constant in other families of monocotyledons.

The ovule may mature and function before it has reached the full anatropous form; it is then partly curved or, even, so rudimentary that it is straight (Fig. 81 D, H). While there are usually two integuments, some palms appear to have only one, though whether this is a generic feature is not known. The ovule is attached to the central partition of the syncarpous ovary near the middle, the apex, or the base, or it may spring from the base of the ovular cavity; it never occurs on the sides of the carpel or the ovary-box. Its position may remain unchanged in fruit or, especially in Arecoid palms, it appears to move to one end or the other of the fruit because of asymmetric growth of the ovary. In other words, the small and simple ovary has complicated potentialities and these are explained as the fruit develops. Thus, unlike the ordinary monocotyledonous state with six vascular bundles in the ovary, there are many in the palm ovary, indicative of the derivation of the carpel from the massive leaf-primordium. All these vascular bundles come to have particular functions as the fruit develops, and so do the finer bundles in the outer integument of the ovule; at the time of pollination they may be scarcely defined. To follow these changes satisfactorily calls for much more investigation and illustration. We know, as so often happens, the adult differences and use them generically, but we lack the knowledge of development so necessary for understanding. For instance, the micropyle points usually to the base of the ovary on the side of the ovule away from the longitudinal axis of the ovary; in *Calamus* it is on the inside towards the long axis (figure 81c). In the Arecoid *Oncosperma* and its allies, the micropyle points upwards to the apex of the ovary but this direction is reversed by asymmetric growth of the fruit-wall.

Within the ovule there is the small embryo-sac with the egg-cell. It seems to be constructed generally on the normal plan with eight nuclei, but there are certainly aberrations; nipa, for instance, is said to have no antipodal cells [179]. The enlargement of the minute embryo-sac of the coconut flower into the cavity of the developing coconut, filled with the embryo-sac juice, is, as Drude remarked in 1877 in his fundamental study of palm ovules, truly colossal.

The embryo develops from the fertilized egg-nucleus which is situated at the micropylar end of the embryo-sac. There it remains while growing in the developing seed but, as in other features of the palm, strange asymmetries may intervene in the developing endosperm which displace the embryo to one or other side of the seed, even to the opposite end. In seed-terminology, the embryo may be basal, which is next to the micropyle or the attachment of the seed, or apical at the other end, or lateral. As the style and the seed may appear to be shifted by fruit asymmetry, so the embryo appears to be shifted by endosperm asymmetry. In the nipa seed the embryo may have little connection with the micropyle which is usually obliterated in the course of development. The position of the embryo is used in the generic definition of palms, but its significance is far from clear. Its variation in *Phoenix* is merely specific between species so closely related that they may hybridize (figure 103). Palms experiment in ways denied to most monocotyledons with simpler and smaller construction.

Even when the fruit is ripe, the embryo may have little differentiation. As a short cylindric mass a few millimetres in length, a stem-end and a root-end can be distinguished, with the root-end pointing outwards, the stem-end inwards into the endosperm. Without microscopic examination the stem-end may seem homogeneous, but it differentiates sooner or later after fruit-fall into the cotyledon and the stem-apex where the seedling leaves develop. The embryo proceeds to attack the endosperm with the cotyledon. The surface of the cotyledon secretes, apparently, enzymes which hydrolyse the proteins, oils, and reserve cellulose of the endosperm cells. As these cells are killed and more or less absorbed, the cotyledon enlarges and digests its way until it has absorbed practically all the endosperm and taken its place; in doing so it often develops minute papillae in the regions of contact. The most familiar example is the enormous spongy mass that comes to fill the sprouted coconut; it is the cotyledon, soft, sweet, and nutritious so that it is used as a vegetable delicacy. In the still bigger double coconut the cotyledon develops into a large bilobed brain-like mass [180]. While starch and sugar do not occur in the endosperm, they are formed in the cotyledon from the hydrolysis of the mannans which make the reserve-cellulose, deposited as the thickenings of the cell-walls of the endosperm. Nipa does not show, however, the presence of starch in the absorbing embryo. Though palms offer through their bulky tissues abundant material for biochemical study, this aspect of their lives has also been neglected [181].

As a matter of fact it is not easy to tell what part of the embryo is absorbing the endosperm until the other parts are thrust out of the seed. Then it is clear that the seedling has emerged by elongation of the cotyledon stalk. This structure sheaths round the seedling at one end and joins up with the cotyledon (and endosperm) at the other. The only palm in which there is some doubt is the nipa; it has been reported that its absorbing organ is really the radicle of the seedling and that its first root is actually the adventitious root (figure 95). Something of this sort happens in the Chinese lotus *Nelumbium*, so that it may happen in the nipa palm, but the situation is not clear.

The seedling has no difficulty in forcing its way out from the seed of most palms. The thin stone or fibrous shell of endocarp which

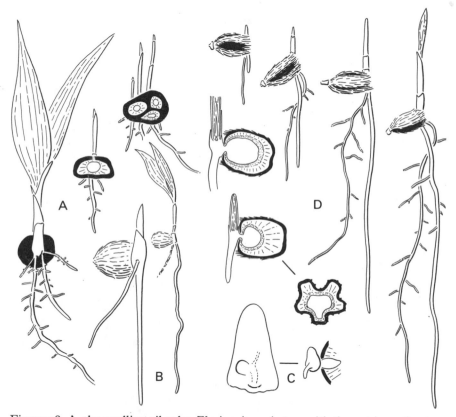

Figure 98. A, the seedling oil palm *Elaeis guineensis*, two with the nut in section to show the 1-seeded and the 3-seeded states, × ⅔. B, the Arecoid *Archontophoenix* to show the early disappearance of the radicle, × 1 and ⅓ (after Gatin, 1906). C, the embryo of *Archontophoenix* × 2 (after Gatin, 1906). D, the Arecoid *Ptychosperma* with 5-fluted nut covered with fruit-wall fibres, the largest seedling 67 days old, the radicle more persistent than in B, × 1; sections of the nut showing the narrow layer of floury endosperm digested by the cotyledon as it expands into the horny endosperm, × 2.

193

surrounds it is easily ruptured and may, indeed, be decaying at the time of germination. In those palms with a strong hard stone, such as the Cocoid palms, there are three thin places in it which enable the embryo to be pushed out. These are the germ-pores, not the micropyles as they are sometimes erroneously called, and within each is an embryo though usually, as in the coconut, two are 'blind' and distinctly harder than the soft pore which shuts in the one embryo. In the case of the palmyra *Borassus* with three thick stones in the fruit, there is a soft placc on the side of each where it was attached to the central core of the ovary.

In palms with relatively small seeds, the seedling is thrust by the cotyledon stalk just outside the seed where it sends the radicle into the soil and takes station at once [182]. The other and colossal extreme is that of the double coconut *Lodoicea*. The stout cotyledonar stalk, which is one inch thick, grows out from the huge nut, carrying with it the plumule and radicle. It is forced into the ground, even to a depth of two feet, and grows underground for several more feet until it plants the seedling up to a distance of, even, twelve feet from the nut [183]. In intermediacy there are several examples among

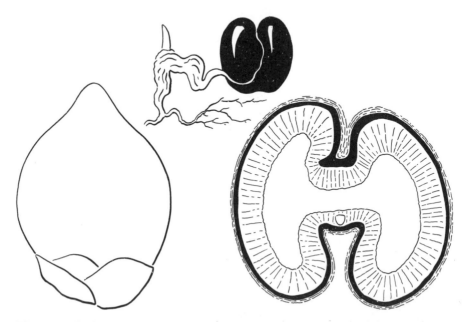

Figure 99. *Lodoicea*; the entire nut $\times \frac{1}{8}$, and a section of the bilobed stone with hollow endosperm $\times \frac{1}{5}$ (after Bailey, 1942); the seedling $\times \frac{1}{32}$ (after Hooker, 1827).

other Borassoid palms as *Hyphaene* with cotyledon stalks to two feet long and, among Coryphoid palms, *Copernicia* and *Pholidocarpus* to six or eight inches long. *Borassus* and *Phytelephas* sink the seedling perpendicularly into the ground for several inches. The date palm is similar on a smaller scale. Doubtless, there are many fascinating aspects of germination to be discovered, followed through and fully

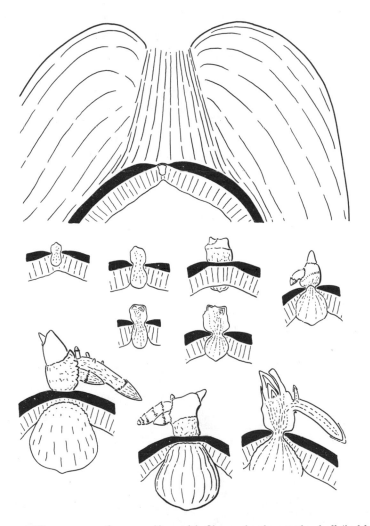

Figure 100. The coconut *Cocos nucifera* with fibrous husk, woody shell (in black), hollow endosperm (hatched), and the small embryo at the soft eye (germ-pore); successive stages in growth of the embryo as the cotyledon swells into and digests the endosperm; note the early appearance of massive roots; × $\frac{1}{2}$.

illustrated. Then, there are the *Iriartea* seedlings on their tripods (p. 91) and the origin of the descending stem in *Sabal* and various Cocoid palms (p. 90). One would like to know the manner of germination in the palms with warted fruits. *Pholidocarpus* resembles *Lodoicea* in miniature and *Phytelephas* resembles *Borassus*. It seems that the planting of the seedling in the ground at some distance from the seed, though exaggerated without doubt in *Lodoicea*, is really the primitive palm method and the simple case of the date is the reduced which becomes the normal method in other monocotyledons. The onion seedling is a miniature of the palm's which is unable to raise the heavy seed in the air.

The first root is short-lived and is soon followed by adventitious roots formed at the base of the seedling stem, to push out by small ruptures of the epidermis. Thus, as the stem enlarges and forms more leaves, it adds the adventitious roots throughout its life [184]. There is an interesting variety, however, in the early leaves produced by the seedling. It concerns the number of scale-leaves which proceed the first foliage leaf to have a lamina, as well as the shape of this first

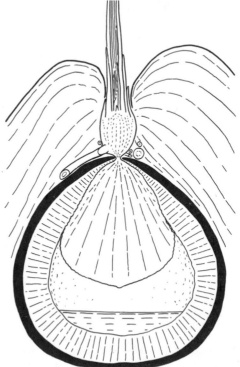

Figure 101. The coconut with three green scale leaves and the first foliage leaf about to emerge from the plumule; the cotyledon much enlarged, the coconut water nearly finished; × ½.

196

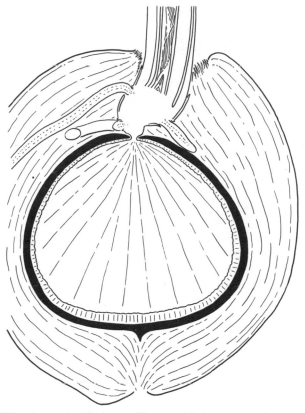

Figure 102. The coconut with the seedling established, rooted in the ground, with several foliage leaves, the spongy cotyledon filling the cavity of the endosperm but still with endosperm to be absorbed; × $\frac{1}{2}$.

foliage leaf which starts the build-up of the sapling leaves to the adult form. In some palms the first leaf above the cotyledon has a lamina, though small. In other palms the first leaf is a scale leaf, consisting of a sheath without lamina, as in *Phoenix* (figure 94). In others there are habitually two or three such scale leaves, or as many as five to seven in the nipa palm, before the first foliage leaf (figure 95). These details may be generic for they commence the character of the adult.

The first foliage leaf may have one or other of five shapes of blade [185]. It may be undivided and either lanceolate (*Phoenix*) or obovate, that is widened distally (*Licuala, Arenga*); in contrast it may be split either from the apex into two halves (*Caryota* and numerous Arecoid palms), or it is already palmate (*Latania*) or pinnate (*Howeia*,

197

*Phytelephas, Raphia,* and some *Chamaedorea*). A modification of the pinnate condition may be that in nipa where the first foliage leaf has two leaflets and a prolongation of the leaf-axis between them as a thin, lanceolate structure like a terminal leaflet. These differences, which initiate the split-lamina, must surely be generic, though they may need finer definition. Thus it is curious that *Caryota* should not begin with the terminal leaflet that its adult leaves have. Then, in *Euterpe* two forms occur; the section of the genus with ruminate seeds has the bilobed seedling leaf, so far as known, and that with non-ruminate seeds has this first leaf more or less palmately divided into leaflets [186].

Successive foliage leaves build up to the adult form by increasing the extent of the lamina in the developing leaves and by splitting off leaflets from the base of the initial apical part (figure 24). If the adult leaf is not split, successive blades increase in length by adding more folds through basal growth. In either case the apex of the leaf is that which is defined first in the seedling leaves. There can be no doubt that groups of species, if not genera and groups of genera, conform to characteristic steps from cotyledon to adult foliage, and this is a field where much more investigation is required to evaluate the palm genera. No land plant, whether it starts as 'sporeling' or seedling, can be fully appreciated until the developmental sequence of its leaves is known. As the eye is accustomed to the juvenile stages, the more characteristic they appear. Seedling and sporeling identification has to be learnt by the ecologist, and foresters have made of it a practical art.

Because the individual shows the build-up of a complicated leaf from a simple beginning, it is sometimes supposed that this is an evolutionary recapitulation. Inasmuch as modern plants habitually repeat what their ancestors have done, this is surely true. There is the well-known instance of the *Acacia* seedlings which build up doubly pinnate leaves and then transform them into the phyllodes (flattened leaf-stalks) of the adult tree; they recapitulate the normal foliage of the ancestral Acacias just as the seedlings of the phyllodic species of *Eucalyptus* recapitulate the decussate Myrtaceous leaf of their family. Though such repetition is hereditary, that does not mean that the cotyledon or scale-leaf, as the simplest leaf-form, was the primitive form any more than the seedling with two cotyledons was the primitive form of the flowering plant. The build-up is a physiological development as the apical bud enlarges and there is a

Figure 103. Embryo position
in seeds. A, *Phoenix dactylifera*
with lateral embryo, × 1.
B, *P. canariensis*, × 1.
C, *P. paludosa*, with basal
embryo, × 2. D, the Arecoid
*Hyophorbe* with apical embryo
and E, the allied *Mascarena*,
with lateral embryo, × ⅔.
(A–C, after Beccari, 1890;
D, E, after Bailey, 1942.)

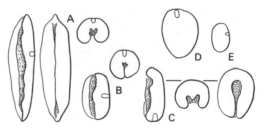

better supply of food and growth-substances to make bigger leaves. The very maximum that a plant can make must be the maximum of its heritage. This maximum may be reduced by stopping the development at any stage from the first instance of the primordium at the stem-apex; it can also be deflected by the transfer of growth and differentiation from one developing region to another. Thus modifications arise such as bud-scales, seedling scale-leaves, and phyllodes. The side-shoot of a palm that starts a sucker begins with scale-leaves which, like those of seedlings, have not developed to the state of forming folds before they are ordered to mature; and it builds up with improving food-supply to the adult leaf more rapidly than the seedling insofar as it begins as a bigger bud and has a better supply from the parent trunk. In counter manner leaves deteriorate as inflorescences are commenced, and are modified into spathes, bracts, and floral parts. We must turn to the biggest leaves of palms to discover their hereditary equipment. We return to the doubly pinnate leaf of *Caryota* as that with maximum endowment, and that through which the origin of the palm leaf must be contemplated. The seedling and the inflorescence show us how, by cutting off the fuel, this living mechanism reacts; it does not stop as an inanimate machine would do, but re-adjusts and simplifies. A hovel may have started architecture, but a sky-scraper does not begin with a hovel; we witness in its construction ontogenetic engineering at an advanced hereditary level.

Finally, in this chapter which brings the palm full circuit, we may note or repeat a few facts that are known about the early age of palms. *Borassus* takes nine years to begin the trunk and another ten to commence flowering. *Lodoicea* remains attached to its nut for at least five years and does not come into bearing for another forty. *Nipa* and *Eugeissona* begin to flower four to five years from seed. The

o

betel palm may fruit in its third or fourth year. The seedlings of the Cocoid *Attalea* grow down into the earth for three to four years, when the stem begins to turn up, and after another five or six years it begins to form the trunk at ground level; some species flower in this state, but others need to wait a further interval of years [187]. The coconut normally requires ten to fifteen years of growth before it comes into bearing, but this time may be shortened to five or six years in a small variety, and even happen abnormally in the seedling [188].

## Chapter 9

# Rattans

*'Nature may be defined as that which exists without guilt.'*
JOHN UPDIKE, *New Yorker* 1946

BETWEEN THE trees of all sizes which comprise the forest, clinging to them and scrambling over them, another form of plant life has evolved. It is the climber. Unlike the epiphyte which stays where it has alighted on trunk or branch, the climber starts at ground-level with other seedlings and ascends by using for its support the trunks and branches of the self-supporting. Its stem is weak and flops over until by some means it catches a rigid object and climbs. There are short climbers and lofty, slender and massive regardless of the height which they may reach. Some climb by short adventitious roots which, as in the ivy and most climbing figs, peppers and aroids, adhere firmly to the bark. Others twine, rotating their tips by lengthening one side of an internode before the other, or grasp with tendrils which are modified leaves, leaflets, stipules, leaf-stalks, and even inflorescences. And there is the vague group of scramblers which simply sprawl or hook their way up with unretractable claws. The climbing habit is found in many families of plants, dicotyledonous and monocotyledonous, and there is a tendency for a family to specialize in one or other way of climbing. The ivy family goes in for root-climbing, the true vines (Ampelidaceae) for tendrils, Annonaceae and Connaraceae for curious twistings, bindweeds for regular twining, though there are exceptions such as the Leguminosae which develop most sorts. It seems that some inhibition of the ordinary manner of growth, which stabilizes the plant by primary or secondary thickening, finds an outlet that is accompanied by a physiological direction to react to rough surfaces; excessive roots are produced, the outsides of which grow into the roughnesses; or young parts become exceptionally irritable and tighten coils. In many cases, there is a lengthening of internodes which facilitates the leaning, or blowing on to the support.

Once evolved, climbers pursue their own course of evolution. It is usually so specialized that there is no difficulty in accepting the general conclusion that, within a family, the climbers have been derived from the self-supporting, which may have been trees, treelets, shrubs, or herbs. Thus, at practically every stage of forest progress, climbers have entered, and it is not correct to suppose that all climbers are advanced plants in every way. They have diverged from all levels of advancement and, then, undergone the same general evolution of the leaf, inflorescence, flower, fruit, and seed according to the heritage with which they started. Climbing composites and orchids are much more advanced than climbing ferns, Annonaceae, or *Gloriosa* lilies. Then, climbers may end up, also, with non-climbing herbaceous forms in parallel with the trees. Climbers complicate the course of forest evolution, but the additional complexity is another and independent check on the general theory.

Palms have evolved climbers, and they start at the early pachycaulous stage of forest evolution. They make the most massive of all climbers, yet they too pass into the leptocaulous with stems narrowing to merely a few millimetres in width. The whole range from the primitive massive climber, little more than a weakening palm trunk, to the slenderest and, then, to the non-climbing undergrowth palm, as a neotenic seedling state, is shown by the genus *Calamus*. It is an extraordinary genus. It has the most elaborate construction of all palms. It is their biggest genus, variously estimated between two hundred and fifty and three hundred species. It is the most wide-

Figure 104. *Calamus* in the forest; left, a young rattan, × $\frac{1}{200}$; right, old rattans × $\frac{1}{400}$.

spread, for it ranges between 30°N and S from West Africa to Formosa and Fiji. It has entered more successfully than any other kind of palm into the forests of the world. It seems at once the height of palm effrontery and an old participant of ancient distribution.

The climbing palm is neither root-climber nor twiner, but the more generalized scrambler that hoists itself leaf by leaf, while the stem hangs as the cable to the root. The big leaf, which it inherits as a pachycaulous plant, does the mechanical work; the stem, relieved of the pressure, responds by becoming a flexible structure with long internodes. The unopen leaf lengthens at the tip. The sword of the palm crown becomes a whip, barbed with hooks. It sways and blows, catching twig, bark, limb, and leaf in the surround. As the leaf opens and projects itself by basal growth, the attached hooks are pushed on and those further down the leaf-axis take over; if they cannot be disengaged the crown is thrust aside on its swaying stem. Once a grip is established, it is seldom released; if other leaves have been unsuccessful, one can hold the crown. But, as more leaves are projected, another will attach itself to the ramifications of the forest; it is the peculiarity of this sort of climber to thrive on the branching exterior of other plants. It often happens, nevertheless, that many leaves do not attach themselves, especially in the early stages of the palm's life when it is growing up from the floor of the forest, or when it is growing by stream, lake, or shore at the edge of the forest, and then hanging whips become a menace to man and beast. To disengage the hooks, it is necessary to back and, in backing, other whips may be encountered; the unwary can become incredibly and most painfully entangled. One needs to be a pachyderm for immunity, and I often think that the elephant and rhinoceros have been the answer. Unattached whips, so fine and tenacious, are an ever present hazard in the forests of south-east Asia and, though apparently just a side-effect of the palm's growth, they surely assist in protecting the edible bud.

Compared with other palms, this manner of growth seems to be fairly rapid. It is caused very largely by internodal elongation as well as by elongation of the leaf-tip. The larger species of *Calamus* may have internodes three to four feet long. The leaves of climbing palms have, probably, no greater photosynthetic ability than those of other palms, but the effort is put into lengthening, rather than massive consolidation. A well-known and commercially exploited climber *Calamus caesius* will produce under forest conditions a stem about thirty feet long in five or six years from seed, and this in the course of ten more years will grow to a hundred feet. Thinner stems may lengthen more rapidly and, though their effective leaf-surface will be much less as the leaves are smaller, yet the greater number of stems that can be produced from a tuft may make up any deficiency; in dense forest with few shafts of light, the leptocaul may win. The longest stem that has been measured for any kind of climbing plant was that of *Calamus manan*, recorded by the Forest Department of Malaya as 556 feet; another, considerably longer, was chewed up and trampled to bits by elephants after it had been pulled down and before it could be carried out of the forest [189]. Thus, like two distant extremities, *Calamus* of the rain forest rivals *Macrocystis* of the sea.

Now, lengths of this kind far exceed the stature of any tree. Either the palm must have scrambled over several trees, or its stem hung in loops and lay in coils on the ground. We do not know the length to which an uninhibited climbing stem may grow, or why it should be limited. The hanging crowns and cables of these palms, however, are heavy. They snap twigs and break branches; they hook blindly on to living and dead. The supports give way, sooner or later; the crown subsides until caught again and the stem loops between the branches and coils on the ground. These are side-effects of slipping which generally cause the great lengths of stem, but they have their consequences. When the spiny sheaths of the dead leaves have rotted away, the old loops and festoons make the runways for the four-handed. And when these runways end in large bunches of edible fruits, there is the contribution of these barbed and horrid growths to the repast in the canopy.

The climbing palms of the Orient are known as rattans or, in Malay, *rotan*. It is thought that the word comes from *raut* (to pare) and to be connected with the cleaning and splitting of rattan stems for the many uses which they have: this is one of their better known aspects. All these climbers belong to the Lepidocaryoid palms, so that the name rattan is a convenient general designation. It can be stretched to the African genera of climbers, which are also Lepidocaryoid, but it is hardly applicable to the American *Desmoncus* which is a genus of climbing Cocoid palms allied with *Bactris* [190].

Two distinct groups of palms, then, have given rise to climbers in two opposite parts of the world, and these plants, like the monkeys which accompany them, run a parallel course marked all along with

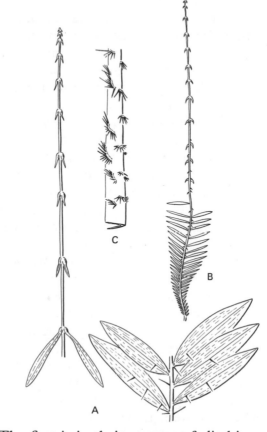

Figure 105. A, the American *Desmoncus*; leaf-tip to show the leaflets modified into hooks deflexed by the pulvinus, and normal leaflets from the mid-part of the frond; × ¼ (after Bailey and Moore, 1949). B, the leaf of the African *Ancistrophyllum* with the distal leaflets modified into hooks; × ⅒ (after Drude in Engler, 1908). C, Combs of spines on the leaf-sheath of *Salacca*; × ⅛ (after Furtado, 1949).

characteristic differences. The first is in their manner of climbing. The fifty or more species of *Desmoncus* have the leaflets set in pairs towards the end of the leaf axis and, where this runs out into the whip, the leaflets are shortened and transformed into tough, reflexed climbing hooks (figure 105). The leaf-sheaths, leaflets, and leaf-axis are usually extremely spiny, as they are in its smaller tree-like ally *Bactris*, and as in the eastern rattans. The arrangement seems by no means as effective as that of *Calamus*, for instance, yet it may be more appropriate for the broken and open canopy of the American forests. These huge tracts of vegetation have still to be compared from the point of view of their fitness for climbing plants. Thus in Central America there occur one or two climbing species of the Arecoid *Chamaedorea* which have no hooks or spines; their weak slender stems with long internodes and arching leaves scramble like the weak trailing stems of some kinds of *Equisetum* [191].

The leaflets of the Lepidocaryoid rattans of Asia generally alternate along the two sides of the leaf-axis and they are never modified into hooks. Instead, groups of spines on the underside of the axis are turned into groups of hooks and these are continued along the underside of the otherwise naked whip (figure 106). The hooks, set in twos, threes, or more up to seven or nine, are fairly short, yet stout, and reflexed and they become so strongly lignified into this position that they cannot be ripped off by any natural means. They make the terrible gliding fronds and catching whips, so successful in the ferocious Old World. Some eight genera, centred on *Calamus* and totalling about 450 species or three-quarters of all the Lepidocaryoid palms, have this habit and they make the most formidable array of any family with climbing plants [192]. It comes as a surprise, then, to discover that three African genera with merely a residuum, as it were, of eight species, are Lepidocaryoid palms that climb with modified leaflets in the manner of *Desmoncus* (figure 105). With them, moreover, grow a few African species of the much more successful *Calamus*, climbing just as the genus does in Asia. If the American climbers evolved with hook-leaflets, then why not some Lepidocaryoid, because most palm-characters have evolved in parallel in different series of genera? Several species of *Calamus* have, in fact, reflexed leaflets, but they are at the base of the leaf-axis and they do not become hooks. Nevertheless it is odd that this should have happened in Africa, halfway between the headquarters of *Desmoncus* and the eastern rattans; unfortunately there seems to be no clear indication of the origin of the African genera.

*Calamus* brings a complication into the nature of the climbing whips. Quite apart from the distinction between leaflet-whips and hook-whips, there are leaf-end whips and leaf-sheath whips. Both of these kinds occur in *Calamus* and in such a way that species with leaf-end whips never have leaf-sheath whips, and *vice versa*. The leaf-end whip is called a cirrus, that from the sheath a flagellum. The cirrus, of course, is the prolonged end of the leaf-axis, but the flagellum is a sterile, unbranched inflorescence. It arises in the manner of the *Calamus* inflorescence (p. 120, figures 63 and 106); it is set sparsely with tightly fitting spathes; it is possible to find transitions between the two that are sparsely branched and bear a few flowers: furthermore, the inflorescence itself of the flagelliferous species generally ends in a flagellum. Beccari was so impressed with the contrast in this respect that he divided *Calamus* into three groups,

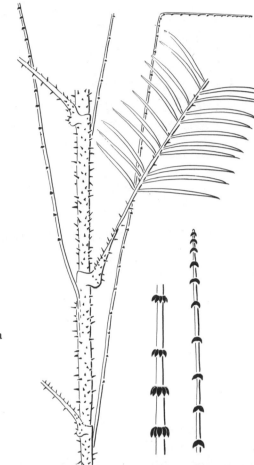

Figure 106. *Calamus*, part of a stem to show the geniculus at the base of the leaf-stalk and the flagellum arising as a sterile inflorescence from the side of the leaf-sheath; × $\frac{1}{8}$. The spine-hooks on the underside of the flagellum, × $\frac{1}{2}$.

namely the cirriferous, the flagelliferous, and a third for species that were not clearly the one or the other [193]. More recently Furtado has changed the classification and given the distinctions the nature of parallels that have arisen more than once in the evolution of the genus [194]. Beccari's third group seems to be a mixture of species truly without whips, of species which have lost the whips, of species in which they are but slightly developed, and, perhaps, of species described from immature material, for the whips may not be present on young climbing stems.

There is another possible distinction between *Desmoncus* and the rattans but it is not so certain. The species of *Desmoncus* build their tufts of climbing stem by short horizontal rhizomatous growth, in the manner of clumps of *Bactris*. It is said, also, to be the habit of the

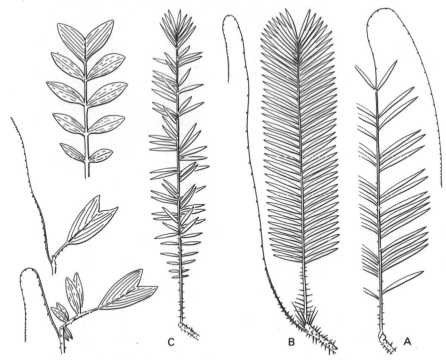

Figure 107. Leaf variation in *Calamus*. A, the cirriferous leaf with apical whip. B, the flagelliferous. C, a non-climbing leaf of the basal rosette, with tufted leaflets. The three other leaves variously reduced with compound leaflets, $\times \frac{1}{40}$.

three African genera which climb in the same way as *Desmoncus*, namely *Ancistrophyllum*, *Eremospathe*, and *Oncocalamus* [195]. It is not, however, in my experience the way of the eastern rattans, which produce short suckers from the rosette of leaves established by the seedling and build very compact tufts in the manner of *Salacca*.

With regard to inflorescence construction, flower, and fruit, there are many profound differences. *Desmoncus* has not the scaly ovary or the armoured fruit of the Lepidocaryoid climbers. Its inflorescence has the two large spathes of the Cocoid palms, unlike the many and often small spathes of the Lepidocaryoid. The fruit of *Desmoncus* is a brightly coloured, mostly red or pink, fleshy drupe with a hard stone. The Lepidocaryoid fruit has the yellow or brown shining armour enclosing rather thin pulp around the stoneless seed. The African genera, in spite of their vegetative parallel with *Desmoncus*, are to be classified as a special offshoot of the Lepidocaryoid palms, and this is borne out by their microscopic anatomy [196].

208

In the large genera *Desmoncus*, *Calamus* and its allies *Daemonorops* and *Korthalsia*, there is the same diversity of leaf-form that occurs in other large genera evolved into stout and slender forms. There are leaves with many narrow leaflets, representing the condition when all the folds of the unopened leaf have split, and there are those with fewer, variously compound, and broader leaflets, the constituent folds of which have not split. In the end, there is the small entire leaf, split only at the apex, which resembles the seedling leaf (figure 107). Not all slender rattans have evolved this way, for others retain the wholly split leaf with fewer leaflets of smaller size. We need a detailed and systematic analysis of the rattan leaf into fold-number and splitting folds, coupled with the study of leaf-succession in the seedling, before we can understand the trends among the species and the reason for these differences being specific. That the specialized rattans should follow the same course as other palm-leaves confirms the suspicion that there is an orthogenetic, or clock-work, trend of evolution to produce the same leaf-forms in all genera that vary greatly in the thickness of the stem.

The leaves of some species of *Calamus* and *Daemonorops* show a construction that is very difficult to understand; it has already been mentioned on p. 61, but it needs emphasis. Their leaflets, narrow and simple, are bunched into groups of three to nine on either side of the leaf-axis (figure 107c). The axis lengthens unevenly to space the bunches unevenly and to leave, as it were, single leaflets between the bunches. This happens differently on the two sides of the leaf-axis without any bending that might be expected when one side of the axis lengthens into an internode and the opposite side, remaining short, accommodates a group of almost contiguous leaflets. The axis, of course, is massive and there must be some graded elongation of cells across it which varies from one side to another and back again along the leaf.

Fish-tailed leaflets, as in *Caryota*, occur in several species of *Korthalsia* to indicate that the once pinnate leaf has been derived from the doubly pinnate. Indeed, it is by no means clear that this genus, habitually associated with *Calamus*, really is so close; it differs much in structure of the inflorescence. It may seem surprising that *Korthalsia* should have this very primitive feature, so far as palm-leaves are concerned, but it must be remembered that climbers have arisen at all levels of evolution and thence been modified.

*Korthalsia* is also the one palm genus to have become myrmecophilous; seeking, that is, association with ants. Where the leaf-stalk joins the sheath in all its species there is a well-developed ligule which may reach several inches long and be so conspicuously convex as to form a sort of legging on the stem; for this reason it is called the ocrea (figure 108). The species are distinguished by the form, size, and spininess of the ocrea. The old and dry leaf-sheaths persist for a long time; stems over one hundred feet long may be clothed with the pallid dead sheaths. The ocreas also persist and, as thin hard convex shells

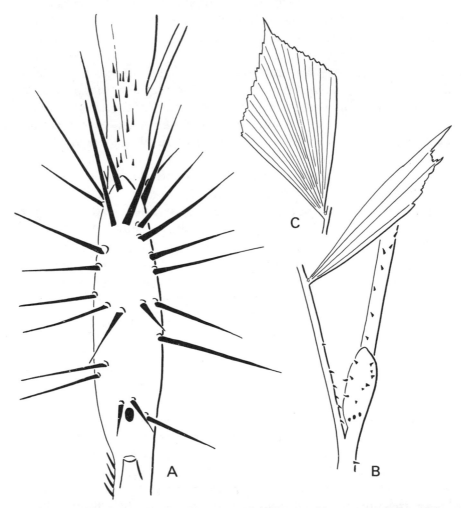

Figure 108. *Korthalsia*. A, *K. echinometra*, the ochrea making an ant-shelter with one entrance hole, × ½. B, *K. scaphigera*, with three small ant-holes, × ½. C, fish-tail leaflet of *Ceratolobus*, × ¼. (After Beccari, 1884.)

firmly pressed to the stem, they make excellent shelters for ants if they can get in. They enter by biting a hole or two in the soft, living ocrea of the young leaf and make a nest inside. As more leaves are developed, they enter more houses until, with strip development, they occupy the whole stem.

We pause in the excitement of a first expedition through the sweating glades beneath the dipterocarps, and a faint rustle fades into the trees. It comes again and vanishes as widely. We think of snakes, wasps, bees, and look around, but can discern no obvious source of the mystery. Yet now it is repeated right, left, and on all sides as a series of tiny rattles through the bushes into the canopy. An uncanny feeling shivers over our clammy bodies that we are watched by a host of invisible onlookers. But is this snake underfoot any more than the trailing stem of an old rattan? We bend down in relief to examine it and, just as the sound commences, a small ant at a hole in an ocrea beats its mandibles on the dry cover. Instantly a rattle comes from the box, to be taken up by the next and the next along the stem into the trees. We are standing in an old clump of *Korthalsia* and all its stems are rattling. The sentry has alerted the soldiers and the alarm is transmitted from post to post as a sort of 'action stations' to repel boarders up to the crown in the tree-tops. We lift the stem and out rush the black ants with ferocious bites.

Beccari maintained that these ants protected the rattans from marauding insects, and thus recompensed it as their landlord [197]. Ridley, less credulous, found that tufts of *Korthalsia* may or may not be inhabited and that, commonly, few stems of a clump were occupied. He found little evidence of marauding insects and observed that palms in general suffered little in this way. He decided that the association with ants (*Camponotus*, *Tridomyrmex*) was merely opportunist and that the function of the ocrea was to help cover the bud and throw off the rain from the young leaf-bases [198]. Considering the story of the coconut, the ants and the sucking bugs, I think Beccari may be right. The ocrea is certainly an opportunist outgrowth from the developing leaf into a space within the bud where it is concealed, but we do not know why the bud of *Korthalsia* should have these particular spaces. The whole phenomenon needs deeper investigation with, it is to be hoped, a sound-recording of what is, even when one begins to understand, the wierdest whispering of the forest.

Small biting ants occupy all sorts of vegetable niches. They nest under the dry persistent spathes of many palms, under the leaflets of persistent old leaves, among the old leaf-bases, and between compact, slowly developing fruits. They shelter, too, even if they may not actually nest, among the long spines on the sheaths of rattan leaves, and they nest in a curious way in certain species of *Daemonorops*.

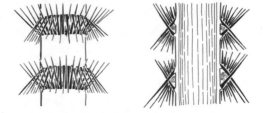

Figure 109. Verticillate spines in *Daemonorops verticillaris*, making ant-galleries; the left figure in section; × 1.

The spines in these species are borne on annular flanges set in pairs, as double rings, with the spines of the upper ring deflexed and those of the lower ring upstanding. Thus intersecting, they protect a secluded gallery, and the same ants which infest *Korthalsia* bite into the soft flanges on the young sheaths to take up their abode. What the biology of the association is, again we do not know, but it is just such little problems that set the mind on the path of discovery.

*Desmoncus* and most rattans have lateral inflorescences. They begin to flower and fruit at lengths and ages characteristic of the species and continue reproductive throughout the rest of their lives. Some are precocious, particularly among the species of *Daemonorops*, and flower before they have begun to climb. Five genera, by contrast, have terminal inflorescences. They flower and fruit at the very end of the life of the climbing stem, which subsequently dies down to be replaced by another, in the manner of the sago-palms *Metroxylon*. One of these five, namely, *Plectocomia*, seems to be a solitary palm, producing but one climbing stem, and, therefore, it is truly hapax-anthic in the manner of *Corypha*. The tufted, hapaxanthic genera are the African *Ancistrophyllum* and the Asiatic *Korthalsia*, *Myrialepis*, and *Plectocomiopsis*. It is difficult enough to study terminal inflores-cences in any palm, but these are the most difficult because they are generally out of sight in the canopy and to be obtained only by the felling of not one, but all the big trees roped together by their stems. Among these genera, *Ancistrophyllum* and *Korthalsia* provide evidence that terminal flowering is primitive. It is associated in them with the primitive bisexual structure of the flower which in all other climbing palms, except the African *Eremospathe*, is unisexual; in fact all the other Asiatic rattans are dioecious. Then *Korthalsia* has the primitive spiral construction of the flowering spikes, as in *Metroxylon*, while the other rattans have passed on more or less completely to the distichous construction with the branches of the inflorescence and the flowers set in two alternating rows. *Ancistrophyllum* has a red and fleshy, though scaly-armoured, fruit which in these two respects seems to be the most primitive durian-type among the Lepidocaryoid palms. In other words, the lateral inflorescences have the advanced constructions.

There appear to be no observations on the pollination of rattans, but bees are the probable agents for the hapaxanthic which unload so many flowers on the market at once. Beccari searched for nectaries and found them only in two species of *Daemonorops*, yet it would seem that rattans, as with other palms, must be among the prime suppliers of such hymenopterous needs. Beccari looked also for extra floral nectaries, associated usually with the visits of ants, but he seems rather consistently to have mistaken the pulvinus at the base of leaflets and spines for such glands, the presence of which in palms is doubtful [199].

With this general acquaintance of rattans, we can begin to enquire into their unique position. As there is constant need to be reminded both of the details and their interrelations in this kind of work, a simple key to the generic differences is given on p. 223. Humboldt wrote: 'Speech is enriched and animated by everything that tends to and promotes truth to nature', and thus it should be with the rather dry statements about genera [200]; they need animation.

Firstly, the rattans belong to one subfamily, the Lepidocaryoid. Their main development is in south east Asia where the dipterocarp trees have built the richest and tallest tropical forest for their abode. Africa has a small contingent but none occurs in America where the Lepidocaryoid palms consist of the three fan-leafed genera *Mauritia*, *Mauritiella*, and *Lepidocaryum*, together with a single pinnate-leafed palm, the wine-palm *Raphia taedigera*. This genus *Raphia* is the only African member of the subfamily, besides its three genera of rattans. Asia has at least eight genera of rattans and four of non-climbing, pinnate-leafed palms, *Eugeissona*, *Metroxylon*, *Pigafetta*, and *Salacca*.

Then, just as the retention of scales or spines on the fruit is the character of the subfamily, so the evolution of the rattans is connected with the retention of this primitive armour on the leaves, where it is regulated into clusters or squads of spines to make the hooks on the undersurfaces. No other palms have copied this feature which must be taken to indicate a common origin for the Asiatic genera. Among these *Calamus* is pre-eminent.

*Calamus* is dioecious. It has lateral inflorescences curiously adnate to the leaf-sheaths and, as has been said, many of its species turn the precocious inflorescences into sterile whips. *Calamus* climbs both by its leaves and by its inflorescences. It occupies, however, the greatest area of any palm-genus, and this could be taken to indicate that it is the oldest on the ground that it was travelling to Africa and Fiji before the present distribution of land and sea stopped the migrations of others. But this need not be true. The rarer a plant becomes, the smaller is its area of distribution. We do not find a rare species all over the world or a continent. And a rare species is very often one that is old and on the way to extinction, for instance, *Metasequoia*, *Sequoia*, *Welwitschia*, and *Ginkgo*: thus old plants and primitive plants linger in small areas. The smaller distribution of the other rattan genera may indicate that they are older than *Calamus*, old as it must be.

*Korthalsia* is the contrast. It has bisexual flowers set spirally on the spikes, terminal inflorescences, and in many species fish-tail leaflets. These are primitive marks. Its specialization is the development of the ocrea, whatever its significance. Its distribution from Burma to New Guinea is not so wide as that of *Calamus* for it does not reach Ceylon or Africa. Its species, however, are much more local, as if they were beginning to die out. These points have lead to the conclusion that *Korthalsia* is more ancient phylogenetically than other rattans [201]. We must look for an ally of *Korthalsia* among non-climbing Lepidocaryoid palms.

We come to *Salacca*, already noted for the primitive form of the fruit-scales in some of its species (p. 176, figure 89). It consists of about a dozen kinds of practically stemless palms, growing in riverine swamps from Assam and Indochina to Java, Borneo, and the Philippines. It fits geographically. Its species sucker freely and develop immensely spiny thickets from which the large bunches of edible fruits protrude. The spines are set in comb-like groups which on the underside of the leaf-axis contract into bunches, just as on the leaf-stalk of some rattans (figure 105) [202]. If they were shortened and reflexed by vigorous extension of the leaf-axis within the sheathing-bud, they would be transformed into rattan-hooks. The flowers are borne spirally on thick spikes, as in *Korthalsia*, and the inflorescences become exposed in an unusual way, which is also typical of the lower branches of the *Korthalsia* inflorescence; they pierce directly through the leaf-sheaths. However, there are important differences. The inflorescences are axillary, not terminal; the flowers are unisexual; and the plants are dioecious. Then, *Salacca*, is clearly on its own route towards the evolution of neotenic undergrowth palms. The smallest of these, *S. flabellata*, is known only from the state of Trengganu in Malaya, where it is common and presents the case of a new species beginning to spread (plate 16). As already noted, it has small bifid, but otherwise unsplit, leaves and the curious habit of running its inflorescences for several feet over the ground, even burrowing into the humus and forming a new plant at the tip (figure 67); in consequence the short flowering spikes project among the miscellaneous dead leaves and seem not to belong [203]. Female flowers and fruits have not been found, but it is probable that they afford the only example of a geocarpic palm; that is, one that fruits in the humus, if not in the soil. Where it grows, there are geocarpic figs, a geocarpic ginger (*Elettaria*), a geocarpic *Cyrtandra* (Gesneriaceae), and the lofty, yet geocarpic, Annonaceous tree *Polyalthia hypogaea*. So *Salacca*, while agreeing in essential points with *Korthalsia* and more primitive in not being a climber, has gone the other way to join the 'geocarpicetum'.

We must look for the ancestor of *Salacca*. We expect a tufted, arborescent palm with bisexual flowers, spirally arranged in thick spikes on a terminal inflorescence, and we meet, again, in eastern Malaysia and Polynesia the sago-palms *Metroxylon*. They are the most robust Lepidocaryoid palms; yet, they are also specialized. Their flowers tend to be unisexual and their fruits are inedible nuts. Though the modern *Metroxylon* cannot be the ancestor of *Salacca* and *Korthalsia*, its ancestor with edible, pulpy fruit may well have been; we notice, too, that the spines of the sago-palms tend also to be in transverse comb-like flanges.

In searching for a still more remote ancestor we return to the small and problematic *Eugeissonia* of western Malaysia (p. 180). It introduces the still more primitive condition of bisexual flowers with many stamens and multilocular ovary. There is, also, the little known *Pigafetta* of central Malaysia, which has a few species of lofty, solitary dioecious palms with axillary inflorescences. The fact is that within the range of *Calamus* in the botanical headquarters of south east Asia there are many signs of rattan ancestry; one day the whole story may be reconstructed.

P

We must return, nevertheless, to *Calamus* because in these evolutionary deliberations it is impossible to deal with all sides at once. *Calamus* has a few tree-species which do not climb. *C. arborescens* (Burma, north Malaya) has tufted trunks up to twenty feet high and three inches thick (plate 24). It has short internodes; its leaves have no hooks or whips, but the long thorns are set in tufts as in *Salacca*. Its Malayan ally *C. ramosissimus* has shorter thinner stems which are subscandent, leaning on to other plants and scrambling with its leaves which possess hooks but no whips. *C. erectus* (Assam, East Pakistan, Burma) resembles *C. arborescens* but, for various other details, it is classified in another section of the genus. The Malayan *C. oxleyanus* in yet another section is subscandent, armed now with both hooks and whips. Thus *Calamus*, unlike *Korthalsia*, provides its own tree-ancestor and it should be possible to learn from the living species of *Calamus* how it has come to climb. At the other extreme of its evolution there are neotenic species so slender and juvenile that they are small, may be stemless, undergrowth palms of the deep shade, even though possessed of hooks and short whips [204]. The nonclimbing species can usually be recognized in the herbarium, if there is no field-information, because they lack the knee, or geniculum, at the base of the leaf-stalk where it joins the sheath; the geniculum is a support, or subsidiary spring, for the leaf that has engaged a support (figure 106).

Now *Calamus*-ancestry, unlike *Korthalsia*, demands a tall tufted palm with axillary inflorescences bearing the bisexual flowers in two rows on the spikes. The nearest approach among living palms seems to be the African *Raphia*, but it has become mainly a solitary palm and its fruits, like those of *Metroxylon*, have been converted into nuts. *Raphia* and *Metroxylon* are usually classified together as tree-genera in contrast to the rattans, but the tree-species of *Calamus* annul the distinction. The two genera may be relics of the ancestral dichotomy which lead to *Calamus* and to *Korthalsia*; and the three African genera of rattans may belong to the *Raphia-Calamus* branch.

The other Asiatic genera of rattans seem also on the *Calamus*-side. *Daemonorops* is certainly related to *Calamus*, but its inflorescence is less specialized and it lacks the whips. *Plectocomia* and *Plectocomiopsis* are massive rattans and their flowers, as in *Myrialepis*, are set in the primitive way of terminal inflorescences; then, instead of the flowers being solitary or in twos, as in other rattans, there are several in a shortly stalked cluster. This suggests a more highly branched, paniculate inflorescence, extensively ramified as in *Metroxylon*, and still more primitive than in *Calamus* or *Raphia*. The suggestion is borne out by the large, non-tubular bracts of *Plectocomia* which seems to be the one truly hapaxanthic rattan.

*Ceratolobus*, according to Furtado, 'appears to represent a transitional stage in the evolutionary history of *Daemonorops* and *Calamus*' [205]. Several of its species, however, have fish-tail leaflets which, as in *Korthalsia*, must represent the primitive leaflet-form on the *Calamus*-side. The final genus *Calospatha* is too little known to be evaluated.

The inevitable conclusion seems to be that the classification of rattans is superficial. The climbing habit, by which they are united, is not a common hereditary property but an example of parallel evolution, just as with the tufted habit, the stemless habit, or the neotenic undergrowth habit with simple leaf. Such palms are not classified together, but are scattered among a great many diverse genera; so it must be with the climbing habit, which *Desmoncus* shows. When the many features of leaf and inflorescence, quite apart from the details of flower, fruit and seed which I have omitted, are worked out according to the common principles of palm-evolution, the genera of Asiatic and African rattans can be traced back to tree-palm ancestors at different levels of Lepidocaryoid evolution (figure 112). A similar parallelism of climbing genera is found in many other families such as Leguminosae, Rosaceae, Sapindaceae, and Moraceae. What is remarkable is the uniform way of climbing in all the Asiatic rattans, and this must refer to a common hereditary make-up.

The make-up consists, clearly, of the grouping of spines into bands or flanges, which can be contracted into clusters to form the hooks, and of the great elongation of the developing leaf within the bud. We must look at this developing leaf (figures 110 and 111). We see at once that the leaf-tip elongates enormously, compared with the ordinary palm-leaf (figures 16 and 26), and that it carries on its back the groups of spines. Then we pause to consider what the tip is. It represents apical growth beyond the blade-forming and folded part of the leaf, and this is the very thing that palm leaves and monocotyledonous leaves in general have been doing away with and substituting with basal growth. They dismiss the primitive apical growth, which makes the fern-leaf and the primitive leaves of dicotyledons, and they develop the blade basally in a manner which at once protects the tender growing region within the bud and projects the adult part for

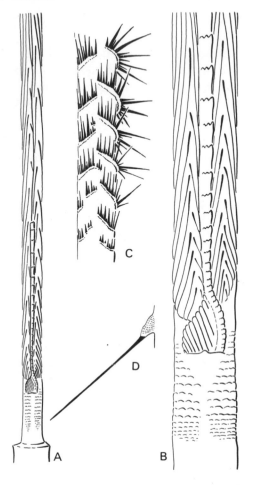

Figure 110. Leaf development in *Plectocomia*. A, a young unopen leaf, enclosing the younger leaf, × 1. B, the base of the leaf in A enlarged to show the transverse combs of spines developing on the leaf-sheath and the long tip of the young leaf with its incipient spines, × 4. C, the sheath of a recently opened leaf to show the spines beginning to recurve, × ½. D, a spine in section to show the pulvinus that has reflexed it, × 2.

photosynthesis. The palm-leaf in the course of its evolution has been losing its apex, distal to the blade-forming part, and reducing the elongation of its axis so that untipped pinnate leaves become costa-palmate and finally, when most curtailed, truly palmate. The rattans possess in their extended leaves the most primitive manner of leaf-development among palms. They climb because of this primitive trait. We must go back to pre-Lepidocaryoid palms for their immediate ancestors, and this is exactly the conclusion to which we were driven on consideration of their other features. The rattan is not the outcome of a modern palm. We may well agree, therefore, with those who regard the Bactrioid palms as distinct from the main body of Cocoid palms, because *Desmoncus* must also retain in some measure

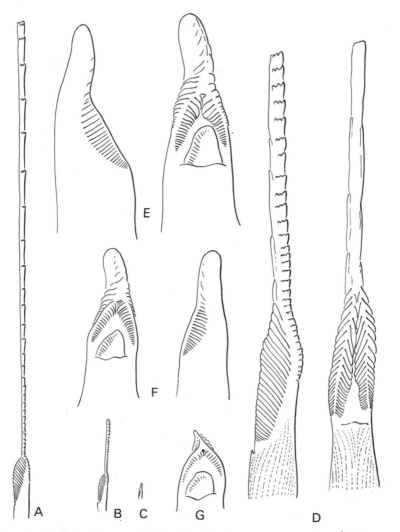

Figure 111. Leaf-development in *Plectocomia*. A, a young leaf with the hooks beginning to form on the long tip downwards along the back of the leaf-axis; × 1. B, C, younger leaves; × 1. D, the leaf B in side-view and front view to show the vestigial leaflet folds on the side of the tip; × 5. E, the leaf C to show the initiation of the long tip with its vestigial (acropetally developed) leaflet folds; × 12. F, a leaf similar to E, × 9. G, the younger leaf of F containing a still younger leaf with the leaflet folds being initiated, × 9.

this power of apical growth and refer to pre-Cocoid ancestry [206].

At length we appreciate two very obvious facts. No climbing palm has a palmate leaf; that is, no fan-leaved palm climbs. America, therefore, had no means from its fan-leafed Lepidocaryoid genera of evolving rattans. The fan-leaf, as the advanced form, is unsuited and this holds for ferns and other flowering plants.

All the subjects of this discussion are living plants. They are for the most part unfamiliar, and they have been introduced not for the sake of erudition but to reveal how much there is in this world on which to build the theory of plants.

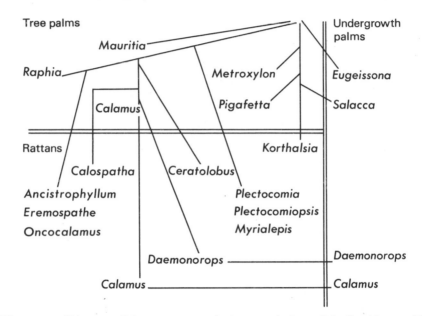

Figure 112. Diagram of the apparent evolutionary relations of the Lepidocaryoid palms.

If the rattans have been studied by few persons scientifically as yet, ever since man had the means of cutting their stems they have been exploited. There are now machines for peeling them, cleaning them, splitting and trimming them before they are put on the world-market as split cane for furniture, basketry, and other purposes. The Portuguese brought this commerce to Europe with the opening up of the Orient, but long before this the rattans were so invaluable to village-life that one can speak of the rattan civilization of the´south east Asia as one can speak of the tree-palm civilization of India and the bamboo civilization of Indochina, China, and Japan. The rain-forests of south east Asia provide ready made countless great lengths of cordage of thickness from a few millimetres to an inch and more, and these have been pulled, cut, coiled, cleaned, and sold since the trade in those parts was developed by the Chinese. The trade still goes through Chinese hands. It starts in the forest, where almost naked men extract the stems. It goes from the village down river to be transhipped to Singapore, Hong Kong, or some other Eastern mart until, at last, it enters sedate Western business. Names change from point to point. Malaysian words receive a Chinese twist and become anglicized. It has been very arduous to establish the botanical identity of the rattans of commerce. They cannot be identified from the finished strips, but must be traced right back to the living source. Many are untraced and, as the stock is diminishing and receding, new kinds are entering, and much more research is needed into their origin, supply, preparation, and possible cultivation. When you sit in a rattan chair at a rattan table on a rattan carpet with a rattan glass-holder behind a rattan blind and with a rattan hold-all, think of the hands through which the rattan came, bless that pioneer of business the Chinese *towkay* who dwells, not at the end of the road, but far beyond where comfort is rapidly fading, and be thankful for *Calamus*, *Daemonorops*, and *Korthalsia*! Be glad that you have not had to cope with *Plectocomia*!

A combined harvester that will pull, coil, and at the same time rub off the spiny old leaf-sheaths from the rattan stems in the forest has not been designed. The labour is accomplished in the primary way by human arms. It is hard, often painful, and always dangerous.

The best rattans live in the high forest. Dead and living limbs, clumps of epiphytes with their biting ants, wasp-nests, and other upper debris tumble down and, if the crown of the rattan should be dislodged, it flops with its cruel whips flaring. The crown of old stems is generally too securely fixed to be dislodged. The puller is content with the loose coils or the younger stems not so firmly established. The last part of the stem with the green leaves is, in any case, too fresh and sappy to be of use, but it does provide a bud which, if bitter, is generally edible. During the pulling, the puller pauses to clean off the dead leaves in order to get a new grip. When as much stem as possible has been pulled down, it is coiled up and carried back on the shoulder to the village. During the cleaning of the stem, especially if the bud is extracted, the puller comes on the wonderful pattern of spines laid flat with red shanks and black tips against the cream-white young leaf-sheath. The Dyaks of Sarawak, among the most eminent pullers, use these pectinate patterns as a motif on their basket-work, bamboo-work and pottery; it is sabre-toothing, though it may degenerate into dog-toothing.

In the village, slender rattans are used for cordage and rough baskets, hen-coops, pig-baskets, fish-traps, and snares. Stouter kinds are used to lash house-poles, ladders, carts, water-wheels, and other such constructions without a nail. Halters, tetherings, guy-ropes, and tow-ropes are made of rattan. About the last thing that an expedition to south east Asia need worry about is string. Most of our lashings, during the recent Royal Society Expeditions to North Borneo, were made from rattans, which abound on Mt Kinabalu to an altitude of ten thousand feet. Above this we carried coils of rattan, and we trailed thirty feet of finger-thick green rattan after us to use as a rope when negotiating the last slopes to the eastern summit. The perilous swinging bridges over the chasms of Assam are rattan. Downstream, sea-going ships are made from forest-timber lashed with stout rattans; the masts and sails are rigged with rattan; anchor-chains are rattan. Footballs are made of rattan, almost every kind of which has its special properties.

Split rattan allows more dexterous use, since the flat slender strips can be woven tightly or used for stitching. Dried palm leaves are stitched in this way to make the *attap* for roof and walls. Fine baskets, bags, belts, and wristlets are made of the split rattan. Axe-heads, parangs, and other instrument-heads are lashed to their handles with split rattan. Perhaps the most ingenious use of palms that I have met was a large thermos carried by a Chinese wood-cutter on a beautifully braided band made from split rattan; the thermos, which contained a pot of hot tea, was the split husk of a very large coconut hinged with rattan-stitches and clasped with a rattan knot.

To be durable, rattan must be thoroughly dried, scraped, washed, dried again, and smoked. This is a lengthy and skilful process which, in world commerce, is now largely dealt with in factories. The rattan must be cleaned of two parts, the outer glassy skin of tissue strongly impregnated with silica, and the softer inner tissue which is hygroscopic and rots quickly. The glassy skin usually fractures on bending. Unpeeled stems are called *sega* in the trade; the peeled or scraped are *lunti*, which is the Chinese modification of the Malay *runti* (to scrape or rub). A trade name for one of these is buckloon, and this is a portmanteau word from the Chinese *bak tin*, for the Malayan class of rattan called *rotan ayer*, and *lunti*.

'Sticks' are short lengths of stout unsplit rattan used for walking-sticks, ski-sticks, sweeps' sticks, sewer-rods, broom-handles, and so on. The best supply is from the flagelliferous *Calamus scipionum*, the Malacca Cane, the internodes of which may be four feet long. It is one of the few rattans which are deliberately planted; it seems to thrive both in the forest and, unlike most rattans, in the open. Two other species are cultivated by planting them along cut lines in the forest. One is *Calamus caesius* in Malaya, Sumatra, and Borneo, and the other *C. leiocaulis* of Celebes. They are, perhaps, the only cultivated climbers that, like many tropical timbers, must be grown wild.

Rattans supply sundry other products. The cabbage, as mentioned is generally edible. Many kinds have edible fruits and a few can be described as delicious, but none is cultivated for this purpose. Some are used in native medicine, chiefly through their astringent properties. Not a few whips, alas, have tortured wretches in the past. And some species of *Daemonorops* yield dragon's blood. This is a mediaeval name for the red resinous exudation of several, very diverse, kinds of plant, used for dyeing and for medicine. It occurs on the outside of the scales of *Daemonorops* fruits. To obtain it the fruits 'when quite dry are put into a basket with cockle-shells and shaken. The friction thus caused detaches the resin which falls through the basket into a cloth placed below, as a gritty powder. This, after being pounded into dust, is softened by means of hot water, and then moulded into cakes, sticks etc' [207]. Even in their industry, rattans are wonderfully primitive. Burkill's account of them should be enjoyed as well as the botanical preface to Beccari's monograph on *Calamus*.

A key to the genera of rattans (*Lepidocaryoideae*)

1. Terminal leaf-whip set with pairs of reduced hook-like leaflets. Africa

    2. Inflorescences terminal. Flowers bisexual ................ *Ancistrophyllum*

    2. Inflorescences lateral

        3. Flowers bisexual. Inflorescence without spathes .......... *Eremospathe*

        3. Flowers unisexual. Inflorescence with spathes ........... *Oncocalamus*

1. Leaflets not modified into hooks; climbing whips with recurved spines. Asia, Australasia, and Africa (*Calamus*)

4. Flowers bisexual, set spirally in cylindric spikes on the terminal inflorescence, its lower branches piercing the leaf-sheaths. Leaves with a prominent ocrea. Leaflets often of fish-tail shape. Endosperm ruminate; embryo lateral
*Korthalsia*

4. Dioecious, the unisexual flowers more or less in two rows on the spikes. Inflorescences not piercing the leaf-sheaths

 5. Inflorescences terminal. Endosperm not ruminate; embryo basal

  6. Spathels large, boat-shaped, overlapping. Apparently not tufted, but with a single stout stem ............................ *Plectocomia*

  6. Spathels small, tubular, sheathing. Tufted rattans

   7. Fruit-scales in vertical rows .................... *Plectocomiopsis*

   7. Scales minute, very many, irregularly arranged ........ *Myrialepis*

 5. Inflorescences lateral, attached to the outside of the leaf-sheath, not emerging from the leaf-axil (except in *Calospatha*)

  8. Inflorescences usually much elongate with tubular spathes, often flagelliferous and scandent. Flowers regularly in two rows. Seeds mostly not ruminate; embryo basal or lateral .................... *Calamus*

  8. Inflorescences with one or more large, boat-shaped spathes; often short, never flagelliferous or scandent. Flowers often not distinctly in two rows. Embryo basal

   9. Inflorescence with one large spathe. Leaflets often of fish-tail form. Endosperm ruminate ........................ *Ceratolobus*

   9. Inflorescence with several large spathes. Leaflets pointed

    10. Fruit with 2–3 cavities and seeds. Endosperm not ruminate
*Calospatha*

    10. Fruit one-seeded. Endosperm ruminate ......... *Daemonorops*

224

## Chapter 10

# Palm Geography

THE DISTRIBUTION of living things over the earth and the thoughts which this knowledge inspires have produced a fascinating and almost endless subject. It grew from the enthusiasm of explorers who discovered the different kinds of animals and plants, and what they learnt is being slowly consolidated through the patient cataloguing of local faunas and floras by resident naturalists. Publications on the subject range from school magazines to the weighty reports of expeditions and massive volumes explaining a life's devotion. Yet knowledge is imperfect. No person or expedition can carry into the field the critical ability to recognize more than a fraction of the living things of the countryside. As many specialists are called for as there are families of animals and plants, and most places where wild life is fullest lack the resident naturalist. Nevertheless the broad outlines of the present distribution of families, genera, and more prominent species, at least among the higher plants and animals, are fairly well investigated.

These facts of distribution are the foundation of biogeography which, as the theory of distribution, develops into the most complicated branch of biology. It introduces ecology, which relates the organism through its physiological processes to its particular habitat in the environment. Geographical distribution becomes ecological distribution, and what was inert space becomes living room; for the presence of one organism enlarges the environment to admit others. Much is known about the ecology of cultivated plants and of those which impinge more strikingly on botanical research, but for most plants the roll-call is blank. This is the state with palms. Their physiology has scarcely been explored. The contribution of their great structures to the environment has scarcely been acknowledged. The ladder of niches for epiphytic life which they raise into the air among the persistent leaf-bases, the giant litter which they cast, and the fruits which they offer bring a world of living as peculiar as the manner in which they enter into the environment. The vista of ecology is brilliant, though narrow.

Biogeography must reckon with past distribution of organisms. In so far as fossils can be identified or related with the living, they help to solve the origin of present day distribution. But investigation is tedious, lengthy, and chancy: where should one look and how extract? Rocks and peat need microscopic sifting to disclose their fossil content. Even the larger plant-fossils need microscopic study for their identification. In many cases there is not the microscopic knowledge of the living for comparison with the extinct. After identification there must come interpretation. Fossil deposits may be re-worked by later geological processes and re-deposited with their fossils at a later period; their content need not have come from plants that lived in the vicinity. The presence of nipa pollen in the apparently unworked Cretaceous deposits of Borneo indicates that the nipa palm grew there then as now; but the water-worn nipa fruits in the Eocene clay of Texas and Brazil may have been drifted from a far source, just as West Indian fruits, even those of the Amazon palm *Manicaria*, are washed up on the coast of Ireland and Norway, perhaps also to become fossilized. Paleobotany is a bright, yet ever hazy vista.

Distribution implies space, descent implies time, and the two in biology spell evolution. Biogeography leads to the heart of organic evolution. The issue comes in many ways. *Phoenix* presents a chain of species from the Canary Islands to Formosa, each with its place in the chain (fig. 114). The question is whether there was one progenitor spread over the whole range which broke up into the modern species as it evolved in different parts of the chain or these species evolved from each other in one or more directions along the chain. Where and from what did *Phoenix* arise? That is its biogeography. Likewise the questions apply to the chain of genera beginning with the Mediterranean *Chamaerops* and extending through the Asiatic *Trachycarpus* over the Pacific Ocean to their Coryphoid allies in tropical America (p. 235). *Phoenix*, structurally, is allied with them, and the questions arise whether they had a common ancestor and where it lived. If India is chosen for *Phoenix*, it is a long way overseas to the West Indies, yet this pattern occurs in other plants and strengthens the conviction. Thus biogeography comes against classification. Both are aspects of evolution, and the only classification that can truly serve biogeography is the natural which attempts to portray phyletic origins. An artificial classification into pinnate and palmate palms, for instance, or tufted and solitary, can serve a purpose but rarely that of biology in its grand problem of biogeography. All who work on the classification of living things know, however, that there is much room for improvement. Text-books maintain thc old traditions; the subject grows stale; and students believe it is exhausted. It is well to realize that biogeography is merely as good as the classification on which it depends. This vista needs clearing.

The unit favoured in biogeography is the genus. *Phoenix* is a good example, which cannot be said of all palm genera. Many have been made, not from obvious distinction, but through splitting large genera into small genera on details of uncertain significance; with better understanding they are being re-valued and already, in some cases, re-united. Is *Cocos* one or ten genera? Are there 130 genera of Arecoid palms or thirty? The status of a genus cannot be defined, for some see many where others perceive one. The issue becomes important when the relative contribution of a part of the world to the origin of a family is considered. The presence of many genera is taken as the sign of an evolutionary centre, weightier than one in which there has been merely a multiplication of subgenera or species. Thus, for some, New Caledonia is an island where many palm-genera have been evolved; for others it is a minor centre of subgeneric modification. Of greater significance and more uncertainty there is the monotypic genus that consists of a single species. It brings in the problem of the evolutionary course of a genus which, if successful, rises from one or a few species to a peak of many and declines, as it is superseded, to a few or one before extinction. The monotypic genus may be new or old, as it is nascent or moribund and, so, floras may in this respect be modern or ancient. Numbers of genera and species and their ratios are meaningless in biogeography unless bound with a system of classification. To overcome this difficulty, Croizat wrote of form-making and implied thereby the whole extent of an evolutionary line, regardless of how it was subdivided; and even this depends on an overall classification which, if we can judge from the current trend, is sure to be improved. Tentativeness takes the edge off many biogeographical arguments.

The interplay of land and water, mountain and desert, or tropical and temperate climates are factors of the environment acting more or less stringently on all living things. As the interplay has varied in the past, so it must be reflected not only in the distribution of palms, for instance, but of all plants and animals with like susceptibilities. The distribution of one must relate, and must be related, to that of others.

227

In fact all genera and species are instruments recording through their presence planetary history. From protozoan to worm, insect, fish, and mammal, and from plant-plankton to seaweed, moss, fern, fungus, lichen, and flowering plant there must be biogeographical facts, stemming from as many different periods in geological time as witnessed their evolution. Biogeography, palaeontology, and geology must be welded into one science which, to emphasize its magnitude and comprehensiveness, Croizat has called panbiogeography. To fit palms into this survey would need a volume of background. It is hypothetical because with so much uncertainty about the origin, evolution, and dispersal of living things, there is no starting point, and one must work backwards hopping, as it were, from hypothesis to hypothesis to see which gives the more comprehensive view.

There are three main theories, and a fourth standpoint. It is assumed, because there is much biological evidence in its favour from present-day distributions, that land-masses have risen and sunk all over the world, interconnecting at one time or another by landbridges across which those living things travelled which then existed. Hence arose the wide and narrow distributions of ancient and modern genera. If their present distributions were known exactly, it should be possible to cut them out and fit them together, side by side in space and superimposed in time, as a jigsaw puzzle in three dimensions which would register the past interplay of land and water. This theory is upheld in botany by Croizat and van Steenis [208], though others regard it as geologically impossible [209]. An enormous mass of evidence from botany and zoology has been marshalled by Croizat to show that world conditions began to stabilize into those of the present time about the Cretaceous period and that much of present day distribution reflects Cretaceous geography. He considers that flowering plants, in particular, have issued from an Antarctic continent of mild climate through three 'gates of Angiospermy'. There is the Magellan gate of Cape Horn, the African gate of Good Hope, and the Polynesian gate of New Zealand. He leads palms through the African gate to Gondwanaland, which has largely foundered in the Indian Ocean, and thence through Africa to America, through Malaysia to India and Europe, and by a re-routing from New Caledonia to Australia, Polynesia, Hawaii and California. This is the most positive contribution to palm biogeography [210].

The second theory is that of continental drift which Good champions in the third edition of his work on plant-geography [211].

The theory, supported by modern geophysics, rams the old continental masses of South America, Africa, India, Australia, Siberia, Scandinavia, and Canada into one land-mass, while the rest of the world was ocean. The modern continents began to separate about the Jurassic period and have since been drifting into their present positions. The most important point for the biogeography of the flowering plants was the separation of South America, Africa, India, and Australia from their common interlocking with Antarctica. We sense again the southern gates of angiospermy.

Then, to both of these theories, there may be superimposed that of polar wandering due to the oscillation of the axis of rotation of the earth. Polar wandering would automatically set the equator pivoting about its present position [212]. The theory, supported by palaeomagnetism, or the direction of magnetization in old sedimentary rocks, could bring at some time the equator near to the present arctic and antarctic circles and warm up the gates of angiospermy [213].

Fourthly there is the standpoint of tropical botany which holds that all the main groups of plant and animal arose under tropical conditions. The problem is where the tropics were in the Jurassic period when flowering plants were taking possession of the world, where the continents, and what their shapes. Let us see what facts palms, so old, so tropical, and so diversified, have to contribute.

The palm family is pantropical, but it has subtropical extensions into California, North Carolina, Chile, Argentina, Italy, Greece, Asia Minor and across north India and China to Korea and south Japan, New Zealand, and South Africa. The extreme limits of distribution are from 44° N latitude in Europe to 44° S in the Chatham Islands off New Zealand. We know now, as a result of palaeobotanical exploration, that these excursions are rearguard actions on the withdrawal of palms from a much wider distribution during the warm Eocene period, if not from the Cretaceous. Present limits mark the frost line where frost damage to living tissues becomes serious enough to impede palm growth in competition with other vegetation. Several are remarkably cold resistant and can stand winter temperatures down to—7° C, for instance *Chamaerops*, *Trachycarpus*, *Washingtonia*, the Chilean *Jubaea*, the New Zealand *Rhopalostylis*, species of *Livistona*, and the date palm; but it is one thing to survive in cultivation and another to succeed in nature where setbacks retard recovery and lead to overshadowing and extermination by hardier trees. Thus, the more usual limits of palm distribution are given by the zone in which *Cocos nucifera* is successfully cultivated, between 20°N and S latitudes. The maximum of palm vegetation narrows to the zone of equatorial rain forest between 5°N and S latitudes.

Perhaps the most striking points about palm distribution are that with one possible exception no genus is pantropical, that with two exceptions the genera belong either to the Old or the New World, and that with four exceptions those of the Old World are either African or Asian. In other words most genera are restricted to the three main tropical continents. The first exception is *Cocos* which in its widest sense of form-making, occurs in America, South Africa, and, as the coconut, on the islands of the Indian and Pacific Oceans. The two genera which occur in both America and Africa are *Elaeis* (the oil palm) with one species in each, and *Raphia* with one species in America and about twenty in Africa. The four genera which occur both in Africa and Asia are *Phoenix*, *Hyphaene*, *Borassus*, and *Calamus*.

A sample of palm floras is given in table 2. The figures have been taken from standard works and checked by recent monographic

## Table 2. *Palm Floras*

| | GENERA | SPECIES | | GENERA | SPECIES |
|---|---|---|---|---|---|
| America (excl. Hawaii) | 92 | 1,140 | Guadelupe (Mexico) | 1 | 1 |
| Africa (mainland) | 15 | 50 | Cocos Isl. (Costa Rica) | 1 | 1 |
| Asia, Australasia (excl. Hawaii) | 107 | 1,150 | Galapagos, Revillagigedo | 0 | 0 |
| | | | Madagascar | 18 | 113 |
| Chile | 2 | 2 | Mascarene Isl. | 5 | 12 |
| Argentina | 4 | 5 | Seychelles | 6 | 6 |
| Paraguay | 15 | 45 | Socotra, Chagos Maldive, | 0 | 0 |
| Paraña (South Brazil) | 12 | 15 | Laccadive Isl. | 0 | 0 |
| Brazil (entire) | 41 | 420 | Ceylon | 9 | 19 |
| Colombia | 56 | 293 | Andaman Isl. | 9 | 15 |
| Guatemala | 22 | 73 | Nicobar Isl. | 4 | 6 |
| USA | 9 | 14AC | Singapore | 16 | 47 |
| Arabia | 4 | 7 | New Caledonia | 14 | 25A |
| Malaya | 33 | 216 | Fiji | 10 | 34 |
| Indochina | 21 | 77 | Samoa | 3 | 8A |
| China | 14 | 30 | New Zealand | 1 | 3A |
| Japan | 2 | 3C | | | |
| Australia | 16 | 31 | Canary Islands | 1 | 1P |
| | | | S. Thomé | 2 | 2 |
| Cuba | 15 | 76 | South Africa | 4 | 4 |

(A, Arecoid palms; C, Coryphoid; P, *Phoenix*.)

studies of the palms [214]; introduced species have, of course, been omitted. Of the three regions with comparable tropical extent, America and Asia plus Australasia have practically equivalent palm floras; that of Africa is extremely poor. Indeed, the small detachment in Singapore Island equals the whole African continent, Madagascar being excepted. Furthermore, the flora of Malaya is double that of Madagascar the area of which is four times that of Malaya. This fact emphasizes the prevalence of palms in the narrow rain-forest belt of the tropics. Brazil and Colombia have rich floras in this part of America, though neither country is in proportion to its size as rich as Malaya. Colombia, one eighth the area of Brazil, has two thirds as many kinds of palm, but Malaya which is one eighth the area of Colombia and is without its Andean diversity, has about three-quarters as many species. We do not know yet how many palms occur in Bornco and New Guinea. The astonishing fact is the unproductive-ness of the rain-forests of the Congo.

The region where the species of a genus or the genera of a family are concentrated is taken to be the source of that genus or family, in so far as this can be ascertained from present distribution. It is possible that the centre may have shifted with climatic change in which case the proof must lie with fossil evidence, but it is obviously absurd to suppose in the absence of such evidence that the Sahara, midway between the concentration of palms in south-east Asia and Amazonian America was the old, extinct source of modern palms. Africa, then, is ruled out from palm-ancestry unless it can be shown that in Mesozoic times the equator traversed it obliquely so as to induce rain-forest along one or other side and that, as the poles gained their present position, the equator swung rain-forest and palms out to America and Asia. The other extreme would be to regard Singapore as the source of the palm family because it has such a high density of genera or species per unit area, but these figures have not been ascertained for districts of comparable area in Brazil or Colombia, Borneo or New Guinea.

We turn to consider what kinds of palms are distributed in these places. Table 3 provides an analysis in which the specific number will be more reliable than the generic in the case of large groups. Three subfamilies, the Arecoid, Coryphoid, and Lepidocaryoid, are pantropical, but the Coryphoid is not truly African because of its two African representatives. *Chamaerops* (Mediterranean) is related to the Asiatic *Trachycarpus* and *Wissmannia* (Somaliland) to *Livistona*: they

Q

## Table 3. *Palm Floras*

|  | WORLD | AMERICA (INCL. HAWAII) | AFRICAN MAINLAND | ASIA AUSTRALASIA (EXCL. HAWAII) | MADAGASCAR | SINGAPORE | NEW CALEDONIA | FIJI |
|---|---|---|---|---|---|---|---|---|
| Phoenix | 1/12 | — | 1/4 | 1/7 | 1/1 | — | — | — |
| Coryphoid | 33/330 | 18/170 | 2/2 | 13/140 | — | 2/5 | ?1/1 | 1/2 |
| Borassoid | 6/24 | — | 3/12 | 3/4 | 3/4 | — | — | — |
| Caryotoid | 3/38 | — | — | 3/38 | — | 1/1 | — | — |
| Lepidocaryoid | 25/500 | 4/25 | 5/30 | 16/450 | 1/1 | 6/28 | — | 2/2 |
| Arecoid | 130/1,100 | 36/484 | 2/5 | 71/490 | 12/106 | 6/12 | 13/24 | 7/30 |
| Cocoid | 27/600 | 25/597 | 2/2 | — | 1/1 | — | — | — |
| Phytelephas | 1/10 | 1/10 | — | — | — | — | — | — |
| Nipa | 1/1 | — | — | 1/1 | — | 1/1 | — | — |

|  | CHINA | USA | CUBA | BRAZIL | COLOMBIA | PARANA | CEYLON | MALAYA | AUSTRALIA |
|---|---|---|---|---|---|---|---|---|---|
| Coryphoid | 5/10 | 7/12 | 7/59 | 4/6 | 5/5 | 1/1 | 1/1 | 7/33 | 3/7 |
| Arecoid | 1/3 | 2/2 | 5/11 | 11/120 | 25/166 | 2/4 | 3/3 | 8/43 | 9/15 |
| Cocoid | — | — | 3/6 | 20/276 | 13/89 | 8/9 | — | — | — |
| Lepidocaryoid | 3/12 | — | — | 4/20 | 4/10 | 1/1 | 1/10 | 12/131 | 1/5 |
| Caryotoid | 3/6 | — | — | — | — | — | 1/1 | 3/5 | 2/2 |
| Borassoid | — | — | — | — | — | — | 1/1 | 1/1 | 1/1 |
| Phoenix | 1/1 | — | — | — | — | — | 1/2 | 1/1 | — |

(The first figure gives the number of genera, the second the number of species) are westerly extensions of the Asian palm-flora to Africa north of the Sahara.

Lepidocaryoid palms are concentrated in Malaysia (Malaya to New Guinea), which seems therefore to have been their centre of origin. Here occur the problematic *Eugeissona*, *Salacca* with the long scales on its fruits, and the rattans with their primitive leaf-character. America has only three or four genera which, as fan-palms, must undoubtedly have been derived from the pinnate stock of the Old World where the fan-leaf has never entered Lepidocaryoid evolution. The fan-leaf with the most reduced leaf-axis develops in this sub-family as far away as possible from the domain of rattans which prolong the primitive apex of the pinnate leaf into the climbing whip. The African Lepidocaryoid palms, *Raphia* and the three rattan genera with reduced leaflets on the whip, need more careful investigation particularly in regard the affinity between *Raphia* and *Metroxylon*; it may speak for the relict nature of the African palm-flora. The Malaysian Lepidocaryoid flora fails in central and western India, except for the extension of *Calamus* into Africa, where a few species extend across the continent. Eastwards the flora peters out in the usual way of Malaysian flowering plants for which Fiji is the last substantial vanguard. The subfamily is absent from New Caledonia, though this island is confronted with rattan-dwelling Queensland, Solomon Islands, and Fiji; and there would seem to be no connection with the American genera across the Pacific. But the fan-leafed American Lepidocaryoids must have come from somewhere. One possibility is via *Raphia* over the Atlantic. The other is via *Metroxylon* over the Pacific. Anatomical similarities strongly suggest that the American genera are nearer to *Metroxylon* [215], which is also the one Lepidocaryoid genus that gathers strength in the Pacific theatre, and seems to have originated about New Guinea and the Solomon Islands, that is the Melanesian foreland [216].

This conclusion confirms Beccari's that *Eugeissona* of west Malaysia is the remains of the link between the Lepidocaryoid palms of the Asia plus Australasia and the American Cocoid Palms. The link must have been trans-Pacific, for there is no such evidence in Africa. If, now, the land-bridge had the form of island stepping-stones rather than continental masses, as recent considerations prefer [217], it is highly improbable that it would have been a seat of major palm evolution. As table 2 reveals, palm floras dwindle on oceanic islands and, as we shall see, where they have multiplied in species this has been the ultimate radiation of their genera, not that of their primary evolution. The palm biogeography introduces ancient plants and ancient problems, and it requires ancient land-masses.

The Arecoid subfamily is equally distributed in number of species between the American and the Asian plus Australasian floras. The greater number of genera in the Asian-Australasian flora probably stems from the insular nature of the region and the tendency to split genera on very minor details corresponding with island differentiation. Arecoid palms peter-out westwards of Central India and the two African genera, *Podococcus* and *Sclerosperma* seem to be related with the American *Geonoma*. Towards Polynesia, the Arecoid palms predominate in the island floras. Thus the subfamily masses on both sides of the equatorial Pacific, and practically avoids, or has barely reached, Africa.

The Coryphoid palms confirm the Arecoid conclusions. They have developed strongly in central and north America, and this northerly extension is reflected in the preponderance of Coryphoid palms in China; with five genera and ten species they comprise a third of its palm flora. They are the only palms which reach Japan and they extend furthest north into the United States of America. The affinity between the Sino-Japanese flora and the North American is well known; there are the cases of *Cercis*, *Gleditschia*, *Platanus*, *Castanea*, *Nelumbium*, *Rhododendron*, *Magnolia*, and *Lilium*. The affinity extends far back into Eocene floras which seem to have swept with a homogenous warmth across the whole of the north temperate region. Now there is left the Coryphoid front which makes the whole north

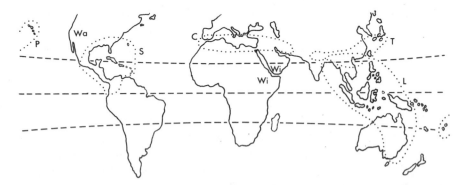

Figure 113. Distribution of the northerly Coryphoid palms *Chamaerops* (C), *Livistona* (L), *Pritchardia* (P), *Sabal* (S), *Trachycarpus* (T), *Washingtonia* (Wa), and *Wissmannia* (Wi). Equator and tropics indicated in broken lines.

temperate boundary of palm distribution. It is commanded by the Mediterranean *Chamaerops*, the Sino-Himalayan and Japanese *Trachycarpus* and *Rhapis*, the Californian and Mexican *Washingtonia*, the Florida *Rhapidophyllum*, the big alliance of *Sabal* in Central and Caribbean America, and, even, the complex of *Cryosophila*, *Chelyocarpus*, and *Trithrinax* in South America. Then dropped, as it were, into the middle of the Pacific break there is the Hawaiian *Pritchardia*. There is no Atlantic link, and no African. On the principle that massing indicates a site of origin, this front must be read as the post-glacial line of Coryphoid palms which issued from their source in tropical America, where the durian-fruited genera *Chelyocarpus*, *Haitiella*, and *Thrinax* occur, and travelled north-west into Asia and Europe. Yet, there is another massing in south east Asia about *Livistona* and the durian-fruited *Pholidocarpus* and *Teysmannia*, and this must surely have extended northwards and met the Sino-American contingent. The two monospecific Malayan genera *Liberbaileya* and *Maxburretia* of the limestone hills are relics of the vast limestone mass that must have been a scene of Coryphoid evolution since the Cretaceous era. What we need to solve this problem is the deeper analysis of the Coryphoid genera [218].

The separation of the tropical world into two palm centres is emphasized by the Cocoid and the Caryotoid palms, and by the so-called anomalous palms *Phytelephas* and *Nipa*. The Cocoid with *Phytelephas* are American except for two African Cocoid palms and the uncertain coconut itself. The Caryotoid palms with *Nipa* are Asian-Australasian and rigidly exclude Africa. Though the theory of continental drift separates America from Asia on the two sides of the united land-mass with Africa in the centre, and might explain this fact of modern distribution, it does not explain where the centre of origin of the palms lay or how the Arecoid, Coryphoid, and Lepido-caryoid palms got to both sides of the land-mass. If the equator were stationary, the central position of Africa should have caused a climate too dry for palms, the origin of which must have been on the river flats. If the equator pivoted even to an angle of 45°, it would have removed Brazil and Malaysia, China and North America remotely from continuous tropical contacts. If these events were post-Jurassic, they were too late to affect the primary distribution of palms which seems to have been accomplished by the Cretaceous period. Perhaps the climate of the world was uniformly tropical, but this is not in accordance with geological evidence. If there is any truth in the suggestion that Africa, now so poor in palms, was once their centre, it must be proved by fossils. However, this problem must be viewed from all sides and we wait a modern review of palm classification. We may be deceived in allying the Arecoid palms of the Old and New Worlds into one subfamily for they may be two parallel groups; yet it hardly seems possible that this argument could apply to the Coryphoid and Lepidocaryoid palms.

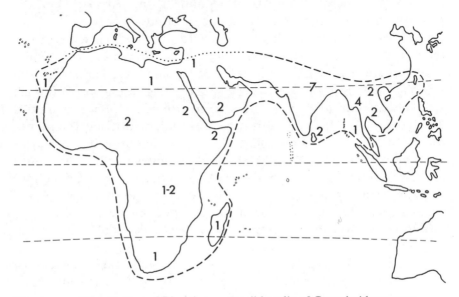

Figure 114. Distribution of *Phoenix* as a possible relic of Coryphoid ancestry. The number of species in the geographical regions indicates the present centre in Indo-Burma. Dotted line indicates the distribution of the cultivated date palm along North Africa; the wild species follow the *Hyphaene*-line south of the Sahara in Fig. 115. Equator and tropics indicated in broken lines.

In contrast to the other subfamilies, the fan-leafed Borassoid has a distribution which is particularly African and Indo-Malayan, that is to say around and in the Indian Ocean. It is a small subfamily with merely six well-marked and diversified genera. When their construction is better known, it should be possible to follow the changes which have lead to their evolution. Two genera have free carpels, as in *Phoenix* and some Coryphoid palms. One is the dichotomous *Hyphaene*, which has a distribution similar to that of *Phoenix* in Africa and west Asia (figure 115) and, thus, impinges on the Coryphoid group; its species are variously estimated from ten to twenty-eight. The other is the small genus *Medemia* with two species in East Africa and one in Madagascar; thus it falls within the compass of *Hyphaene*, possibly as a derivative with unbranched trunk. The remaining four genera have syncarpous ovaries. *Lodoicea* and *Latania* have many stamens in the male flower and perhaps, therefore, as primitives, they have the relict distribution of *Lodoicea* with one species in the Seychelles and *Latania* with three species in the small Mascarene Islands Mauritius, Réunion, and Rodriguez. *Borassus* and *Borassodendron* are reduced to the normal six stamens (as in *Hyphaene* and *Medemia*). *Borassus* has five species, one in Africa, two in Madagascar, one in continental Asia and Java, and one in New Guinea. *Borassodendron* has a single species in north Malaya (Perak). Yet, anatomically, *Lodoicea* is said to agree rather with *Borassodendron* [219].

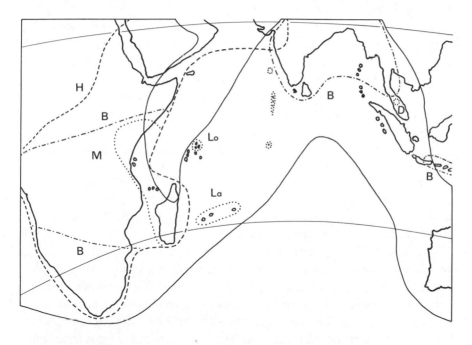

Fig. 115. Distribution of Borassoid palms around the Indian Ocean, with the early Jurassic tract of Gondwanaland superimposed. *Hyphaene* (H, broken line), from Africa to N.W. India. *Borassus* (B, dot-dash line), with African, Indo-Malayan, and Java to New Guinea distributions. *Medemia* (M, dotted line) in East Africa and Madagascar. *Latania* (La) and *Lodoica* (Lo) in the Mascarene and Seychelles islands respectively. *Borassodendron* (D) in Perak. The tropics indicated in thin lines. Gondwanaland indicated by the S-shaped outline. (After Oakley and Muir-Wood, 1964.)

The distribution, on the whole, emphasizes a connection with hot dry climates, rather than true rain-forest climates which seem to be avoided. It is, in fact, a distribution that would be expected from the theory of continental drift with a Jurassic subfamily specializing to the central dry climate. It is in agreement also with the postulated Gondwanaland of botanists and Lemuria of zoologists which, as a land-bridge, connected East Africa, Madagascar and India. Within itself, however, it shows a remarkable diversity which has restricted *Lodoicea* to the pre-Cambrian granite of the Seychelles and *Latania* to the Mascarene Islands, without *Hyphaene* or *Borassus* having reached there; while Socotra and the other islands of the Indian Ocean to the north east, excepting Ceylon, have no palms. Ceylon has *Borassus*, whether naturally or introduced it is impossible to decide, but it links with India.

The problems of *Cocos*, *Elaeis*, *Raphia*, and the Arecoid *Juania* are akin but differ again from the preceding. They concern connections between Africa and America, that of *Elaeis* and *Raphia* affecting the equatorial region and that of *Cocos* and *Juania* the south tropical or subtropical. The case of *Elaeis* and *Raphia* has been mentioned, (p. 230). If South America drifted from West Africa and, as is supposed, the bulge of Brazil separated last from the Gulf of Guinea, this would explain how *Elaeis* had a foot on each continent and *Raphia* got a species into America. Others have supposed that prehistoric man carried their vagrant species across the Atlantic; the considerable specific differences in *Elaeis* and the wide distribution of *R. taedigera* in South America seem to militate against this idea. The second point is not conclusive for man has distributed the date and the peach palm *Gulielma* as widely (p. 281) and the coconut still more widely (p. 291); and *R. taedigera* is very close to the African *R. vinifera*. As for the first, it is difficult to estimate the significance of the differences which have been given generic character, and yet the two species of *Elaeis* are said to hybridize [220]. The geological explanation would also account for the distribution of the African Arecoid genera *Podococcus* and *Sclerosperma* if they are truly to be related with the American *Geonoma*. The remarkable point is that, when this separation was supposed to have taken place in the Cretaceous-Eocene time, palm evolution was surely far advanced into modern genera and, yet, so few took the opportunity to go to West Africa. If the mountains laboured, a mouse was born!

The problem of the coconut palm is insoluble (p. 291). It is the only

Asian or Australasian member of the Cocoid subfamily and all its immediate allies, to the number of over sixty species, are American, chiefly South American. They have been separated into eight or nine other genera, though the value of these genera has recently been strongly disputed [221]. The fact is that there is an alliance in form-making which links the vagrant *Cocos nucifera* of Indo-Pacific shores with South America as the home of the alliance, to which even the southerly *Jubaea spectabilis*, or Chilean wine-palm, belongs. Then there turns up another remote and relict palm of the same alliance in the south-east corner of South Africa, namely the Pondoland Palm *Jubaeopsis caffra*, in the primitive habitat of riverine bush. It differs very little from *Cocos* but has the germ-pores of the nut almost equatorial instead of basal, the little nuts one and a half inches wide, and the dwarf habit of many Brazilian members of the alliance [222]. It certainly suggests a southern land-bridge, via an extension of Antarctica, when conditions were better, or by means of the consolidated continental tips of South America, Africa, India, and Australia on the theory of continental drift. Pondoland is the situation, too, of the African Cycad *Stangeria*, but it can hardly be said to link the Asian-Australasian *Cycas* as closely with the American genera as *Jubaeopsis* does with *Cocos*. Then, Croizat has drawn attention to the single palm of Juan Fernandez *Juania australis* which, as a monotypic Arecoid genus may be related either to the American *Iriartea*, *Chamaedorea* (*Morenia*) or *Ceroxylon*, to the Mascarene *Hyophorbe*, or the Asiatic *Orania*; in any case, as an instance of form-making, the resemblance points also to this south Atlantic connection [223].

There remains the impression that this route, like the mid-Atlantic crossing of *Eleais* and *Raphia* and the north Pacific crossing of the Coryphoid palms has, in fact, achieved remarkably little in bringing together the widely different palm-floras of America, Africa, Asia, and Australasia. It seems to me that the Antarctic continent has played little part in palm-distribution, that the gates of angiospermy were either closed to palms or served as minor exits, that continental drift gets trifling evidence in its favour from living palms, but that Gondwanaland must come into play with the Borassoid palms. Madagascar and the Mascarene Islands must be examined more closely.

Most tropical islands are renowned for their abundant and peculiar palms, though there are remarkable exceptions such as the Galapagos Islands, Revillagigedo Islands, Ascension, St. Helena,

Socotra, and Easter Island, without palms. This goes with the fact, emphasized by Good, that over ninety per cent of all palm species are so narrowly limited in their distribution as to be considered endemic to small areas. The great island of Madagascar is no exception [224]. It has seventeen genera with 112 species of which twelve genera and 110 species are endemic. The non-endemic genera are the African *Phoenix*, *Hyphaene*, *Borassus*, *Medemia*, *Raphia*, and *Elaeis*, all with a single species in Madagascar except *Borassus* with two; and the only non-endemic species to the island are *Phoenix reclinata*, *Raphia ruffia*, and *Elaeis guineensis*, which are spread over a great part of tropical Africa south of the Sahara. These continental genera happen, also, to be those which are spinous, with thorny petioles or leaflets (*Phoenix*, *Elaeis*) in an otherwise thornless and therefore advanced palm-flora. For the rest it is made up of twelve endemic Arecoid genera with their total of 106 endemic species. There are no Coryphoid or Caryotoid palms, no *Nipa* or *Phytelephas*, and no climbing palms. *Nipa* seems to have been excluded from the area of Gondwanaland, but it is assuredly a very advanced palm. Yet, the rattans are also excluded and they, as pachycaulous climbers which used a primitive form of leaf-development to scramble in the primitive upward struggle of the flowering plant forests, are a trace of ancient palm-life. The Arecoid palms of Madagascar are too numerous to analyse in detail, but there emerges one fact that the abundance of them arises from the faculty which at least four of the genera (*Dypsis*, *Neophloga*, *Phloga*, *Chrysalidocarpus*) display in producing many species of small undergrowth palm (p. 301). This is the potentiality of advancing palms of reduced stature, by which they evolve into neotenic diversity. Thus the Cocoid *Bactris* (140 species) and the Arecoid *Chamaedorea* (80 species) and *Geonoma* (200 species) swell the advanced palm-flora of tropical America, just as the Coryphoid *Licuala* (80 species), the Arecoid *Pinanga* (115 species) and the dwarf rattans swell that of Malaysia; Africa, in its ill-reception of palms, has never produced them. The absence of spinous palms and of climbers and the presence of so many small palms, more than sixty species, indicate that the Madagascan palm flora is an advanced one. Though isolated from Africa since the early Tertiary period and long out of contact with the main struggle of continental life, Madagascar has received a small number of African palms and a large number of Malaysian or Australasian as the ancestors of its Arecoid development. Their affinities are said to be, even, with the Arecoid palms of New

Caledonia. The point is supported by the presence of other advanced plants of this geographical relationship, such as *Nepenthes, Hibbertia*, and *Ficus* sect. *Sycidium* and subgen. *Pharmacosycea* [225]; but these are really problems of intervening Malaysia. I conclude that the palm flora of Madagascar is recent in so far as the family is concerned, and that it does not show in any way an Antarctic or Gondwanaland derivation for palms; its origin must lie with land-bridges to Africa and Malaysia long after the rise of palms, figs, and pitcher-plants; these connections may be Cretaceous or Jurassic (225a). It is note-worthy, therefore, in this connection that the African Arecoid genera *Podococcus* and *Sclerosperma*, which others relate with *Geonoma*, may have greater affinity with the Madagascan evolution [226].

Between the north tip of Madagascar and the African mainland there lie the Comoro Islands with merely four species of palm; they are the African *Phoenix reclinata* and three endemic species of Madagascan Arecoid genera (*Chrysalidocarpus, Ravenea*). This flora, non-Borassoid, confirms the previous conclusion.

East of Madagascar there are three Mascarene Islands with a small palm flora of five genera and twelve species, all endemic and, at first sight, distinctly different from the Madagascan. They have no genus of the African mainland, but there is a Borassoid genus *Latania* related to the African and Madagascan *Medemia*. The two closely allied Arecoid genera *Hyphorbe* and *Mascarena* may connect with the Madagascan *Dypsis* (or with *Juania*, p. 239). The Arecoid *Dictyosperma* seems essentially east Malaysian. The fifth and, also, Arecoid genus *Acanthophoenix* is a spiny palm related perhaps with the Malayan *Oncosperma* or more directly with the thorny Arecoid palms of the Seychelles. Thus their palm-floras suggest an intermediate step from eastern Malaysia, just approaching the influence of Borassoid Gondwanaland, and according to the small size of the islands with the same Arecoid prevalence as Madagascar. Bespeaking their long separation, each island has its own endemic species, Mauritius six, Réunion and Rodriguez three each [227].

As far north from Madagascar as Rodriguez lies to the east, that is about eight hundred miles, there is the Seychelles group [228]. The affinity of its palm-flora of six endemic genera and six species appears to be entirely with west Malaysia. It has one Borassoid genus, the renowned double-coconut *Lodoicea* (p. 311), which is thought to be related with the Malayan *Borassodendron*, and five spiny Arecoid genera *Phoenicophorium* (*Stevensonia*), *Deckenia, Roscheria, Nephro-*

*sperma*, and *Verschaffeltia*, which are related with *Oncosperma* of Ceylon and Malaysia. In fact the palm-flora is in this respect more continental and Indo-Malayan than insular Malaysian. The palm-flora, however, is not the only key by any means to the biogeography of the Seychelles where the figs are African and there is the Madagascan Leguminous genus *Brandzeia* related with the African and American *Pentaclethra*. These plants might travel by islands and could have reached the group after the passage had been closed to the palms.

We come to Ceylon where the palm-flora is undoubtedly Indo-Malayan. *Phoenix, Corypha, Borassus, Caryota, Nipa, Areca, Oncosperma*, and *Calamus* relate it with India and Malaya, though its one endemic genus *Loxococcus* (one species) may extend the affinity to eastern Malaysia [229].

The islands of the Indian Ocean suggest through their palms two arcs. The more southerly, passing through Madagascar and the Mascarene Islands connects Africa south of the Sahara with eastern Malaysia. The less southerly passing through the Seychelles connects with western Malaysia and may graze the first about the Mascarene Islands. Perhaps they were the receding frontiers of Gondwanaland but, if so, they do not enclose a primitive centre of palms; the Borassoid palms are advanced in leaf, inflorescence, and fruit. In fact the biogeography of these Indian Ocean palms hardly fits with modern geophysical conclusions [230].

The Caribbean islands, the Malaysian, and the Polynesian have their particular palm-floras which hang together in their respective geographical affinities, though the flora of each diminishes in species and genera both with the size of the islands and its displacement towards the geographical periphery, Atlantic for the Caribbean and Pacific for the eastern islands. The majority contain endemic species and many have endemic genera, which emphasize the ancient dismemberment of the palm-front which advanced into them. The endemism, however, needs careful scrutiny for it may be exaggerated. The three genera which were said to be endemic to the Marianas and Caroline islands of Micronesia have been reduced to genera of the more central New Guinea alliance [231]. The flora of the Caribbean islands is predominantly Coryphoid and Cocoid, to a lesser extent Arecoid of South American affinity, while the Malaysian and Polynesian are Arecoid with some Lepidocaryoid and Coryphoid genera of Asian affinity. Cuba, as the central and largest island in the geological upheavals, connections, and disconnections of that long troubled region between North and South America, has an exceedingly rich palm-flora. Similarly New Guinea is said to have thirty-two genera of palms, though the full number of its species is not known. New Guinea is supposed on the theory of continental drift to have been pushed northwards with Australia and not to have contacted Malaysia before the late Tertiary or early Quaternary period. Yet, neither Australia nor New Guinea bring a new or Borassoid palm-element into this region. Their palm-floras are essentially Asian. Even if the great Arecoid concentration in eastern Malaysia and Polynesia is thought to be the special New Guinea contribution, so late a contact with Malaysia could not possibly explain the wide dispersal and differentiation of Arecoid genera to Ceylon and Assam. In fact, with the exception of *Metroxylon* and the Marquesan *Pelagodoxa* (p. 178), there does not seem to be any really primitive feature among the palms of eastern Malaysia and Australasia. What is needed certainly is a more penetrating enquiry into the evolution of the Arecoid palms of America, Asia, and Australasia, and their alliance across the Pacific. Palm biogeography should be thought out with the map of cycad distribution before one, because the pattern of this very old group is essentially the same as with palms [232]. Then both should be compared with that of *Ficus*. This very advanced dicotyledonous genus, with numerous allies in the Moraceae, reveals the same problems [233].

If a species arises in one place, it will sooner or later spread to a different situation. If a tree or lofty climber, it will indeed grow up through different ecological conditions. The species may, then, adapt peripherally into new forms and incipient species, as well as centrally, in reaction to these changes. Furthermore the isolation of groups of individuals, which promotes differentiation by excluding pollination with the parent stock, operates both peripherally where the incipient new species exceed the parental range and centrally under natural conditions of closed vegetation. The high forest is a tremendous speciator. The dense stands isolate not only the trees of a kind individually or in small groups but also the pockets of undergrowth, and all tend to preserve their peculiarities as inbreeding populations [234]. It is to be doubted whether any tree or shrub, which does not reach the canopy, is pollinated from sources beyond the immediate vicinity. So the extensive range of *Phoenix* or *Trachycarpus*, impinging on the temperate floras and the desert, may exemplify peripheral evolution, whereas the density of speciation in the undergrowth palms like *Geonoma* and *Pinanga* exemplifies central evolution internal to the parental range. The royal palms *Roystonea* exemplify peripheral evolution in the Caribbean area (p. 331). The Bermudan palmetto *Sabal bermudiana* may be only a varietal extension of the continental *S. palmetto* [235].

When the natural vegetation is cleared or broken up by man, pollinators may travel freely and break down by hybridization the speciation that had been developing. Hence arise so many of the 'hybrid-swarms' that baffle botanical classification in the civilizing countries. Hence, too, there arise artificially the hybrids of *Phoenix*, *Howeia* [236], and, possibly, of *Roystonea* and *Cocos*, when the wild species are planted together. The problem among palms reaches its acutest in the Hawaiian *Pritchardia* where it may be questioned if there are thirty species or only one or two (p. 328).

Island life, especially in volcanic regions, has lead palms to develop local endemic species, but their character seems generally to have been rather trifling. Unless, for instance, a rattan entered, the local palms have failed to fill this blank in the forest with a climber of their own invention. The island floras, with one exception, have harboured ancient unresponsive genera, such as *Lodoicea* and *Metroxylon*, or slightly altered the more recent. The exception is Madagascar. Acting as a small continent of long isolation, it has evolved new series of undergrowth palms from its Arecoid heritage, but it has not produced a new subfamily or a new manner of palm life; it has restricted the potentialities of its original palms with neotenic effects. The island floras prove the continental origin and major evolution of palms. We have to consider what may have been their original progressive habitat, though its geographical location is unknown. We come to ecological biogeography about which there is generally no more information than the more obvious features of palm occurrence. That this habitat was tropical follows from the temperature requirements of most palms, and that it was abundantly supplied with soil water follows both from the evidence of great root-pressures manifested in nearly all subfamilies and from the need for abundant water-supply in savanna and desert palms.

The alluvial plains of large rivers from the mud-banks of their tidal flats to the gently rising ground provide the domain of the majority of living palms, where they grow in immense numbers. The Magdalena, Orinoco, Amazon and Paraguay rivers provide the richest palm floras of America. Here thrive such characteristic genera as *Mauritia, Copernicia, Acrocomia, Astrocaryum, Bactris, Desmoncus, Euterpe, Geonoma, Manicaria,* and *Iriartea,* and force the botanist by their numbers to become a palm student. They are substituted in West Africa by *Elaeis, Raphia,* and the African rattans. In South-East Asia *Salacca, Calamus* and its allies, *Licuala, Livistona, Pholidocarpus, Pinanga, Oncosperma,* and above all the nipa palm set the scene. It is difficult to conceive what a big river in these parts of the world could have looked like before the advent of palms, mangrove trees, and other flowering plants. In a forest of tree-ferns and seed-ferns palms must have begun the ample, thorny, smothering, and repellant life which has been their way ever since. It persists even with such relatively slender undergrowth palms as *Eugeissona tristis* in Malaya; to the botanist this plant is an ancient, fascinating relic, but to the forester a tiresome weed that checks regeneration. The spinous thickets of *Salacca, Licuala,* and *Bactris* with their lively fruits represent to us the impenetrable denseness of this early invasion during which, it would seem, among the low stalwart pachycaul beginning of dicotyledon and monocotyledon the palms began to climb.

From the swampy origin palms ventured with diminishing variety and greater specialization to the hill-sides, mountains, savannas, deserts, seashores, and borders of the temperate regions, according as they were able to survive the increasing adversity of lowered temperature and lowered water-supply [237]. The mountain palms of Asia and Australasia are lowland genera ascended. Some kinds of *Phoenix* mount to eight thousand feet in the Himalayas and thrive with pine and oak. On Mt Kinabalu in Borneo a few species of *Calamus* and *Pinanga* reach ten thousand feet, and a *Salacca* occurs in montane swamps at five thousand feet. But in the wet Andean parts of Bolivia, Peru, Ecuador, Colombia, and Venezuela there has been a great development of Cocoid, Arecoid, and Coryphoid palms. Here the wax palms *Ceroxylon* reach the frosty altitude of thirteen thousand feet (p. 289). This mountain range rose in the Miocene period in the midst of the rich American palm flora, but it is incredible that its palm genera should have evolved in so short a time. The botanist, seeking the origin of Andean palms, must co-operate with the geologist and reflect on the table-land represented by the flat-topped mountains of Brazil and the Guianas.

The Americas contribute two other features to palm ecology in addition to mountaineering. There are the stemless savanna palms, mainly Cocoid, which develop underground branches or descending stems and, thus protected, with deep roots to the water-table, survive the summer droughts and now, since the advent of man, the periodic burns. The habit is paralleled by the Coryphoid *Sabal* and has led in Florida to the evolution of sand-dune palms, such as the saw-palmetto *Serenoa* and a few low-growing species of *Sabal* [238]. In south-east Brazil the stemless Cocoid palm *Allagoptera arenaria* binds the Atlantic dunes with massive subterranean rhizomes near the southern limit of the tropics, just as *Serenoa* in the north [239]. *Phoenix*, *Hyphaene*, and *Nannorhops* have this tendency to form low thickets in the dry regions of Somaliland and Arabia, but they lack the rhizomatous ability, and no African or Asian palm in spite of the abundant opportunity can be considered as a dune or sea-shore pioneer. It is not the habitat of a primitive palm.

The dryer conditions of hillside and savanna introduce deeper or more extensive rooting and specialization to particular soils. Bondar has noted the preferences of several Brazilian palms; *Acrocomia sclerocarpa* indicates alkaline soils, several species of Cocos the acid granitic soils. *Lodoicea* grows on deep laterite soils of granite origin, which seems also to be the preference of the rich palm-flora of Malaya. *Nanorrhops* thrives in alkaline regions of north west India and Pakistan. A few palms grow chiefly, if not exclusively, on calcareous soils and limestone. This is said to be the character of the American Coryphoid palm *Brahea* and *Haitiella* and of the relict Malayan genera *Liberbaileya* and *Maxburretia* which relate in some way that has yet to be explained with *Chamaerops* and *Trachycarpus*. The Arecoid palm *Gulubia* is said to be calcicolous in eastern Malaysia and Melanesia. When we consider the vast extent of calcareous deposits exposed during the Cretaceous and Tertiary of south east Asia, the significance of this habit is immediately clear.

The extra tropical limits of palms are set mainly by Coryphoid genera in the north and pinnate-leafed genera in the south. Thus, *Washingtonia* and *Sabal* mark the extensions into North America; the Cocoid *Jubaea* of Chile and Argentina and the Arecoid *Juania* of Juan Fernandez, mark the limits in South America. *Chamaerops* and *Trachycarpus* mark the northerly limits in Europe and Asia, *Phoenix* and the Cocoid *Jubaeopsis* in South Africa, the Arecoid *Rhopalostylis* in New Zealand, but the most southerly palm in Australia is said to be a *Livistona* in Gipps Land in the state of Victoria (37° S.).

Since the family of palms is such an ancient one, the questions arise whether any of its members are verging on extinction and whether any represent recent species and nascent genera. The answers to each turn on the interpretation of monotypic genera; the single species may be the last or the first. Nascent genera and new species should have obvious allies in their geographical neighbourhood whereas the moribund should be isolated. There can be no doubt that excepting *Hyphaene* and *Borassus*, the other Borassoid genera *Medemia*, *Latania*, *Lodoicea*, and *Borassodendron* are relics. *Nipa* is also a relic in a sense, but it may be doubted if the genus or its antecedents ever consisted of more than one or two species (p. 319). Though their ancestors have gone, there is no evidence that these palms are enfeebled. The Borassoid have suffered through loss of territory and become restricted to diminishing areas or islands. *Nipa* has ranged widely and successfully. It is difficult to evaluate the problem in other subfamilies because of their much larger number of genera and the intricacies of structure in flower, fruit, and seed by which they are distinguished. The Coryphoid subfamily has about twelve monotypic genera, Cocoid fifteen, and the Arecoid thirty-five to forty. The more advanced the subfamily, the more numerous these genera; yet some may be relics and others nascent. The Arecoid genera on the islands of the Indian Ocean are, presumably, relics similar to the Borassoid, but we cannot assess the position of *Loxococcus* in Ceylon or *Howeia*, for instance, in the Lord Howe Islands, until Arecoid theory has been worked out. So it is with the other groups, though the Coryphoid genera of limestone districts seem to be relics; and they may have arrived at this status also by loss of territory. In contrast, all those stemless or small palms of under-growth must be regarded as advanced and comparatively recent. Among these the case of *Salacca flabellata* may be recalled as a nascent species restricted, so far as is known, to Trengganu (p. 215).

It seems, therefore, that palms have prospered and evolved in the dense extensive forest and that they have diminished in variety and progress where this has been broken up, isolated and degraded. Yet they persist with vitality. The Coryphoid *Washingtonia* survives in scattered canyons of California, Arizona, and Mexico; as a relic, it may need to be traced back to the Cretaceous forests of that region [240]. Diagonally across the Pacific, in similar canyons of central Australia, the Coryphoid *Livistona mariae* lingers as an outpost of Asian colonization when with wetter climate it travelled with the rain

R

forest across Australia [241]; it is not a relic of Gondwanaland or Antarctica. Then, beyond the western limit of *Livistona* there has been found in recent years a close ally *Wissmannia* which thrives in the mountain gullies of Somaliland and south Arabia; it must date, too, from the rainier period of the early Tertiary when the Indo-Malayan flora reached across the Middle East and *Nipa* flourished by the Black Sea [242]. *Phoenix* and *Hyphaene* have dwarf species in the same region as *Wissmannia*, but they appear as relics adapted to the conditions of the lowland desert in consequence of the hardier heritage of their genera [243]. *Phoenix canariensis*, often seen in cultivation as a vigorous and massive species, had become geographically isolated on a few islands (Tenerife, La Palma, and Gomera) of the Canary Islands [244]. The Pondoland palm *Jubaeopsis* is a similar relic of South Africa where it may refer to Gondwanaland. Such is the evidence of the shrinking frontiers of the palm scene. The Arecoid *Pseudophoenix sargentii* lingers on two or three small islands of the Florida Keys; these occurrences may be merely chance landings from the Bahamas where it grows more freely but, even so, such sporadic happening is a relic of Tertiary history when the palm must have extended to a much higher latitude in North America [245].

These examples of later geological history merge into the disagreeable record of human contempt, the consequence of urbanization and 'dodo-ism' in sheer brutality. The relic *Juania* of Juan Fernandez has become so rare from destruction of forest that it is imperilled and it seems to have been lost from cultivation [246]. *Jubaea* on the Chilean mainland is vastly diminished in numbers through the felling of the palms to obtain the sugary sap and wine. Of the Mascarene palms, *Dictyosperma alba* is already extinct on Mauritius, but it survives in many botanic gardens of the world. Now the second species on Rodriguez has nearly been exterminated by cutting of the palm for the edible cabbage [247]. The two species of *Acanthophoenix*, one in Mauritius and the other in Réunion, are suffering the same way. Likewise *Deckenia* in the Seychelles has been devastated for its cabbage, but it is protected by law, if not in fact, in the reserves of *Lodoicea* on Praslin Island. The Arecoid *Clinostigma savoryana*, endemic to the Japanese Bonin Islands, was practically exterminated during the second world war by starving soldiery that ate the bud [248]. The Coryphoid *Erythea edulis*, once described as the only plant of tropical luxuriance on the Mexican Island of Guadelupe in the Pacific, has been almost eaten out. Already at the turn of the century the Coryphoid *Pritchardia pacifica* was stated to have become a rare plant in Fiji [249]. The habitat of the one Bermudan palm *Sabal bermudiana* is being threatened by the encroachment of buildings [250]. The Florida royal palm *Roystonea elata* nearly met the same fate through another means; its seedlings were removed in large numbers for sale as ornamentals, but it is now preserved in the Everglades National Park. The two species of *Howeia* provide also this happy contrast for they are carefully tended to secure the export of their seeds to nurserymen throughout the world [251].

The fate of palms is not senescence or debility. Their races have lasted too long to be overcome now with this sort of phyletic weakness. The extinction of their ancestors seems to have occurred mainly during the Mesozoic instatement of the flowering plants and their upward struggle in progressive forest [251a]. Then followed geographical isolation, dislocation, increasing aridity, harder winter, and loss of territory. Man may remedy his record with botanical gardens, parks, and nature reserves.

## Fossil Palms

Bits of trunks and roots, fragments of leaves, more or less water-worn fruits, some flowers in amber (said to be *Phoenix* and *Sabal*), possibly fragments of inflorescences, and microscopic pollen grains are the vestiges of the extensive geological history of palms. Where identification seems firm, such names as *Nipadites*, *Phoenicites*, and *Sabalites*, are used. More often the fossil bits cannot be referred definitely to existing genera and they are classified for convenience into 'organ-genera'. *Palmoxylon* is the genus for trunks, *Rhizopalmoxylon* for roots, *Palmophyllum* for leaves or *Flabellaria* for fan-leaves, *Palaeorhachis* for inflorescences, *Palmocarpon* for fruits, and *Monocolpites* for pollen-grains. The difficulty in identification arises both from the imperfection of the fossil material which, besides being fragmentary, may not show microscopic details to clinch the identification, and from our imperfect knowledge of these essential details in the living palms. Thus palaeobotany is always forcing plant-anatomy [252].

Fossil leaves and trunks have been recognized as belonging to palms since the middle of the eighteenth century. Unger brought together the knowledge of them in the *Historia Naturalis Palmarum* [253]. Many of the trunk-fragments are petrified and preserve their microscopic structure in cellular detail, but too little is known about the microscopic anatomy of living palms to develop satisfactorily what seems to be the most promising clue to the past occurrence of palms [254]. Most specimens of *Palmoxylon* come from the Cretaceous and Tertiary beds of Europe, Asia, North Africa, and North America; yet there are said to be examples of a fan-leafed palm from the Triassic of Colorado which would accord with the antiquity that must be assigned to palms already in modern form by the Cretaceous period [255].

The fullest and most extensive record for any particular palm belongs to *Nipa*. It starts in the Cretaceous, for its pollen has been found in beds of this age in Borneo [256]. Fossil fruits, more or less dehusked to show the internal nut, occur in Eocene strata of south England, Belgium, France, and India as well as in Borneo. Then the record stops in Europe but it is continued into the Miocene of India, the east coast of which is now the westerly limit of the distribution of living nipa palms. With the fruits in southern England there occur pollen grains and fragments of leaves assignable to *Nipa* and along with them, to prove that this palm grew in Europe in those days sixty million years ago, there are fragments of the mangrove trees, the mangrove palm *Oncosperma*, and the mangrove fern *Acrostichum* which still grow wherever nipa survives [257].

*Nipa* seems to have receded south-eastwards. This is the history of the Tethys Sea which at the beginning of the Tertiary era stretched across Europe, North Africa, and most of southern Asia to unite what are now the Atlantic, Indian, and Pacific Oceans. The world climate seems to have been much warmer then than now. As far north as Greenland and Alaska there are found in their early Tertiary beds fossils which can be assigned with certainty to subtropical, if not to tropical, genera of flowering plants. As modern lands emerged, the climate cooled, and the Tethys Sea broken up and receded from Europe. The mangrove, nipa-belts, and, in fact, the Malaysian type of forest in general which seems from the fossil record to have stretched along the shores of the Tethys Sea withdrew as the conditions became unsuitable.

Nevertheless, this cannot be the whole story because nipa has never established itself, apparently, in Africa and there are no fossils of nipa from Australia and New Zealand. Nipa fruits have been recorded from Brazil and Texas, but it has still to be proved beyond doubt that they are not the fruits or seed-casts of other tropical

American palms, particularly the Cocoid, and, if truly those of *Nipa*, they may have been drifted there from the Tethys shores just as *Manicaria* fruits arrive on the west of Scotland from tropical America [258]. The fact is that nipa does not grow in the American tropics. If it had reached there in a living state during the Eocene, it would surely be there now.

The conclusion seems to be that *Nipa* in the form of its present single species lived in what was Cretaceous Borneo and thereabouts [259]; that it spread northwards along the Tethys shores and back again without colonizing Africa or America and without extending south-west to south Australia and New Zealand. In the early days of these palaeo-botanical discoveries the fossil fruits were called *Nipadites*, but the hesitancy was overcome as knowledge increased and it is generally agreed that the whole record is that of one species which, of course, may have undergone some modification in the course of so many millions of years.

The conclusion is remarkable. Structurally, *Nipa* is a very advanced genus of palms. Thornless, stemless, with unisexual flowers, capitate female inflorescence, ovary with a single ovule, and dry fibrous fruit, it could be reckoned the most advanced palm. The very dryness of the fruit seems to have provided the durable husk and woody nut prone to fossilization. The swamps where it grew provided the conditions for the collection and sedimentation of its pollen. No palm is better fitted for the fossil record. Yet there is no trace of its ancestor. It can be said of all palm-fossils that none indicate palm-ancestry. Fruits of *Attalea* and *Astrocaryum* have been found in the Tertiary beds of tropical America, but no proto-Cocoid relic. It is the negative record of palms rather than the positive which reveals their antiquity.

Together with the remains of *Nipa* in the London Clay of Eocene age in south-east England there occur pollen grains referable to several Malaysian palm-associates of nipa, namely *Calamus*, *Caryota*, *Livistona*, and *Phoenix*. There are also grains assigned to the American fan-palms *Sabal*, *Serenoa*, and *Thrinax* which do not grow with *Nipa*. Here is a problem, perhaps, of identification, but there is another aspect of the association. Numerous fossil leaves and flowers of *Sabal* (or *Sabalites*) have been found in the Tertiary of Europe, Asia, and the Aleutian Islands. Now *Sabal*, as well as *Serenoa* and *Thrinax*, are centred in the Caribbean region, but they have species which extend into Florida and south Carolina. It may have been these subtropical

251

species which migrated northwards during the early warm phase of the Tertiary to spread into Asia and thence to Tertiary Europe, just as *Sequoia* seems to have done; and, like *Sequoia*, they disappeared from Europe and Asia. If the tropical species could have reached the Old World from their American centres, then *Sabal, Serenoa,* and *Thrinax* would surely be established now in Asia. There is the converse record of a seed of *Phoenix* in the Tertiary of Texas; it may have reached North America from Asia and have then disappeared, for the genus is nowhere wild now in the Americas [260]. *Phoenix* may have followed the route of the elephants and horses. The facts of the modern distribution of palms are so firm that fossil records must be examined in this light. And, of course, there is always the possibility that the fossil represents a generic ancestor or an extinct descendant parallel to a living form. A much deeper analysis of the Coryphoid front is required and the relation of this to the distribution and origin of *Phoenix*.

Thus the fossil record tests knowledge of living palms and these test the interpretation of the rocks. Knowledge in all respects is too imperfect to answer satisfactorily any question about the past history of the family. We may wonder to what palm the fossil pollen-grains *Monocolpites* belong, that are so abundant in the Tertiary of Colombia that they seem to register by the fluctuation in their numbers climatic fluctuations over millions of years [261].

## Chapter 11

# Evolution of Palms

A LIVING organism is a state of protoplasm manifested by the way in which it works. Given a living and undifferentiated cell, no biologist could prophesy what were its powers unless he could recognize the cell as that of a particular organism. The cell must be grown in order to discover into what it may turn. The protoplasm in this cell has existed since the beginning of life and has reproduced itself generation by generation through geological time. During this enormously long period the cell, owing to its very complexity, has varied and developed its powers in adaptation to the environment. Thus we speak of its evolution, in which both the biochemical alteration of the protoplasm is implied and its expression as an organism. Some cells have made little progress and, unicellular or in microscopic aggregates, persist in the humbler, primitive, and aquatic situations. At the other extreme there has been the mighty progress which in land plants has led to the flowering tree, climber, palm and herb. They exist, but their ancestors are dead; their offspring may continue to change. In considering the evolution of higher organisms, we must think of their past, their present, and their future. The past should carry us right back to the beginning of life, but it is too long a journey to book from one station. We may have a rough map on a very small scale, but the number of lines, stations, halts, bridges, and intersections on this railway of life is so vast and they have been laid, re-laid, closed, side-tracked, and re-opened so many times that we do not know how they are to be reached. Just as we do not know where to begin the geographical distribution of palms, so we do not know how to begin their ancestry. We must develop a theory which will work back to a junction; and this theory must be founded on the manifestation of palm ability. The test of the theory will be the importance of the junction.

Thus the initial enquiry must be limited. Our problem is the palm sector and its immediate ancestral route. Then it may be related with other sectors of the flowering plants and a grand junction may be discerned from which they radiate. For the present effect of palms, we refer to the preceding chapters which have dealt with the manner in which they impinge upon and interfere with the rest of nature. For the future effect, we must consider what powers of evolution palms still have and how they may fit the new environment which man is creating. Yet, there is a collateral problem whether the palms have produced from some part of their sector another family of monocotyledons.

Firstly it must be questioned whether, in treating palms as one group, they are a natural sector or evolutionary unit, from a single origin. This must be ascertained through comparison with other monocotyledons, on the assumption that they are a natural unit in contrast with the dicotyledons. The answer lies in the family character of the palms, the features of which have been singled out by this comparison (p. 346). The leaf is highly distinctive; folded in the bud, it opens by actively splitting along the ridges. The ovary has a single ovule in each cavity or in its single cavity and ovary and ovule develop into an indehiscent fruit. The large seed has a hard mass of oily (not starchy) endosperm, and it lacks a seed-coat of distinctive structure. The epidermis of leaf and stem is typically spiny, except in those palms which have clearly disarmed and become almost glabrous. Then, less easy to define, there are the massive stem, massive leaf, massive inflorescence with massive flowering spike, and the relatively simple, radially symmetrical flower in which the perianth consists of two whorls, each with three segments. There are certainly aberrations, such as *Nipa* and *Phytelephas*, and strong contrasts such as between induplicate and reduplicate leaflets, or pinnate leaves and fan-leaves, but they fall within the general compass which excludes all other flowering plants. The assumption of the natural unit seems justified, and implies that there was a pre-palm with the necessary ability.

Most botanists look to the fossil record as the source of enlightenment. But with palms, as with all groups of flowering plants, no such help has been discovered. There are records to the mid-Mesozoic era, if not earlier, but they are all palms of recognizably modern respectability. There is no evidence of the ancestry of, even, existing genera; either their fossils have not been found or they have never fossilized. But it is also doubtful if they could be recognized without a hypothesis of palm evolution to point out what should be expected. What seems generally to be unrealized is the amount of information that can be gathered from the diversity of living palms; it is greater than that which any other family or order of monocotyledons can supply.

This information comes mainly from the construction of living palms. It must be read in conjunction with that from other plants, and the result is morphology in its full sense. Botanical morphology is the science of plant form. It is the outcome of multiplying, arranging, and differentiating cells. Morphology co-ordinates all the facts from ultimate details of adult cells to their initial projections from the zygote; and no sharp line can be drawn between this and the internal construction of the cell. The science began with the description of shape and structure but it has progressed and the morphology of the leaf, for instance, embraces everything that is known about the way in which this object in all its manifestations is thrust into space. If we know nothing about the genetic code of palms, we know so much about the structures which it makes and their modifications in the large number of genera and species that here is already material for the theory of palm evolution. My own faith in morphology is implicit. When the recondite problems of protoplasmic organization are understood to the extent that it may be manipulated, it should be possible to re-construct genetically palm ancestry in living form [262].

Morphology has arrived at certain principles for flowering plants which are to be attributed in the main to the overriding one that apical growth is the primitive way that stems and roots develop in land plants. To this there must be added the primitive radial construction of the stem which produces leaves in spiral succession around it, and of the root which develops side-roots in connection, it seems, with its protoxylem strands. The leaf, however, has inherited in land plants bilateral or flattened construction. Apical growth of the stem implies continuous production of many leaves; hence come the tall leafy stem and the long primitive flower which, as a bud, contains the neotenic leaves transformed into perianth and reproductive structures; it is the sort of flower which *Magnolia* best exemplifies [263]. Limitation of apical growth leads to short, slender stems with small leaves which, as seedling and sapling features, become the herbaceous habit. In the case of flowers it leads to the shortened axis on which the few appendages are set in alternating whorls, as the common state in the majority of flowering plants.

Apical growth of the leaf has given place in many instances to basal growth. It is the character of the monocotyledonous leaf and of the flower parts in general, the protective value of which is obvious

(p. 166). It has produced the leaf-sheaths, which enclose the bud, the spathes which swathe the young inflorescence, the bracts which protect the flower buds, the over-arching perianth segments, the stalked stamens and the styles. It is also the process which leads to perianth tubes, staminal tubes, and ovary-tubes or syncarpous ovaries, which distinguish advanced flowers, and in the extreme to the inferior ovary.

Thus there can be discerned at once the primitive nature of *Phoenix* and some Coryphoid palms in regard to their apocarpous ovaries; the advanced state of the syncarpous ovary in Borassoid, Cocoid, and most Arecoid palms; and the relatively primitive nature of the multilocular syncarpous ovary of *Phytelephas* compared with the single loculus or cavity developed by the more advanced Arecoid palms and by the nipa palm. In fact, most of the subfamilies of palms show independently the tendency to cut down the ovary to one functional ovule. Alternatively, they indicate derivation from a multilocular syncarpous ovary which in turn indicates derivation from an apocarpous ovary with many free carpels.

As for the stamens, *Phytelephas* shows the reduction from over a thousand to a countable fifteen or thirty, while the Coryphoid, Borassoid, Cocoid, Arecoid, and Caryotoid subfamilies show the simplification from many stamens to six, even three in some Arecoid genera. There is abundant evidence that the primitive palm-flower had many stamens and many free carpels. It must have been Magnoliaceous, and in the same way it seems very early in its history to have stabilized the perianth into two whorls of three sepals and three petals. The argument may appear circular but it is based on deductions from dicotyledonous flowers and the evidence of palms gives independent support; for the palm-flower has never really been considered in this light. The pre-palm flower has been experimenting through its surviving families into the simplified flower with its parts in threes, which is the general outcome in monocotyledons. This simple flower is no more a common inheritance in monocotyledons, however, from a trimerous ancestor than the pentamerous construction is to dicotyledons; in both the typical flower is a common experience or parallel result. Consequently no living palm has anything like a primitive flower. To invert the argument and derive, as some have done, palms from monocotyledons with stabilized trimery, would be to give them nearly all a primitive flower, which is absurd in the face of floral morphology and no solution to the problem of the flower.

The palm-fruit fits dicotyledonous theory in the same way as the flower, but since the fruit is the older construction it carries fewer vestiges of its ancestry. The one-seeded drupe and nut, both indehiscent, are also common experiences in many separate families of flowering plants, and end-results. They lead back to two or more seeded fruits which then become dehiscent fruits. There are vestiges of several-seeded fruits in a variety of palms but the only vestige of dehiscence seems to be that of *Astrocaryum*. The fruit of *Phytelephas* brings us at once to the durian-theory and its syndrome. That of *Phytelephas* resembles the fruit of the durian-ally *Coelostegia* if it were completely indehiscent and not so lignified. So we interpret the warts on other palm-fruits and the long precise register of Lepidocaryoid fruits. There must have been a pre-palm stage when Magnolia-like flowers gave rise to apocarpous durian-like fruits. The idea of the pre-palm in fruit is conveyed by the terminal infructescence of the banana-ally *Phoenakospermum*, which lives in the swamps of tropical America. It carries many capsules, each with many arillate seeds, but the capsules are smooth and the seeds small. The apocarpous arillate fruit, as the antecedent to *Phoenix*, seems to have disappeared completely from monocotyledonous families; and this loss may indicate the greater age of monocotyledonous families than dicotyledonous.

Palm seeds and fruits are large compared with those of most seed plants. Some are certainly exaggerated, such as the coconut and double coconut. The reduction in the number of ovules to one and the loss of a restricting seed-coat may well have been accompanied by increase in seed-size exploiting the problem of seedling competition on the forest floor. But a primitive carpel with a dozen seeds twice the size of those of *Phenakospermum* does not seem beyond the power of a massive palm. It is accomplished by *Sterculia*.

In respect of the inflorescence, the argument has been advanced in chapter 5 that the lateral inflorescences of palms have been derived from the terminal. It is based in no small measure on the fact that the terminal inflorescence has the primitive racemose form with a conspicuous main axis along which the branches are developed in declining vigour from below upwards. The lateral inflorescence, in contrast, leads to the sympodial or cymose construction with inhibited and shortened axis around which the branches develop with equal, if not greater, vigour. If these alternatives were presented in a herbaceous family, such as the crucifers or the grasses, there would be no difficulty in accepting the morphological argument, but the massiveness of palms and the curious spectacle of the gigantic terminal inflorescence has appeared to temperate botany a wondrous creation of the tropics at the climax of palm evolution. To the tropical botanist, surrounded with more or less arborescent Scitamineae for comparison and their herbaceous products, the ultimate progress is that which has specialized the tiny grass into something far smaller than the smallest palm seedling, yet working with the same terminal inflorescence in the brief occasions of temperate existence. The order Scitamineae is an instructive parallel to the palms. They have retained the terminal inflorescence, except in the two genera *Ravenala* and *Strelitzia*, and they have progressed on the different line that has specialized the flower into bilateral symmetry with bird and insect pollination from which there results the fertilization of many ovules in the ovary and the development of a fruit with many relatively small seeds. The order has developed, accordingly, a very great number and variety of herbaceous plants to fill the gaps on the forest floor. Palms and Scitamineae are an example of that compensating evolution that occurs in numerous successful families and orders; some take one path, others another, and if it had not been so, they would not have come into existence. As pointed out in chapter 5, the evidence implies that all monocotyledons are framed primarily on the terminal inflorescence.

The most difficult problem appears to be the origin of the palm-leaf. It is called compound, pinnate or palmate, but these terms are not strictly applicable to both palm-leaves and dicotyledonous leaves. In the first, the leaflets are disengaged from a continuous lamina. In dicotyledons they are discrete outgrowths of the leaf-axis, which becomes webbed at the tips, just as in fern-leaves. The pinnate dicotyledonous leaf grows apically and produces the branches of its axis acropetally, or from below upwards in conformation with the apical growth: as leaflets, they unfold from below upwards. The palm-leaf soon stops its apical growth in the minute primordium and changes to basal growth which produces new folds at the base and matures them distally; the folds split into leaflets from above down-wards. There would seem to be little in common between the two except the final appearance which may be merely analogous as they are superficially similar. Accordingly the theory has been developed which supposes the palm-leaf to have originated from the simple strap-shaped leaf, familiar in many small monocotyledons, through the widening and folding of the base and the splitting of the folds to free them, as it were in delight; that is, there must have been a spontaneous mutation to give a new genetic code for the palm leaf [264]. The theory is akin to that of spontaneous creation which says let there be light, and there is light; it negates reason. It discards the evidence of clear examples of plant evolution where progress has come through modification and curtailment of the existing code; this is the history of the seed, the fruit, the flower, and, indeed, of the leaf. It runs contrary to the evidence in many palm genera that their simpler forms of leaf are derived from the pinnate. It gives to *Pinanga*, *Chamaedorea*, and *Geonoma*, for instance, a primitive leaf in contrast with the advanced inflorescence, flower, and fruit in these thornless Arecoid palms. The same reasoning would give to the phyllode of *Acacia* a primitive status in Leguminosae.

Palm folds have their counterpart in many dicotyledons. The lamina of some species of *Dillenia* is five or six feet long. It develops by apical growth, having the apex incurved in the primitive fern-like manner (figure 116). The side-veins correspond with branches or leaflets and are developed in the acropetal manner from below upwards. They are webbed into a single blade, toothed at the margin as the vestiges of the branched and compound construction, and the whole is thrown into folds alternating with the side-veins along the leaf-axis. It opens with a pulvinus at the base of each fold: if it had splitting lines, it would become pinnate as the palm-leaf, but the dicotyledonous net-veining of the lamina prevents this development; and this enormous leaf modifies with restricted growth in other species of the genus into the small, familiar tree leaf. Other examples are *Dipterocarpus*, *Ficus*, and the American *Cespedezia* (Ochnaceae) in three very different families from the Dilleniaceae, and all show the same simplification into the small leaf with few veins. This is the usual, highly evolved, simple, efficient, and readily deciduous leaf of advanced dicotyledonous trees; it is the parallel product in all their families as the small strap-shaped leaf with parallel veining in the monocotyledonous. The *Dillenia* leaf relates the fern and the palm leaf, but it requires conversion from apical to basal growth.

This conversion happens in many dicotyledons. It is well shown in *Ficus*, where the familiar leaf of *Ficus religiosa* has basal growth to widen the heart-shaped blade and strongly curtailed apical growth to form the 'drip-tip'. In other species of *Ficus* the basal growth develops the heart-shaped blade into the palmate (figure 117).

259

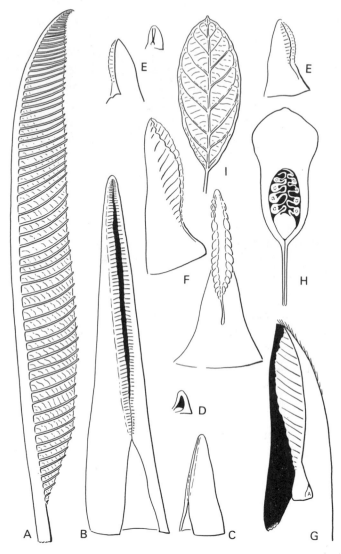

Figure 116. Leaves of the dicotyledonous trees *Dillenia*. A–D, *D. reticulata*, sapling leaves 3–4 ft. long with about 70 pairs of side-veins. E–H, *D. suffruticosa* with 11–14 pairs of side-veins. I, *D. pulchella* with small neotenic leaf, 7–9 pairs of side-veins, analogous with a pear-leaf (*Pyrus*), × ½. A, 7th leaf from the stem-apex, completing its apical growth in the bud, × ½. B, 3rd leaf with about 70 folds already formed along the narrow lamina, × 15. C, 2nd leaf with narrow lamina before the folds start, × 15. D, 1st leaf with stem-apex, × 15. E, 1st and 2nd leaves at the stem-apex, the 2nd leaf in section, × 15. F, 3rd leaf, × 15. G, the bud in section showing the 1st and 4th leaves, × 7. H, the winged leaf-stalk in section enclosing the younger leaf with folded (plicate) lamina as in the palm, × 4.

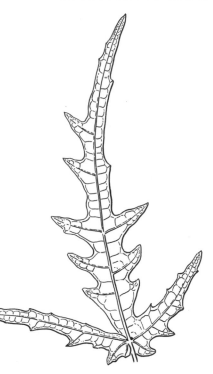

Figure 117. Palmate-pinnate sapling leaf of *Ficus ulmifolia*.

Thistle leaves are pinnately lobed leaves which begin with apical growth, but this is soon retarded and the spinous tip developed, corresponding with the long tip of the fig leaf. The leaflets become webbed to the leaf axis and tipped with their spines in retarded apical growth. Then this leaf begins to grow at the base and to develop more leaflets downwards so that, in the manner of basal growth, they unfold from above downwards. The pinnate leaves of *Solanum*, crucifers, poppies, and many Rosaceae develop in this basipetal manner and produce an adult form that may be indistinguishable from the apically developed. Finally, in scattered examples among the dicotyledons, there are the phyllodic leaves which have eliminated the lamina with reticular veining and produced the falsely-monocotyledonous leaf with parallel veining [265]. But, in all these examples, it seems that the pulvinar mechanism has disappeared.

The pinnate construction has led to the webbed and plicate lamina [266]. But pinnate and plicate construction can be converted from apical development to basal. The peculiarity of the palm is that it combines pinnate construction with the plicate, separates the folds by the pulvinar mechanism acting on lines of weakness in the folds,

261

and bases all this on the so-called parallel venation of the monocotyledons. There seems to be no inherent objection, therefore, as
if some spontaneous innovation had to be invoked, to deriving the
palm leaf from a pinnate leaf with apical growth in the manner in
which the phyllode of *Lathyrus*, *Acacia* and, indeed, *Eucalyptus* has
evolved from the pinnate dicotyledonous leaf. There is the evidence
of the rattan leaf which retains apical growth to make the climbing
whip, analogous to the drip-tip of *Ficus* but far superior in accordance
with the massive construction of the palm. This demonstrative leaf,
however, has never been considered because it seems too outrageous
to impose on the classical concept of a simple short-lived leaf; it fits,
nevertheless, as a missing link in the chain of palm theory. What we
learn is that the fundamental difference between the dicotyledon leaf
and the monocotyledon lies in the vascular construction that pervades
each major group with such distinction. The monocotyledonous
character with numerous longitudinal vascular bundles and little
or no intervening network enables the palm to extricate the folds
from the webbed lamina and re-instate them as leaflets.

The pinnate form of the dicotyledonous leaf is, therefore, not only
strictly comparable with that of the palm, but it can show how that of
the palm may have arisen through commonplace methods of leaf
evolution. We may start with a leaf such as the Leguminous, which is
supplied throughout with pulvini to operate the 'sleep movements'
characteristic of the family. But, in the first place, the venation of the
leaflets and leaf-axis must be monocotyledonous. Webbing will
render the lamina entire with parallel veining and plicate folding will
contain it in the bud. Then basal growth will develop this folding by
intercalary means, inserting in the subapical tissue. The pulvini will
open the full-grown leaf. There is an exact parallel which the palm
leaf now explains. It is the relation between the superior and the
inferior ovary which splits open in fruit. The superior is developed
by apical growth followed by basal growth in the free carpels; the
extent of basal growth is increased to produce the syncarpous ovary,
and finally the whole structure of the ovary is transferred to the floral
axis to make the inferior. The palm leaf could, by analogy, be called
the 'sympterygoid' with incorporated leaflets. It seems clear that palm
ancestors experimented along much the same lines as the monocotyledon and dicotyledon have done with their flowers, and
produced the palm leaf. Theoretical botany has been puzzled with the
problem how a pinnate sporophyll with apically growth, as that of

*Cycas*, could have been transformed into a basally developed carpel, and here is the answer in the manner in which the palm leaf has evolved and transformed into the unsplit leaf, the spathe, the bract, and so on. The mutability of the living parts of plants is astonishing. We shall see the transformation that has taken place in the inflorescence of *Cyclanthus* (p. 269). The leaf of a giant pitcher-plant *Nepenthes* calls for an amount of explanation still greater than that of the palm. Cycad allies show us, also, how leaflets acquire the parallel venation of the monocotyledon, but this goes beyond the scope of our enquiry.

The problem set by the doubly pinnate leaf of *Caryota* now begins to clear. The once pinnate Leguminous leaf is undoubtedly derived from the doubly pinnate, and other families such as Araliaceae, Umbelliferae and Bignoniaceae reveal that the doubly pinnate is derived from higher ramifications, the ultimate branchings of which become webbed into the leaflets. The doubly pinnate leaf of *Caryota* represents the basipetally developed palm leaf with the lobes (or folds) lobed (or folded) themselves and, as we have noted (p. 79), these secondary folds carry traces of tertiary folding, or the trebly pinnate form. The fish-tail leaflets that occur in many pinnate-leafed palms, such as *Arenga*, *Ptychosperma*, and the *Iriartea* complex of Arecoid palms, are not the strivings of these palms to evolve the bipinnate form, as if the upgrade evolution of palms was incomplete, but vestiges of the conversion of the bipinnate palm leaf into the once pinnate. That extraordinary complicated foldings, indicative of the degree of ancestral branching of the leaf, can occur in undivided, basally grown leaves is shown by the common rhubarb *Rheum*. Indeed, floral morphology must contemplate the doubly pinnate megasporophyll.

The combination of large leaves and large growing point to give a massive primary stem undoubtedly inhibits the axillary branching of the stem. It is characteristic of pachycaulous plants to develop such branches from the lower part of the trunk far removed from the effect of growth-inhibitors proceeding from the crown. We should expect pre-palms and palms to have unbranched trunks, at most suckering from the base, even though nothing is yet known about the nature, seat of formation, or direction of flow of palm growth-substances. The branching palm *Hyphaene* introduces the completely unexpected idea that pre-palms may have had dichotomous trunks, inasmuch as dichotomy is a very primitive character which cannot have come 'out

s

of the blue', even in the desert where *Hyphaene* thrives. Dichotomy is probably unaffected by the growth substances which inhibit axillary branching, but we know nothing about the biochemistry of dichotomy. So *Hyphaene* becomes the greatest challenge to the morphology of higher plants.

The inflorescence, sharply set off from the vegetative part of the palm and devoid of large photosynthetic leaves, presumably does not inhibit its own system of branching. We should expect a big inflorescence with many spathes to be highly ramified, as it is in all terminal inflorescences and many lateral ones. But among the lateral a reduction steps in. With small palms, reduced in other ways, this is understandable. In the massive, such as *Borassus*, *Lodoicea*, and *Hyphaene*, with stout, unbranched spikes there must be some other explanation to be sought, perhaps, in what may be called 'positional physiology'.

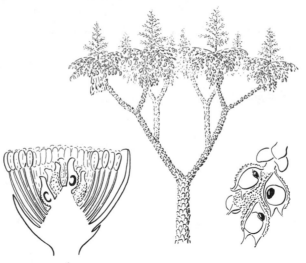

Figure 118. A sketch of a primitive palm based on the features of *Caryota*, *Corypha*, *Hyphaene*, *Phoenix*, and *Phytelephas*; dichotomous stem, persistent leaf-bases, doubly pinnate leaves, terminal inflorescence, and spinous; × $\frac{1}{200}$. Left, the primitive flower with many stamens and carpels; × 1. Right, the primitive apocarpous arillate fruit with persistent perianth; × $\frac{1}{8}$.

The highly branched inflorescence is associated with small flowers. Now one principle of floral morphology asserts that the large solitary terminal flower is the primitive state and that, by progressive ramification of the reproductive axis and consequent diminution in size of its branches and flowers, the highly branched, small flowered inflorescence is a peak of evolution [267]. The terminal inflorescence of the palm is a fit example because it receives from the palm trunk a limited, even if very large, supply of food with which it must make do. Either there will be many slender branches with small flowers or few stouter branches with large flowers. If, then, this principle applies in full force, and there is no reason why it should not, there will be in place of a sparingly branched or unbranched inflorescence with large flowers, a single terminal flower of such magnitude that the ovary will approach the size of the fruit and the bracts and perianth will resemble reduced leaves. There would be, in fact, a 'flower-fruit' with pollination, not of ovules, but of seeds ready for distribution. If this were supported on a stout stem set with doubly pinnate leaves and provided with a spiny epidermis, as the pre-palm requires, there would be the 'ancestral pachycaulous flowering plant' which I have elsewhere attempted to delineate [268]. Because of its massiveness, the pre-palm comes nearer to this hypothetical prototype of the flowering plants than any other pre-family ancestor that must be postulated.

The obvious rejoinder to this hypothesis, based on the evidence of living palms and on accepted principles of morphology, is the absence of supporting fossils. But, then, there are no fossils to support anything about the origin of flowering plants, and the gymnospermous fossils that have been used to derive flowering plants through the minutiae of gymnospermous specialization are not flowering plants [269]. The fossil record is invaluable, its poverty deplorable. There were palm spines a thousand years ago, a million years ago and, assuredly, a hundred million years ago for bits of palm-trunks and leaves occur in Cretaceous beds, but not a palm spine seems to have been fossilized. There are variously lignified fig-fruits throughout the tropics of a distribution which suggests Cretaceous geography, and there are Cretaceous leaf-impressions which could have come from species of *Ficus*, but neither fig-fruit nor fig-seed has been fossilized. The negative objection has no force. The positive evidence of living plants must, however, be stated and faced. Proof will come when an experimentalist works a terminal flower on to the palm-stem.

While a great many palms are successful competitors with trees and have evolved surely larger leaves, stouter stems, bigger inflorescences, bigger fruits, and better spines as improvements on the pre-palm during the ascendancy of flowering forest, more than half the species of living palms are climbers or undergrowth 'palmlets', and these last seem to preponderate. It is difficult, however, to measure the success of plants by the number of their species; monographers differ in assigning specific limits and small plants always gain in specific numbers because this rank is attached to small differences with which no one can be bothered in the study of the larger. Nevertheless most palm genera show in some way the tendency to produce species of smaller stature; either the so-called stemless, which may have as massive leaves as those with tall trunks, or the dwarfed and slender with smaller leaves, and most of these developments are accompanied by increase in suckering. Under the trees there is a tendency to carpet with palmlets, shrubby or herbaceous, for little palms a few feet high are as herbaceous as the majority of gingers, liliaceous plants, and other monocotyledons with this habit. This is the neotenic tendency which prevents full growth and, thus, induces smaller growing-points with smaller leaves and inflorescences; it begets, as it were, species which mature precociously at a less advanced level of development than the large tree-form. It is not progressive evolution in the sense of the upward struggle of vegetation, but it is a very popular method in the sense of that which has populated the forests most abundantly with small plants under, between, and, even, on the trees. Most families of dicotyledonous trees and arborescent monocotyledons have, thus, contributed their variety to the herbaceous flora.

An instance of the inherent tendency to evolve, yet without any call upon it from nature, so far as is known, is given by the coconut palm. It has a well-known variety, the King Coconut, which is not above the normal stature, as its name may suggest, but a dwarf that starts to flower at the age of three, not seven or eight or upwards to the fortieth year in the tall varieties, and produces smaller nuts more abundantly. Thus the variety is being developed as a more manageable crop with a quicker return. It is reported that Brazil had in 1962 ten million dwarf King Coconut palms, all of which were the offspring since 1942 of two palms that had survived importation from Ceylon in 1925. But most remarkable is the seedling coconut reported from Java, to which we have already drawn attention; it flowered when still attached to the nut and consisted of a very short stem bearing eleven leaves, the largest fifty-six centimetres long, most of seedling form with only a bifid apex [270]. The most recent contribution to the climbing of palms seems to have been from the American genus of very advanced spineless palmlets *Chamaedorea* (p. 205), but it is doubtful if such late comers, deprived of several of the hereditary advantages of the rattans, can make much headway.

The future of palms is considerable. Left to nature it is doubtful if circumstances will call upon any innovation, but man is altering these circumstances. Many palms will be exterminated from the wild. Deforestation, burning, ploughing, and building are doing this in Madagascar, Mauritius, New Caledonia, India, and Brazil. The vast tracts of wild land occupied by species of *Copernicia*, *Attalea*, *Mauritia*, *Metroxylon*, and, even, *Nipa* will largely, if not entirely, disappear. Nature reserves will have to safe-guard them, as they are doing for the double-coconut palm in the Seychelles and the few palms of Florida and California. Others will be propagated still more extensively by agriculture which will select the neotenic, and by forestry so long as the rattans have their market. Agriculture may develop fruiting palms, if it ever turns its attention to the needs and the pleasures of tropical village life. Town and country planning will propagate the ornamental; politicians and mayors may be commemorated with palm-avenues. Botanical gardens will have to expand their 'palmeta', if only because of their national duty to preserve and display the floras of their countries. Perhaps the greatest interest will come through private horticulture which, in recent years, has given the liveliest interest to the study of palms by means of its periodical *Principes*, published by the Palm Society of the United States. Lastly, I feel sure, botany will awaken to the meaning of palms and not only the morphologist, but the physiologist, the geneticist, the ecologist, and the experimental taxonomist will develop them. Hitherto, in its histories, the science of palms and its makers have scarcely been mentioned. As Bondar wrote: '*E nas escolas que devemos ensinar as novas geraçoes a conhecer e amar as palmeiras, destecando a sua singular beleza e suas multiplas utilidades*'[271].

One family, that is seldom encountered either in books or in nature, is considered by all who have studied it to be related to the palms. It is that of Cyclanthaceae, of which there have been found in the American tropics only, from south Mexico to Bolivia and, then, mainly Andean, eleven genera and 178 species, according to the latest review [272]. The small, much reduced flowers and the many ovules in the ovary, giving rise to numerous small seeds one to four millimetres long in the peculiar fruits, seem to have little in common with those of palms, except that they are borne on a thick spike with several large spathes on the stalk. The resemblance which is so telling lies in the vegetative habit for, without flowers, the plants are often mistaken for small palms. The rather dry and fibrous leaves are constructed in the same way. They are folded in the bud and, on opening, split in most cases at the apex so as to appear bifid, or almost to the base into two halves, which have the characteristic furrowed

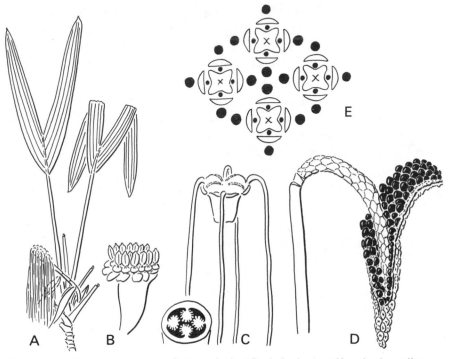

Figure 119. Cyclanthaceae. A, *Sphaeradenia (Carludovica) ensiformis*, the spike hidden by the hanging staminodes; × $\frac{1}{10}$. B, male flower of *S. ensiformis*, mag. C, the female flower of *S. ensiformis* with four long staminodes, four stigmatic grooves, and four sepals; ovary in section; mag. D, the fruiting spike of *Carludovica rotundifolia* peeling to display the berries with many small seeds: reduced. E, diagram of the flower arrangement in the family; each female flower with four staminodes (small black circles) surrounded by four male flowers (large black circles). (A–D, after Hooker, 1879, 1889; E, after Harling, 1946.)

or plicate surface; in a few species they are split into four fan-shaped parts like the compound costa-palmate leaves of the fan-palm *Licuala*. Some species have a short erect stem unbranched above ground, but suckering to form tufts from below ground. Others are apparently stemless but are developed from a short rhizome which in branching builds the tufts. And yet others are short, slender climbers though a few reach nearly a hundred feet long. They, thus, have the appearance of reduced, simplified, undergrowth palms of the rain-forests where they grow. Some of the more slender have even simple, though plicate leaves as would be expected by analogy with the palms, and this may be accompanied by the retention of the juvenile distichous arrangement of the leaves.

Resemblance in vegetative habit is important among monocotyledons. Most of their families have subsided into their own distinctive herbaceous manner of growth, unlike the families of dicotyledons which, in evolving the leptocaulous tree-habit, have produced a great similarity among their derivative climbing and herbaceous forms. Thus grasses can be distinguished from sedges, and both from rushes. Gingers, arrowroots, cannas, bananas, pandans, aroids, orchids, bromeliads, and many other monocotyledons can be recognized from the leaf, the way in which it develops, how it is attached to the stem, and how the stem grows. Several monocotyledon families have plicate leaves, but they are simple or unsplit. Only the Cyclanthaceae have splitting plicate leaves strictly comparable with the advanced fan-leaf of the palms. By monocotyledon standards this is most significant. The family seems to have been derived from the ancestral palm stock before the flower was reduced to the palm character of one ovule per loculus, and then it specialized over a long history, which is entirely lost, into herbaceous forms which have diminished the size of the seed and increased their number in the fruit, in strict contrast with the palms. At the same time the flowers have undergone neotenic reduction similar to that of the grasses, sedges, and aroids.

The unarmed Cyclanthaceae parallel, therefore, the reduced unarmed palms of the undergrowth, and this is borne out by the habit of their climbers. Having no pronounced apical growth of the leaf, they are not leaf-tip climbers, like the palms, but root-climbers like the ivy. They creep over the ground or low vegetation, emitting adventitious roots, and they climb by fixing themselves to the support with these adherent roots. Some send slender roots to the ground where they ramify to provide additional supplies of water and mineral salts to the leaves, in the manner of the aerial roots of climbing aroids. A few, also, are epiphytes. Thus they fit modes of life which the palms never managed.

The Cyclanthaceous inflorescence and flower show the ingenuity of reproduction possible in advanced plants. Starting from the large, generalized flower-cum-fruit of ancestral similarity, flowering plants have worked down on family lines to particular little flowering and fruiting mechanisms. Of these two, the flowering becomes generally the more elaborate as it enters the insect world. Cyclanthaceous inflorescences resemble the aroid, and the two should be compared as an instance of parallel evolution. The inflorescence is unbranched but, in place of the one large spathe of the aroid, there are two or more which lack the clasping base of the aroid inasmuch as they are not enrolled in bud in the way of the aroid leaf. Moreover, the inflorescence is lateral in the manner of so many derived palms, not terminal as in the aroid. The small unisexual flowers are crowded on the thick

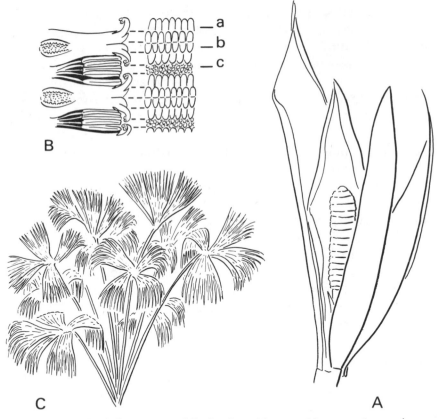

Figure 120. A, the inflorescence of *Cyclanthus* with several large spathes, $\times \frac{1}{8}$. B, part of the inflorescence to show the cycles of flowers in surface view and in section, cycles of female flowers separated by cycles of stamens; *a*, staminodes; *b*, styles; *c*, stamens; magnified. C, *Carludovica palmata*, $\times \frac{1}{60}$. (After Harling, 1958.)

270

axis of the spike and in all cases, except *Cyclanthus*, they are set in clusters of five; a central female is surrounded by four males in such a manner that the cluster comes to function like a single large flower with many stamens. The parts of the flower are in fours, not threes as usual in monocotyledons; but while the stamens in each male flower are numerous (10–150, according to the species) there are four sterile stamens in the female flower. The ovary in most genera is more or less inferior, unlike that of the aroids, and it contains a single cavity on the sides of which the many ovules are set, typically in four rows. The female flowers open first, when the white staminodes give a bizarre fluffiness of silken festoons of threads several inches long, spiralling up the inflorescence; this, like the aroid inflorescence, which may also develop tails, heats up during its rapid growth and gives off a strong odour, fragrant and not foetid like the aroid. Small beetles (weevils) are attracted in large numbers and remain among the flowers till the next day when the staminodes wither and the stamens open. It seems that, as with the aroids, these beetles pollinate the flowers but they also lay eggs in the ovary, for beetle-larvae may take the place of seeds in the developing fruit. Bees have also been seen hovering round the inflorescences, which are not worked into the concealing spathe, as they are in many aroids. It seems, nevertheless, that all the female flowers on the inflorescence operate together on one day, and then the male flowers on the second day, so that the inflorescence acts as a single protogynous flower, just as in the aroids. It is the outcome of the reduction of a branched, many-flowered inflorescence, that operated over many days, such as the palms have, into a compact inflorescence of small flowers co-ordinated to work briefly as a single flower.

As the ovaries of the numerous, compact female flowers enlarge into fruits, they become confluent and at their tips, where there are the shrivelled remains of the perianth and styles, there forms a thin woody layer. At maturity this dull green or brown surface dries up, splits off as a crust over the whole fruiting spike, and carries away the red inner tissue with the small berries filled with their slimy seeds. There is an almost exact parallel in the long, self-peeling fruits of the aroid *Monstera*.

In the case of *Cyclanthus* the inflorescence has become graded transversely into whorls of flowers so compacted as, practically, to have lost their individuality. A whorl of female flowers or ovaries is flanked on either side, above and below, by a whorl of many stamens, each of these male whorls separating a female whorl along the whole inflorescence. In some instances the whorls are combined into a gradual spiral winding round the inflorescence in a double strand, one part as a row of male flowers, the other as a row of female flowers. The configuration shows how the whorled arrangement must have arisen from the spiral phyllotaxis. Hence comes the name of genus and family. At maturity, the whorl of fruits developed from the female flowers split open individually, detach themselves from the axis of the fruiting spike which is now bent downwards by their weight, and slip off the end on to the ground, like rings off a curtain rod.

After all this preparation, the inflorescence and infructescence are said to fizzle out and let the slimy seeds be carried off by ants or washed away by rain. The happy thought that birds could be attracted by the bright red, orange, and pink colours, revealed as the dull crust peels away, pick at the appetizingly disorganized berries, and carry off the seeds, appears illusory. We labour under misapprehension. Inflorescence and infructescence are not elaborations but simplifications of the ancestral construction which in the huge panicles of palms is so immensely more complicated that no one has ever analysed it, and evolutionary thought disregards it. The small Cyclanthaceous inflorescences can be analysed. We admire their precision but it is inherited, and the course of reduction to this short-lived, well-timed, intricate construction can be followed along the well-accepted principles of floral evolution. So it must be with the compound fruit. The diffuse dehiscence in neighbourly co-operation is the survival of the mechanism of individual fruit-dehiscence, and the bright internal colour a survival from the time when the Cyclanthaceous ancestor had a brightly coloured fruit with brightly arillate seeds. It is the old elaborate method which has evolved into brief primordia, neotenically active, to get through as quickly and as simply as possible with the old life-cycle that has had to be adapted to herbaceous existence. The Cyclanthaceae show us how a massive palm-like ancestor with many ovules in the ovary turned into a particular kind of undergrowth family distinguished by an inflorescence which is admirable and an infructescence which is disappointing.

Deceptively similar, the aroids have achieved the same effect and prove that there is this mode of life under the palms and the trees of the forest, which works with beetles. Deceptively similar, the pandans prove that this can be effective at higher levels in the forest in direct competition with palms. Vegetatively the aroid and the pandan are so unlike the Cyclanthaceae and the palms that we cannot suppose that this conveyance is the result of descent from a common ancestor possessed of this specialized inflorescence. The aroid leaf is, like the Scitamineous leaf, wrapped round itself in the bud, not folded, and so unpalmlike that it may lead back to another line of monocotyledonous evolution. The pandan leaf, plicate like an enormous sedge-leaf, may be a modification of the palm's, in which only the distal initial folds are developed and prolonged by basal growth. Thus it is the antithesis of the Cyclanthaceous leaf which has retained the basal folding and lost the apical development. The differentiation of such extremes from a generalized ancestor is a common process in evolution. The remarkable point is that in tropical America the so-called anomalous unarmed palm *Phytelephas*, roughly co-extensive with Cyclanthaceae in distribution, has the reduced multistaminate flowers set in thick spikes and the compacted female flowers, while in the Old World, where Pandanaceae exist, there is the anomalous *Nipa* with female flowers set in heads astonishingly like those of pandans [273]. Cyclanthaceae are monoecious, though unisexual in the flower; *Phytelephas* is dioecious. In the Old World *Nipa* is the monoecious and Pandanaceae dioecious. As pinnate-leafed palms, neither *Phytelephas* nor *Nipa* can be regarded as ancestral to Cyclanthaceae or Pandanaceae, but from the ancestry of these palms the two families may have sprung. Among these matters for investigation, there is the question whether the midribs in the leaflets of *Cyclanthus* are not a relic of the doubly pinnate leaf.

Since the plicate leaf is so important, its presence in other mono-cotyledons must be equally significant. There are many examples but they are scattered, as one would expect from their relict nature, in various families which possess more generally the simple flat and strap-shaped leaf [274]. In all these cases, too, the plicate leaf is never split into leaflets; there is the pulvinar mechanism to open the folds but, like the seedling leaf of the palm, it gets no further; the two are often mistaken in the forest. A familiar example is the north temperate *Veratrum* (Liliaceae). In the tropics there are species of *Panicum*, *Setaria* and their allies among the grasses, the grass-like *Joinvillea* (Flagellariaceae), *Curculigo* (Commelinaceae) and a number of ground-orchids such as *Corymborchis*, *Phajus*, *Spathoglottis*, and *Sobralia*, as well as the allied family Apostasiaceae (p. 17). In all these families the simplification of the plicate leaf into the ordinary flat monocotyledonous leaf can be followed as a process of neoteny. It is accompanied by other means of containing the leaf in the bud, which parallel the rolling of the Scitamineous leaf and explain how it may be derived from the plicate. Nevertheless, it is not clear that the

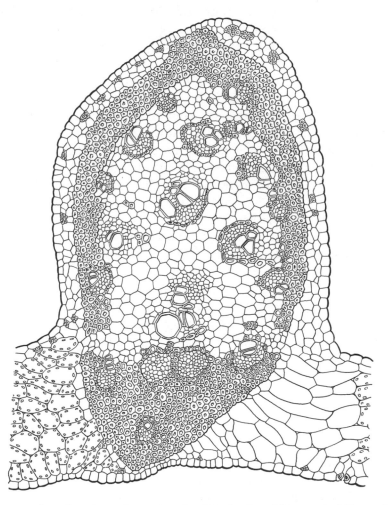

Figure 121. A section through a main vein of the leaflet of *Pinanga kuhlii* near its origin from the leaf-axis, to show the complexity of palm-structure; × 80. Note the large number of thick-walled fibres in a sheath round the vascular bundles and in small subepidermal groups; vascular bundles with small-celled phloem and comparatively few large vessels. Note, also, the fundamental asymmetry as shown by the aqueous pulvinar tissue on the right of the midrib. Compare Fig. 122.

aroid leaf, or those of *Tacca* and *Dioscorea*, has this origin; they seem to relate to a non-plicate form of pinnate leaf with apical growth, but it is a problem for investigation [275].

The object of this excursion has been to point out the abundant evidence in favour of the derivation of the flat monocotyledonous leaf from a pinnate and plicately folded leaf, such as the palm's. The course of this evolution accompanies the trend from the arborescent habit to the herbaceous, evinced so clearly by the palms in genera too numerous for repetition. The possibilities of palm-ancestors surge to the front. Their survivors make the family with most immense variety among the monocotyledons. They are by far the tallest, and among the shortest. Their leaves range from sixty feet to half a foot in length; they are doubly pinnate, simply pinnate, palmate, and undivided, reduplicate or induplicate. Their inflorescences range from highly branched structures twenty feet long to simple spikes of a few inches and compact heads. The flowers are bisexual and unisexual, with a

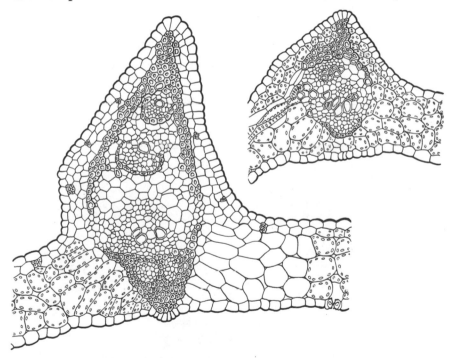

Figure 122. Sections of the same vein as in Fig. 121 but taken half-way along the leaflet and near its tip, × 80. Note, again, the asymmetry, and the simplification of the structure into the ordinary monocotyledonous condition towards the small tip of the leaflet.

thousand stamens to three. The ovaries are apocarpous through all degrees of union to syncarpous, and they are multilocular to unilocular. The pollen-grains are too varied for a family distinction. The ovules have one or two integuments, often many vascular bundles, and considerable variety in shape. The fruits, in spite of their uniform indehiscence have a range in size and structure far exceeding that of other monocotyledons. The seedlings are no less remarkable and some must be measured in feet. The dichotomy of *Hyphaene* puts the orbit of palm ancestry outside the realm of other flowering plants.

If to this equipment there are restored the presence of many ovules in the ovary and the arillate dehiscent fruit, there is practically nothing in the array of monocotyledons which cannot be derived from this source. It must have originated far back in the Mesozoic era and, perhaps, earlier. If it was not the source of monocotyledons, the consistent feature of which has been to produce one massive leaf at a time, the question must be answered from what else they could have been derived.

The study of monocotyledons becomes the biography of particular lines of specialization from palm ancestors. The Cyclanthaceous is the example. Therefore it is not that palms are monocotyledons, which has been so frequently repeated, but that monocotyledons are palm derivatives. In contrast, the study of palms leads through their ancestry to the beginning of flowering plants. It is not, therefore, that

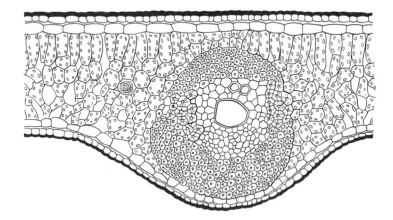

Figure 123. Section of the main vein of a leaflet of *Caryota mitis*, for comparison with Figs. 121 and 122. Note the better developed palisade tissue, the presence of stone-cells as well as fibres in the sheath of the vascular bundle, and the absence of sub-epidermal fibres; × 80.

this is such a mystery, as has often been repeated, but that our eyes have been closed to the significance of palms. There is no dicotyledonous route so clear.

The ancestral portrait is one of massive, spiny, dichotomous trunks ten or fifteen feet high, with rosettes of large compound leaves and terminal inflorescences on which the massive flowers developed into spinous arillate fruits. They stood in dense low formidable forest along the rivers where the ancient reptiles were beginning to achieve their maximum size and diversity. The scales, armour, and protuberances of these beasts may have assisted in their endeavour to force a passage through this forest, for they had to contend not only with teeth but spines. Their size may have enabled them on their hind-legs or by their long necks to have reached the flower and fruit or the small creatures that worked them, and among these were the toothsome warm beginnings of birds and mammals; perhaps the gaping jaws were traps, and the green lizard their miniature. But the dicotyledonous tree began to raise the canopy and the high table was carried beyond the reach of ground animals, unless they could climb. Into the gaps that opened between the trunks there evolved the herbaceous flowering plants that competed with the sapling trees and set a lower commons. Some palms went up; others persisted in the shade; many stayed in the ground flora; and a few became rattans.

At that time, when the last great steps in plant and animal progress were being tried out, there were being offered honey, pollen, flower remains, and arillate seeds much superior to the produce of flowerless predecessors [275a]. Palms figure feebly in the background of Mesozoic restorations. They should be brought to the front as the medium through which we evolved, and in whose vigour we still delight at the palm scene.

## Chapter 12

# Generic Notes

## Areca—Attalea, Maximiliana, Orbignya, Scheelea, Parascheelea, Markleya—Borassus—Caryota—Ceroxylon—Cocos

*'And they came to Elim, where were twelve wells of water,
and threescore and ten palm trees: and they encamped
there by the waters'*

EXODUS 15:27

### Areca

Linnaeus established this name in botany when he described in 1753 the betel palm *Areca catechu*. All these words are euphonous corruptions. *Areca* is a Portuguese variant of the Malayan words *adeka* or *adaka* for this palm. *Catechu* is the Portuguese *cacho* (English cutch) transcribed into Japanese as *catechu* and used originally for the drug obtained from *Acacia catechu*, which was imported from Japan to Germany in the seventeenth century as *terra japonica*; Linnaeus misapplied it to the palm [276]. *Betel*, too, is not an oriental word, but again a Portuguese corruption of the Malay *vetila* for a leaf, the betel nut being chewed with the leaf of the pepper *Piper betle* [277]. From this confused beginning 'the genus expanded very rapidly so that about seventy-five years later there was hardly an Asiatic or Australian palm having an erect stem, tubular sheaths and small fruits that could not be called an Areca, even some American palms were included in the genus' [278]. With too many characters it became characterless. It baffled Martius, but Blume stepped in and with his characteristic attention to detail began the carving up by separating numerous genera according to the position of the flowers and ovules, the nature of the endosperm and the position of the embryo in the seed. He set the stage for the microtaxonomy, as it can be called, of the group Areceae, which has expanded into more than a hundred genera, and it may still be wondered why these characters should indicate genera, and what is an Arecoid genus.

*Areca* was monographed by Furtado in 1933. If the sectional

## TABLE 4 Sectional characters in *Areca* (after Furtado, 1933)

(the evolutionary direction in a character reads left to right except, perhaps, in the stem-column)

| Sections (species) | Infl. branches | | | Flower clusters | | | ♀ flowers | | Stamens | | | | Calyx | | Leaf | | Stem | | Distribution |
|---|---|---|---|---|---|---|---|---|---|---|---|---|---|---|---|---|---|---|---|
| | m | f | n | sp. | dist. | sec. | t | b | 24 | 12 | 6 | 3 | f | j | d | s | s | t | |
| 1 *Microareca* (8) | + | + | + | + | | | | + | + | + | + | | | + | + | + | + | ? | Malay, Lingga, Borneo |
| 2 *Mischophloeus* (4) | + | + | + | + | | | | + | | + | | | | + | + | | + | | Celebes to Solomon Isl. |
| 3 *Oeotheanthe* (9) | + | + | | | + | | | + | | + | | | + | + | + | | + | + | P.I., Celebes, N. Borneo (? Ceylon) |
| 4 *Axonianthe* (13) | | + | | | + | | + | | | + | | | + | + | + | | + | | P.I., Celebes to Solomon Isl. |
| 5 *Arecella* (9) | + | + | + | | | + | + | | | | + | + | + | + | + | | + | + | Assam to Borneo, Queensland |

Explanation: Inflorescence branches many (m), few (f), none (n). Flower clusters spirally arranged (sp), distichous (dist) or secund (sec). Female flowers more or less throughout the inflorescence (t) or towards the base (b). Stamens, the number in a male flower. Calyx (male) with free sepals (f) or joined (j). Leaf divided into leaflets (d) or undivided (s) or tufted, branched at the base (t).

characters are set in the form of a table (table 4), an idea can be obtained of the evolution which they have been undergoing. The decisive character is in the arrangement of the flowers which separates three groups, namely sections 1 and 2, sections 3 and 4, and section 5. It represents the simplification of the inflorescence from that with radial construction to the distichous with two rows of flowers and the secund with a single row of flowers all set to one side of the spadix. Thus sect. *Arecella* appears as the most advanced group with six or three stamens in the male flower. It has the female flowers, however, distributed throughout the inflorescence and not restricted to the base, which is the advancement in sections 1–3. The first two sections have also developed the joined sepals, which is an advance on the state with free sepals, and both states occur in section 3. The first sections consist of slender palms and, as one would expect, it has developed the neotenic simple leaf. Sections 3 and 5 have developed the tufted habit and all have the tendency to reduce the branching of the inflorescence, three sections having unbranched inflorescences.

We learn that in this considerable genus evolution has been towards reducing the size and complexity of the palm. Nothing wonderfully new has been evolved, unless the tufted habit is such, but the genus has been dissipating its heritage, as a great estate may be broken into small units. It is so common a manner of generic evolution in all kinds of plants that it may be regarded as typical generic evolution into species. It is the way in which the ancestral palms have diversified into subfamilies and these into tribes and genera. In a sense it is downgrade evolution for the equipment is running down into little things. Upgrade evolution, such as the making of vascular bundles, seeds, fruits, and flowers is a different process and it is not clear that the origin of genera and species since the Cretaceous period of flowering plants implies the same process as the pre-Cretaceous evolution of flowering plants. Hence some speak of micro-evolution, which is the Tertiary history of flowering plants, and macro-evolution which was the major phyletic upgrading during the Mesozoic era.

We notice, also, from table 4 that the sections specialize in different ways, and then specialize in much the same way by parellel micro-evolution. No section is entirely primitive, none entirely advanced. The more sharply defined sections could be made into genera, for this is the way in which many small Arecoid genera have been distinguished. It is mainly a matter of convenience; general botany prefers one large genus to numerous small ones on the principle that entities should not be multiplied.

The ancestral *Areca* must have been a stalwart palm of the kind that section *Mischophloeus* represents. Furtado describes this section with '*caudex crassissimus*'. In searching for an ancestor among other Arecoid genera we are lead to the tribe Ptychospermeae where several genera occur with multistaminate flowers, but a difficulty arises. The tribe is divided into genera with pointed leaflets and those with truncate and toothed, that is praemorse, leaflets [279]. The praemorse leaflet of *Ptychosperma* owes its fish-tail appearance to the retention in some degree of double folding or double pinnation (figures 16b, c). Presumably this is the explanation in the other praemorse genera. It will not do for the 'erose-truncate' leaflet tip of *Areca* for its leaflets have several longitudinal veins and folds to show that they are compound leaflets; they are leaflets which have arisen through splitting not at every fold, but at every third, fifth, seventh or later fold and, hence, the ability to produce species with unsplit leaves. The eroded tip represents in *Areca* the several pointed tips of the primary folds from which the marginal strip broke away. Hence we must pursue the group of Ptychospermeae with pointed leaflets such as occur in *Pinanga* which is closely allied with *Areca*. We are led, accordingly, to the lofty and solitary palm *Actinorhytis*, one species of which is widely distributed from Malaya to New Guinea and the other is restricted to the Solomon Islands. The widespread distribution speaks of the antiquity of the genus and it would fit well the conception of proto-*Areca*; in fact, the reason why *Actinorhytis* and *Areca* should be placed in different tribes, even why they should be separate genera, needs reinvestigation. *Actinorhytis* leads in turn to the Polynesian genus *Veitchia* in another arc of distribution from the Philippines to Fiji [280]. Thus we are led not merely to analyse structural differences in the classification of palms but to synthesize their natural history in the way that phyletic or natural classification requires. The tribe Areceae, with so many and varied living palms distributed over the west Pacific archipelago, where every one of the numerous islands and island groups has its own geological history, offers an unrivalled opportunity.

The betel palm belongs to the third section *Oeotheanthe*. Though cultivated in almost every village of India, Burma, Thailand, and the Malay Archipelago, a wild plant in primary forest has never been found. It resembles Humboldt's peach palm *Gulielma gasipaes* which, as the pupunha palm in the Brazilian Amazon and the pirajau or chiquichiqui in Spanish speaking parts, is cultivated for the flour obtained from its fruit over a vast continental area without a truly wild specimen being known. Its ancestor appears to be G. *microcarpa* of eastern Peru, where it is known locally as the wild pupunha [281]. It seems to have originated in the Andean part of the Amazon where the other species of the genus occur. So the betel palm may have originated from central Malaysia on or about Celebes where its section of *Areca* occurs. The suggestion fits the old tradition of the pandan-eating people of the Gilbert and Ellice Islands, who trace their origin from red-mouthed ancestors – the betel eating Malays, sea-rovers from the Molucca or Sulu Islands, as the nearest and most likely provenance [282].

The betel palm is cultivated for the hard endosperm of the seed which on chewing is pleasant, stimulating yet soothing, and narcotic. Betel-chewing

is the most complex of luxuries of its nature, requiring several ingredients . . . therefore the custom of chewing betel cannot easily be transplanted into a new country unless several materials can be assembled there. The result is that the habit has spread more slowly than, say, the habit of smoking tobacco, or drinking coffee. Yet it has obtained a very wide distribution and an extremely firm hold among the people who use it, none of their feasts or greetings being polite without it [283].

The dried seeds, previously boiled or not, are split or cut into pieces and a piece is placed on a fresh leaf of the betel-pepper (*Piper betle*) with a dab of lime and a little cutch or gambier; it is then folded up, put into the cheek and slowly chewed. 'The most important fact of betel-chewing is that the quid is spat out, relatively little of what is in it going into the system' [284]. It causes continual salivation and the saliva is turned red; hence the bloody gouts that spatter roads in betel districts. 'Beginners do not find chewing pleasant, but acquire the taste; at first they feel dizzy, and the throat burns and feels constricted' [285]. The nut contains numerous alkaloids of which arecoline and arecaidine (arecaine) are said to be the most important. Excess chewing is detrimental, but the late Professor J. B. S. Haldane, on being asked what betel-chewing was like, rolled his eyes to heaven and continued chewing.

Betel palms live for sixty to a hundred years, and reach up to sixty feet high. They begin to flower from the fourth to the seventh year. The fruit takes about eight months to ripen. Usually an inflorescence produces fifty to a hundred fruits, but in varieties with smaller fruits there may be 150–250. The male flowers begin to open as soon as the inflorescence branches escape from the two spathes. They open from the ends of the branches to their bases. Each flower lasts but a few hours but the whole period of male flowering of one inflorescence is three to four weeks. When the last male flowers have opened the female open near the bases of the branches. Usually four days elapse between the end of the male flowering and the beginning of the female, but this period varies from one to eleven days. Each female flower remains open for three to four days. The male are fragrant and visited by insects for the pollen. The female appear not to be insect-visited. Flowering is perpetual in Malaysia but confined to the dry months November–February in India [286].

### Attalea, Maximiliana, Orbignya, Scheelea, Parascheelea, Markleya

These stately and robust palms of South America form the tribe Attaleae, distinguished among Cocoid palms by the absence of spines, the presence of germ-pores at the base of the elongated nuts, and the generally unisexual inflorescences. The long leaves are completely split into many leaflets, each representing one fold of the young lamina, and very usually the leaf-axis curves so as to put the leaflets in its distal part into a vertical plane: in others, the leaf ascends steeply and the leaflets droop apart on both sides. It is probable that these enormous structures take several years to grow. The many species of these genera contribute grandly to the landscape. They shelter and feed a host of wild creatures from animalcules to arthropods, rodents, pig, deer, and tapirs. They combat the forest trees and pioneer the burnt plains. They enter extensively into rural life and commerce for the oil extracted from the fruit-wall and seed-kernel, much as the oil-palm *Elaeis*. As a major feature of vegetation, they call for botanical investigation in every respect. For example, the babaçu *Orbignya speciosa*, cohune *Orbignya cohune*, piassava *Attalea funifera*, and inajá *Maximiliana* [287].

The genera are distinguished by details of the flower and the stone of the fruit. They may well be regarded as one large genus particularly if, as Bondar has implied, all have the curious seedling growth into a descending subterranean stem before ascending to develop the trunk on the surface of the ground [288]. This peculiarity is recorded for

*Acanthococos* (figure 45), which also has the basal germ-pores on the nut, but is placed rightly or wrongly in the tribe Bactrideae because it is a spiny palm. Other Cocoid palms seem to lack this feature unless it is present in the stemless species of robust habit, such as the *Syagrus* group of *Cocos*. The growth habit in these genera is too massive to produce small shrubby palms but several species of *Attalea*, *Orbignya*, and *Scheelea*, if not of *Maximiliana*, are stemless.

Their geographical distribution raises the point which Spruce emphasized (p. 36) and Croizat has taken up in his panbiogeographic analysis of South America with respect to the old Brazilian shield of Palaeozoic age and the tertiary rise of the Andes [289]. *Attalea*, with twenty-five species in Colombia, Venezuela, Central America, Haiti, and Brazil, has twenty-one species in Brazil where they occur mainly in the eastern part of the country. *Maximiliana*, with ten species in Peru, Colombia, Venezuela, the Guianas and Brazil, has four species in Brazil in the Amazon region. In contrast, *Orbignya* has twenty species which are mostly Andean in Peru and Venezuela, but fourteen penetrate the Brazilian Amazon, though none reaches the eastern states; the genus is also absent from Colombia. *Scheelea* has forty species, chiefly Andean, with ten in Colombia, and twelve enter western Brazil. *Markleya* has a single species in the Brazilian state of Pará, and *Parascheelea* has a single species in Colombia where it is said to link *Scheelea* and *Orbignya*. These are the bare bones which need covering.

### Borassus

After *Hyphaene*, this is the second largest genus of Borassoid palms. Its species are numbered variously at four to seven, but as they are based mainly on fragments of one of the largest kinds of dioecious palm, which no one has ever studied in the full detail from the immense numbers of wild and semi-wild trees from West Africa to New Guinea, there is much doubt. Probably no one cares for there is too much to do in botany than analyse these hulks of vegetation. Yet, there are said to be more *Borassus* palms in the world than there are of any other kind except the coconut. One or two African species have been distinguished, two more in Madagascar, one in Asia, one in the Sunda Islands, and one in New Guinea. The range is not peculiar or ancient, for it is that of a common fig-tree, *Ficus racemosa*, and its immediate close allies; the fig reaches also to Queensland where the *Borassus* may occur.

The best known and, perhaps, the only species is *B. flabellifer*, centred in India where it is the palmyra palm. The best and most original account of it is that of Ferguson, but it is difficult to obtain; one can, however, refer to the excellent summary by Blatter [290]. 'Every part of the Palmyra Palm is turned to account in some way or other.' Thus he introduces fourteen pages of the description of these uses and another eight pages for Ferguson's translation of the Tamil poem *Tala Vilasam* by Arunachalam. This poem extols the 801 uses of the palm, which date far back to the prehistory of the Indian people. The palmyra symbolizes the palm-civilization of Asia where food, drink, firewood, timber, implements, clothing, writing material, toys, medicine, and intoxicants were supplied and most probably indicated by the palms, and to them animals flock for the same purpose of sustenance and shelter. When the vegetable constructions of the tropics have been seen and their forests dwelt in, the source of curiosity, invention, and raw material is reached. As ancient Egypt symbolized them, Thout, his baboon, and the doum palm are an old trinity (p. 309).

Blatter put first, for good or evil, the making of toddy which is palm juice, preferably fermented. I follow his example for the benefit of plant physiology. The juice comes from tapping the inflorescences, the male yielding better than the female. The young inflorescence is bound up with vegetable thongs so that it cannot open. It is beaten with a mallet for three days or more to encourage the flow of sap. The tip is then shaved off daily for four days. 'On the eighth morning a clear sweet liquor begins to flow from the wounded spadix, which is indicated by the "Toddy Birds" and crows fighting and chattering amongst the trees.' It is the primeval setting when subman, as was his apish wont, licked the fermented wound on the broken or diseased inflorescence. The liquor is now collected in bamboo receivers or in gourds, and in this way, tapping with daily slices several inflorescences on a tree, there is drained off over several months, about two litres a day per inflorescence. Large palms yield eleven to twenty litres per day. A single palm is estimated to give about 120,000 litres during its tapping life [291]. The wild date palm of India is tapped in the evening, the palmyra in the morning. The juice is fermented and drunk, turned into vinegar, distilled into arrack or palm brandy, or evaporated to jaggery (palm sugar).

Fruits raw, roasted, or pulped into confection, soft immature seeds, seedlings, and, of course, a share in palm-honey increase the value of a grove of palmyra palms. The outer part of the trunk from old palms makes good timber, the female now being preferable to the male; stem fibres are spun into rope. The leaves are used for thatching, fencing, mulching, matting, baskets, umbrellas, fans, hats, and, as braided leaflets, fancy-ware; their fibres are extracted for string and cord. But the greatest contribution of the palmyra to civilization, which it shares with the talipot *Corypha*, must be its establishment of literature. The oldest Hindu reference to writing is over four thousand years ago. 'Pliny says expressly that the most ancient way of writing was upon the leaf of the Palm tree, an assertion with all the weight of evidence in its favour' [292]. The dry leaflets are ready ruled by parallel veins and the softer tissue between them was lightly inscribed with a stylus or, may be in the first place, with a palm thorn. The leaflet was held in the left hand and, with the right forearm rigid, the leaflet was pushed to the left between fingers and thumb. There flowed the horizontal line of circles, dots, and dashes from left to right, which distinguishes Sanskrit from the vertical flow of Chinese painting on unyielding bamboo rotated to the right. No table was needed, and the peripatetic philosopher could at once inscribe his meditations. Later, with a table, the stylus was loaded with a metal weight at its upper end and the rounded hand was improved. The leaflets were bound in books, which had to be wider than long; the maximum width of two feet for a line is given by the spacing of the veins, and the maximum length of two inches by the breadth of the leaflet. Hence come folio and leaf. And palm leaflets are still in use for letter-writing.

### Caryota

The fish-tail palms of this genus and those of its close ally *Arenga* have many peculiarities. The leaf-axis ends in a terminal leaflet. All the leaflets are induplicate as in *Phoenix*, but they end in broad or obtuse ends which are toothed like eroded fish-tails. They have no distinct midribs, but many equally strong veins issue from the short stalk of the leaflet and traverse its length. The fleshy fruits have no woody stone (slight in *Arenga*) and their tissue is rendered inedible to most higher animals through the abundant, irritant, microscopic needle-crystals (raphids). Further their trunks are hapaxanthic in the peculiar way of flowering from above downwards (p. 128).

Four genera were made for this alliance, namely *Caryota*, *Arenga*, *Didymosperma*, and *Wallichia*. *Didymosperma* has already been reduced to *Arenga* and it may be only a matter of time before they are all telescoped into *Caryota*. They evince in this subfamily all the usual trends in palm evolution. *Caryota* begins the series with doubly pinnate leaves, unique in the palm family and, as argued on p. 199, to be regarded as the primitive form of the palm leaf. The leaflets are short and widely dilated to the broad, toothed margin, so as to appear wedge-shaped. The small flowers are bisexual with many stamens, and the seed has ruminate endosperm. The other genera are reduced to once pinnate, or simply pinnate, leaves with oblong leaflets inasmuch as they represent the long primary folds of the *Caryota* leaf. Their flowers are unisexual and set in male and female inflorescences on the same trunk. The endosperm is not ruminate. Then, the male flowers of *Arenga* have many stamens as in *Caryota*, whereas in *Wallichia* they are reduced to six.

In all three genera there are species with tall massive solitary trunks that are truly hapaxanthic; for the whole palm dies after fruiting from the lowest inflorescence. They have, also, less stout species which prolong the life of the individual palm by producing suckers from the base, and in *Arenga* and *Wallichia* this leads to relatively small undergrowth palms of neotenic aspect. *Wallichia* has taken the extreme step in palm-construction and evolved a species with the leaves produced and set in two rows like a gigantic compass plant or prolonged fan, namely *W. disticha* of the eastern Himalayan region. So the hapaxanthic state with massive solitary stems leads to the tufted with small stems and the practically stemless undergrowth palm. The flowers become unisexual and reduced in complexity. But whether the rumination of the endosperm has disappeared in *Arenga* and *Wallichia* or developed in *Caryota* is an undecided issue.

The tall trunks of *C. urens*, forty to sixty feet high, are said to begin flowering when twelve to fifteen years old, but this seems hardly possible for it implies at some time a growth rate of more than four feet per annum, which is the maximum that has been observed. *C. rumphiana*, or a close ally in the mountains of Malaya, develops trunks over one hundred feet high and they would seem to be of much greater age. Nevertheless the sugar palm *Arenga pinnata* of south east Asia is said to grow its trunk, twenty to forty feet high, about the same rate in seven to ten years. The starch in the trunks is turned into sugar which enters each inflorescence as it develops from the leaf-axil in the order from above downwards. Instead of sending the whole of this carbohydrate store up into a terminal inflorescence, as in *Corypha* and *Metroxylon*, it is mobilized in stages, node by node, down to within one or a few feet of the roots.

The young inflorescences are tapped for sugar-production, wine and arrack. They are pommelled with a wooden mallet for several days, like those of the palmyra, until bruised internally. Then, they are sliced gradually down to the stalk by thin cuts once or twice a day, and the sugary sap is collected in suitable vessels attached to the stumps of the inflorescence. At this time the leaves have died. There is no ordinary transpiration stream from root to leaf to carry with it this flow of sugar. We are led to think of root-pressure and exosmosis or glandular activity by the ground-tissue of the stem, secreting sugar into the vessels in the vascular bundles. There may be very much more physiological action than physical. It is recorded that, to promote the flow of sap, the pommelled but uncut inflorescences of *A. pinnata* used to be poulticed with pulp from the re-active tuber of the yam *Dioscorea hispida* [293]. Then, further, the female inflorescences of this palm yield little or no sugary sap; only the male ones are tapped. Most trunks produce early in their flowering two to five female inflorescences which are left to seed, and the remainder are mostly male and can be tapped. Some trees produce mostly female inflorescences and they can be cut down for sago because most of the starch in the trunk is still unmobilized when the upper inflorescences have opened to disclose their sex. Others produce mostly male inflorescences. Thus, this species is tending to become dioecious with male and female individuals. Trees may yield for two years at a rate of three and a half litres of sugary sap a day. Old, thoroughly tapped, and effete trunks become more or less hollow.

The large *Caryota urens*, tapped in the same way, yields seven to fourteen litres per inflorescence in twenty-four hours or, if several inflorescences are tapped at the same time on one trunk, twenty to twenty-seven litres [294]. This prodigious feat exceeds that of the palmyra (p. 285) and, for a leafless tree, throws doubt on physical theories to explain the ascent of sap.

*Caryota* ranges from India to Queensland but, except for the small tufted *C. mitis*, it is nowhere common in the forest. *Arenga*, with similar distribution, is more abundant and plays a considerable part in the lower stories of the rain-forest. *Wallichia* is restricted between the eastern parts of India and Indo-China.

Care must be taken of the juice from fresh, untapped, tissues of these palms. My first botanical monkey died from collecting specimens of the giant *Caryota* in the Malayan mountains [295]. I have suffered anguish over many hours from the embryo-sac juice of immature *Arenga* seeds.

## Ceroxylon

This is the genus of wax palms peculiar to the Andes. Their solitary, unbranched trunks are covered by a film of wax. Their large pinnate leaves are silvered beneath with wax. And among the silver and green, against the blue of the sky, the berries hang in large orange-red clusters. Twenty species have been recorded in pockets or saddles between the mountains from Lake Titicaca in Bolivia to Caracas and Santa Marta in the north. The long range and isolation suggest the breaking up of the extensive distribution of their ancestor into divergent populations, much as with the species of *Pritchardia* in Hawaii. They do not lend themselves to cultivation and there is much still to be learnt about them [296]. Those with shorter trunks, up to forty feet high, occur at altitudes from 4,000–13,500 feet. The highest record is for *C. utile* near Volcan Chiles on the Colombian-Ecuador frontier; the temperature falls, there, at night below freezing point and snow showers lie for a few hours under the overhead sun. It is the highest altitudinal occurrence of any palm. In most places where the wax palms prosper, they dot the landscape with their shining trunks and the crowns surge above the mountain forest. The tallest *C. andicola* on the Quindío pass west of Bogotá grows at ten thousand feet and its trunk attains over two hundred feet as the tallest palm in the world. This species, the first to be discovered, was found by Humboldt on his scientific journey over this difficult route in 1801; and when it was made known to science in 1808, it was the tallest of known plants, for there was no published information yet about *Sequoia* or the giant *Eucalyptus* [297]. A delightful account of Humboldt's travail and of the subsequent efforts of botanists to study these palms, which have become the national emblem of Colombia, is given by Bomhard [298]. The French botanist Eduard André visited the famous pass in 1876 and described the palm house in which he stayed. It was built of the logs of the wax palm. The uprights were waxed trunks that shone like marble columns. The roof was a thatch of waxed leaves that caught the silvery shadows from candles made of the self-same wax; outside the temperature dropped to 2°C. Unaccustomed to marble halls, the German botanist Karsten observed that bears climbed the trunks of *C. utile* to eat the young leaves. He created for this and several other species the genus *Klopstockia* in honour of the German poet whose stanzas filled his head amidst these Andean delights, but by the grace of priority the name has been sunk in synonymy. The German botanist Engel, soaring in symphonic ecstasy among these palms, called them *Beethovenia*, sunk too in ignominious synonymy. How are the mighty fallen! Take care, enthusiastic one, lest you perpetrate a like crime, heedless of Humboldt's cosmopolitan euphony! Botany has suffered enough from the vain association of men and plants. What a jargon are *Warscewiczia*, *Rehderophoenix*, *Liberbaileya*, *Maxburretia*, *Johannesteijsmannia*, *Kingiodendron*, *Merrillosphaera*, and *Cornera*!

*Ceroxylon* has given its name to the subfamily of palms Ceroxyloideae used to cover both the Cocoid and Arecoid palms, though it is customary now to maintain each as its own subfamily. But the position of *Ceroxylon* among the Arecoid palms is uncertain. It is placed with *Juania*, equally uncertain, and also with the alliance of *Iriartea*. It is clearly a problem of the pre-Andean palms.

### Cocos

Under this name, upwards of sixty species of palm have been gathered. The modern trend is to distinguish nine other genera and to leave the coconut palm, *C. nucifera*, as the sole species of *Cocos* [299]. This attitude which was started by Beccari [300], has been hotly contested by the Brazilian botanist Bondar who was probably better acquainted with these palms in the field than anyone else [301]. He considered that it isolated alliances established by intergeneric hybrids and was in no small measure based on misunderstandings; so he reverts to the single genus *Cocos*. Whatever attitude is adopted, the fact remains that here is a South American group of palms with two outlyers, the coconut itself of the Indo-Pacific world and the South African palm *Jubaeopsis*. The genera involved are *Arecastrum*, *Aricuriroba*, *Barbosa*, *Butia*, *Chrysallidosperma*, *Lytocaryum*, *Microcoelum*, *Rhyticocos*, and *Syagrus*, as South American 'splits' from *Cocos*, the Chilean *Jubaea*, the South African *Jubaeopsis*, and the Brazilian *Polyandrococos*; the last three have the more primitive multistaminate flowers. Of these genera, *Syagrus* has about forty species, *Butia* about twelve, and the others merely one or two species. Their general character is the lack of spines on the trunks, leaf-sheaths and spathes, compared with the *Bactris* and its allies; and, to distinguish them from the oil-palm *Elaeis*, the stamens are not joined and the flowers are not sunk in depressions on the spike of the inflorescence. All possess the hard nut of which the coconut is a dry, fibrous aggrandisement, but some of the South American allies have fleshy nuts or drupes as the antecedent condition, for instance *Cocos* (*Butia*) *pulposa*. Several of the South American species, ascribed to *Syagrus*, are dwarfed into stemless or rhizomatous palms, even with unbranched inflorescences, e.g. *C. liliputiana*, *C. campicola*, and *C. vagans* of Brazil, *C. stolomifera* of Uruguay.

The coconut palm is an outstanding exception to this American alliance. Whence came this most widely cultivated and now pan-tropical palm, 'one of Nature's greatest gifts to man?' There are many ancient Sanskrit names for the palm, dating back to 1000 BC, and from these come the Malay *kelapa* and *nyiur* which is widely used through-out south east Asia and far into Polynesia. There can be no question that the palm has not witnessed the rise of Indian and Malayan civilizations. The problem is that all through the Old World it is cultivated. There is no island or shore where its presence is not due directly or indirectly to its having been planted by man. Hence it has been supposed that its origin was Indo-Pacific. It is a conclusion to which I subscribe, and I would add that, since the palm suffers so much from depredation of young foliage and fruit by monkeys, bears, squirrels, and rats, it could not have been native to the continent of Asia, that is from Borneo westwards. Its survival until the coming of primitive man must have been outside the range of these intelligent mammals, eastwards in the ancient Pacific where the problems of *Pritchardia*, *Pelagodoxa*, and *Metroxylon* are to be solved.

In 1906 Guppy suggested that the palm was native to the Pacific coast of tropical America and that it had been carried westwards by ocean-currents or sea-rovers to Polynesia and, thus, to Asia away from the Cocoid home in South America. Certainly the nut can float for three to four months without the growing seedling being destroyed, and during this time it might be drifted three thousand miles; native craft nearly always carry coconuts on their journeys for use or to plant at their destination. In 1910 Cook developed this idea but gave it an improbable turn by supposing the palm to have had an inland origin, quite contrary to its nature. There is some evidence that the palm was on the Pacific coast of Panama in pre-Columbean days. It is certain that it was not in the Caribbean area, the Guianas, or the Amazon region when Columbus arrived, but the Spanish and the Portuguese quickly brought it there from India.

There is the question how the palm got to Cocos Island which lies 250 miles west of Panama [302]. That it thrives on the Cocos Keeling Islands of the Indian Ocean is surely because they lay in the path of the Malaysian sea-rovers that went to Madagascar. The Kon-Tiki expedition proves that all round the world there has been 'Westward Ho!' to the setting sun. For the Amazon region, Wallace wrote of the coconut: 'It is in a foreign land. It flourishes . . . but no part of it is applied to any useful purpose, the fruit only being consumed as an occasional luxury. In the towns and larger villages where the Portuguese have settled it has been planted, but among the Indians of the interior it is still quite unknown [303]. The remarkable point is the absence of all palms from the Galapagos Islands.

Beccari replied to these ideas in 1917 by marshalling an amount of evidence in favour of the Old World origin of the palm. He suggested the Cocos Keeling Islands, Ceylon, or some extinct island of the Indian Ocean. He exaggerated the differences between *Cocos*, defined on *C. nucifera*, and the other American genera split off from it, and he used the argument of the robber-crab or coconut crab *Birgus latro* which appears extremely plausible. This massive crab, limited to islands of the Indian Ocean and again to Pacific Islands east of Celebes and Formosa, seemed to be adapted to feeding on coconut fruits and to be, like the palm, both insular and absent from the Americas. A rigorous examination of the information concerning this crab and new knowledge on its habits belie, however, the idea and make the relation between the crab and the coconut almost incidental [304]. Guppy had already this doubt. Nevertheless, there is the presence of the undoubted ally of *Cocos*, namely *Jubaeopsis*, in south-east Africa, to link as a relic of southern, Antarctic or Gondwanaland distribution *Cocos* of the Indian Ocean with South Africa and South America (p. 239). There is also the fact that, while in tropical America the coconut has only one variety, there are many in south east Asia in evidence of its old establishment. If, however, the coconut was brought to India by man from some island of the Indian Ocean other than Ceylon, it is remarkable that the home of the double coconut in the Seychelles was not known until late in the eighteenth century.

The most recent light on this perplexing subject, in which there are so many leads and no focus, is geological. Small fossil nuts, $3·5 \times 2·5$ cm., in the form of small coconuts have been found in the late Tertiary (Miocene-Pliocene) beds in North Island of New Zealand; they have been called *C. zeylandica* [305]. Pollen, very similar to that of *C. nucifera*, has also been found in these beds, and seems to prove that a species allied with *C. nucifera* lived in this part of Polynesia long before it was reached by man. *Cocos* no longer grows in New Zealand, which is too far south for its cultivation, but the fossil record places the problem of the coconut with that of many other plants which link the floras of Polynesia and tropical America. It has been pointed out, too, that entomological evidence favours this west Pacific origin; various insects infest the coconut palm wherever it is grown but by far the majority of those which are associated exclusively with it occur in Melanesia. Nevertheless, even these discoveries do not exclude the possibility of migration to the Pacific from Gondwanaland or Antarctica [306].

The coconut palm has been planted and multiplied into vast plantations where it grows best, and that is along tropical shores and on their alluvial plains between latitudes of 26° N. and S. It cannot tolerate drought or cold. Dry weather impedes its growth. The production of leaves, roots, inflorescences, and the all-important nuts declines as rain becomes infrequent. The water-table must be near the surface or the roots must be refreshed with continual rain; heavy water-logged soils are unsuitable. It can be grown up to some two thousand feet in altitude and, though fairly tall palms may be seen at four thousand feet, they do not flower. It has been said that it will not fruit far inland, but this may be a question of dry seasons rather than distance from maritime conditions. The fruits fall into rivers and into the sea to be drifted about for several weeks while the embryo is developing inside. They may be stranded and take root on mud-banks or beaches, but it is extremely doubtful whether they could have established themselves among the trees under the heavily forested primeval conditions. There are still abundant opportunities and coconuts floating in the sea are common objects round many Malayan and Pacific islands. Perhaps the rising atoll is their preference. Certainly it is the activity of man that is turning coastline, estuary, and even rocky headland, in the tropics into coconut plantations.

The seedling requires five years to make the base for the trunk. In eight to fifteen years, when the trunk is as many feet high, it begins to flower. It continues in this way, flowering and fruiting incessantly in the manner of numerous unrestrained tropical plants, until it reaches a height of eighty to a hundred feet, when the size and yield of the nuts decline and the tree is cut down. The dwarf coconuts begin to flower at four to five years (p. 266). The trunks do not normally branch, except to bear the axillary inflorescences, but occasionally palms are seen which at some considerable height divide into two to four trunks each with its crown of leaves, as if the result of some injury. It has been observed, too, in India that occasionally young palms may produce suckers, as happens normally in several South American allies, and that small vegetative buds (bulbils) may be produced on the inflorescence instead of flowers; by each of these means the palms may be propagated vegetatively, whereas the usual method is necessarily by seed [307].

The young crown builds up to a total of twenty-five to thirty-six leaves according to the variety of the palm. The leaves vary sixteen to twenty feet long and have seventy to one hundred pairs of leaflets. It is said that twelve to sixteen leaves are dropped per annum. The total age of the leaf, therefore, seems to lie between four and five years, half of which time is taken up by development in the bud (p. 44). The sword leaf has been observed to lengthen at a rate of an inch in twenty-four hours. The quantity of water transpired from a large palm has been calculated as twenty-eight to 75 litres per day, the amount being much increased by wind and, particularly, sunshine. Cut leaves and roots, however, fail to absorb water and, in the way of bamboos dependent on root-pressure, they progressively wilt. With the daily increase in transpiration the pulvinar tissue along the midrib loses water and contracts the sides of the leaflets together; hence, to the observer on the ground, who then sees the uppersides of the leaflets more readily, the glitter of the coconut palms increases during the middle of the day.

The male flowers begin to open about 6 a.m., are fully open by 8 a.m., and fall off in the afternoon. As in the betel palm, they open from the ends of the inflorescence branches down to the base, and when all have opened, the larger female flowers, of which there are one to two at the base of each inflorescence branch, open and remain receptive for a few days. The male flowers are three to six millimetres wide, the female thirty to thirty-five millimetres.

The fruits grow to nearly their full size in five to six months. Then the endosperm (meat) begins to develop. They ripen when ten to twelve months old. When the nut is only three inches wide, the central hollow begins to appear and is filled with the watery embryo-sac juice which increases in quantity until the endosperm is nearly fully developed: then it diminishes in amount as the fruit ripens, but it does not disappear completely until germination is well started.

The young endosperm begins as an almost gelatinous tissue round the embryo at the base of the nut, whence it spreads over the interior, thickens inwards, and hardens into the firm meat from the outside next the shell by thickening of the cell walls. There is a variety in which the endosperm hypertrophies to fill the whole nut and, as it seems, to exclude even an embryo. The juice of the giant embryo-sac, developed after fertilization, becomes the coconut water that is drunk from the green coconut; it must not be mistaken for the coconut milk of cookery which is made by stirring the mature grated endosperm with water. The coconut water in the fresh green nut is remarkably cool, slightly aromatic, and saturated with carbon dioxide, derived from the respiration of the internal tissues of the nut, particularly the endosperm and embryo, and this self-effervescence, though slight, adds to its delectableness. It contains, as one would expect, an appreciable amount of plant growth-substances and it has consequently found a variety of uses in the experimental culture of the tissues of flowering plants [308].

Ripe nuts vary according to the variety from green to ochre-yellow and orange-red, but they dry up to a dull brown on the palm before falling. Sometimes the seedling begins to sprout from nuts which are still attached. There is, in fact, no period of dormancy, the delay in appearance of the seedling being due to the delay in its early growth compared with that of the nut.

About four months elapse from the falling of the ripe nut until the seedling emerges. This equals, roughly, the period of viability of the nut when drifting in the sea. The seedling breaks through the soft eye of the three coconut eyes and this rupture presumably lets in the sea water to destroy the young plant and the endosperm, which is a living tissue. The seedling develops four to six scale-leaves or leaf-sheaths without blades. They are followed by two to six plicate leaves which are split only at the bifid apex. Then the pinnate leaves come and lengthen successively as the lower folds are split off as leaflets. During this time the cotyledon has enlarged to fill the cavity of the nut. It forms a voracious spongy tissue that erodes the endosperm almost completely and converts the cellulose-like substance of the cell-walls of the endosperm into sugar which it stores as starch for the use of the seedling [309]. Occasional nuts have two or three embryos (p. 153).

Trunks of old trees are used for timber. Dead trunks should be felled and split and, if not required for use, should be burnt for they

U

allow the large and destructive rhinoceros beetle and coconut beetle to develop. They have plagued the coconut countries after the strife of the last world war. The leaves are used for light thatching, mats, and sundry decorations during festivals. The cabbage is edible, but expensive for to eat the cabbage is to kill the palm. Palm-sugar and wine can be obtained by tapping the inflorescence, but the most valuable part and that for which the palm is cultivated is the endosperm. Ripe nuts are split and the halves exposed to the sun or to kiln-drying to make copra, the sickly sweet smell of which pervades most tropical wharfs and is accompanied by the swarm of small copra-beetles. From the copra the coconut oil is extracted for cooking oil, margarine, soap, candles, and so on; a particular virtue of the oil is its tolerance, so to speak, of sea-water and it has been the basis of marine or salt-water soap. The fresh grated endosperm is also used very extensively in villages either in cakes and confectionery or as the coconut milk. The dried, grated endosperm of first quality is used in the world trade of confectioners. The fibrous husk produces coir, which is made into ropes, matting, brooms, and bags. The shells are made into bowls, spoons, tea-sets, toys, and the finest medicinal charcoal. Inside some coconuts, which seem to have no power of germination, there are found the rare coconut pearls, half to one inch long, made of calcium carbonate, not siliceous as the bamboo pearls, but endowed also with magic properties. Thus the coconut palm displays the whole range of human dependence on palm-products.

The annual harvest of copra is estimated at more than three million metric tons, of which at least three-quarters comes from the Far East. For comparison, palm-kernels and palm-oil from *Elaeis guineensis* are estimated at two million tons, mostly from Africa, and olive oil, mostly from Europe, at a little less than a million tons per annum [310]. This amount of copra comes from over ten million acres of plantations or about six hundred million palm trees [311]. The last figure is certainly an under-estimate because it will not include the considerable number of village trees. But, as a basis for world statistics, it means that with a world-population of three thousand million, there is a coconut palm for every five persons or, roughly, one per family. As the palm bears fifty to a hundred nuts annually, there should be ten to twenty nuts for everyone every year; the distribution must be unequal.

There are many varieties of the coconut palm in Asia. There are tall palms and dwarf palms, those with orange-red, ochre-yellow, or green fruits when ripe, those with fragrant endosperm, and others with varying proportions of husk, shell, and endosperm. These are the sort of varieties that give rise to specific differences among wild species but not to generic distinctions. A non-hereditary difference, observable in many plants, is that called right-handed or left-handed in reference to the direction of the spiral formed by the leaves in their successive development on the trunk; it depends on which side of the cotyledon the second leaf develops in the embryo or seedling. Left-handed coconuts, which slightly predominate, are said to yield twenty per cent more nuts than right-handed, and there is no explanation [312].

## Chapter 13

# Generic Notes

Copernicia – Corypha – Dypsis – Elaeis – Geonoma – Hyphaene – Licuala – Livistona – Lodoicea – Metroxylon.

## Copernicia

This is the fan-leafed genus of wax palms in the subfamily Coryphoideae, analogous to the feather-leafed wax palms of *Ceroxylon*. A fine monograph has recently been devoted to them and it should stimulate the study of their natural history [313]. There are twenty-three species, all of limited and endemic distribution. Three occur in South America, two in Hispaniola (those twins, Haiti and Dominica), and the remainder in Cuba. Several of those in Cuba are said to hybridize, but the South American species live too far apart for promiscuity. They have unbranched trunks, without suckers, and a stately crown of long-stalked leaves, worthy of a Copernican planetarium, but some of the Cuban species develop incredibly condensed, tussock-like crowns of stiff, barely stalked, crowded leaves below which the old and dead hang like the tattered petticoats under a new Andean poncho. *C. macroglossa* and *C. rigida* are, indeed, guerillas in the vegetable warfare of Caribbea; their leaves have astonishingly long ligules, and these tongues, one to three feet long, may remain on the trunk after the blade has fallen, like the rude spouts of innumerable gargoyles.

Their inflorescences seem quite primitive. They are long, much branched, axillary, and in most cases all the branches have their subtending, tubular bracts. The flowers are bisexual and in some species fragrant. The fruit is rather small with one seed, the endosperm of which is ruminate. *Pritchardia* and *Washingtonia* seem most closely allied and differ chiefly in the non-ruminate endosperm. Indeed, the differences between *Copernicia* and its several American allies seem to be the details of sections rather than distinctions of generic character.

298

Figure 124. *Copernicia cerifera*, the carnauba of Brazil (left) and the Cuban *C. vespertilionum* with dense crown of shortly stalked leaves and persistent dead leaves; × $\frac{1}{200}$.

The South American species are the carandá palm (*C. alba*) of Paraguay, north Argentina, east Bolivia, and south-west Brazil; the carnauba palm (*C. cerifera*) of the dry north-east sector of Brazil, between the Amazon estuary and the long south-east Atlantic coast [314]; and the llanos palm (*C. tectorum*) of the central coastal districts in Columbia and Venezuela. Between all these regions, separated by hundreds of miles of land, there are said to be no *Copernicia* palms. Yet, it has been estimated that there are over a hundred million carnauba palms in Piaui and Ceara; and that the carandá palms are even more abundant occurring 'in solid stands hundreds of square miles in extent,' the largest estimated to contain about five hundred million palms, and the whole numbering at least ten times as many as the carnauba palms. They grow, as most species of the genus and unlike the hardy wax palms of *Ceroxylon*, in flat lowlands, subject to periodical inundation with constantly high tropical temperatures. One can fly for long stretches over these monotonous forests relieved only by the glint of sunshine on the water beneath them. At other times of year, they live under excessively dry heat when the wax-covering of the leaves will act as a waterproof against loss of water rather than as an insulator against lower temperatures in the species of *Ceroxylon*. Their physiology is not studied, but it is said that they grow slowly and that carnauba palms may attain seventy-five to a hundred years, but reports of greater age are fallacious. That these vast stands of giant monocotyledons have scarcely been explored ecologically, though they must be almost unique relics of forest-geography, while the tiny tussock-grasses of Europe and North America have been studied by hundreds of botanists, shows our ignorance of monocotyledonous science. These palms must tell the tertiary history of the Rio São Francisco, R. Paraguay, R. Madera, R. Orinoco, and R. Magdalena, as separated by the later Amazon river; and what greater riverine history is there in the world?

The genus is divided into two groups. Subgenus *Copernicia* has no tubular bracts on the flowering branches of the inflorescence, whereas subgen. *Coperniciopsis* has. If this is a natural subdivision, then the carnauba *C. cerifera* of Brazil and the llanos palm *C. tectorum* of Venezuela-Colombia are related with the two species in Hispaniola and one species *C. gigas* in central and east Cuba. The most southerly, most distant, and most abundant carandá *C. alba* is related with the remaining local species of Cuba several thousand miles away. Link, then, Asuncion and Habana as an alligator-walk, and you will perceive the historical wanderings of these palms. This grand vista has been opened to us not through biological deliberation, but through the investigations promoted by commercial interest in the wax.

## Corypha

The very large, fan-leafed, and hapaxanthic palms of this genus are grouped in six to eight species, but they are so huge and the enormous terminal inflorescences so lofty that they are exceedingly difficult to study. Five species, at least, occur on the Asiatic mainland. One is known only from Biliran Island in the Philippines and two are known only from herbarium-material of uncertain origin [315]. The most widespread gebang palm of Malaysia, *C. elata*, is distributed from Bengal and the Andaman Islands, throughout the drier parts of Malaysia to north Australia but is absent from the high rain forest between the southern half of Malaya and New Guinea. Its trunk, when approaching the flowering time after some thirty to forty years growth, develops a faint but characteristic, broad, longitudinal spiral banding as if it had shrunk upon itself along lines of leaf-arrangement. The best known species, the talipot, *C. umbraculifera*, is widely cultivated in Ceylon and, like the palmyra *Borassus*, served for writing material and books in the days of the stylus [316]; but, like the betel, coconut, and date palms, it has never been found wild. The origin of cultivated plants is a problem that concerns not only the history of the cereals and fruit-trees of Europe, but many of the trees of south east Asia such as the mango, mangosteen, jack-fruit, and wild fig; they join with these palms and lead back to the dawn of civilization in the palm world.

The talipot is possibly the most massive palm for it exceeds in several respects the double coconut, though its fruits, merely an inch and a half wide, are in comparison midget. The trunk reaches eighty feet and two to three feet in thickness. The leaf-blade is eight to sixteen feet in width and is supported on a stalk six to ten feet long. The terminal inflorescence, developed after fifty to seventy years, reaches fifteen to twenty feet high and thirty to forty feet across; it is almost the largest of all inflorescences. The small fruits, borne in vast numbers, evidently compete in their growth and require thirteen months to develop to maturity [317]. The shortest species *C. talliera* has a trunk thirty feet high, but the leaves are practically as large, and the inflorescence is said to be larger; the fruit, of the same size, takes nine to ten months to develop, but the period may not have been accurately measured.

Related to these huge solitary unbranched palms are the small tufted palms of *Nannorrhops* which extend from north-west India to Afghanistan and Arabia. They have terminal inflorescences but they proliferate, after the flowering stem has died, by means of suckers. We have noted, however, the curious branching in the aerial stems of one species (p. 86). The connection between these extremes, *Corypha* and *Nannorrhops*, of Coryphoid evolution needs investigation.

### Dypsis

Twenty-one species of small, pinnate-leafed palms make this genus which is confined to Madagascar. They are undergrowth palms in the high forest. The larger have slender trunks up to fifteen feet high; the smaller reach two or three feet and not half an inch in thickness. We should observe at once that the tall stately palm, often cultivated as *Dypsis madagascariensis*, belongs really to the related *Chrysalidocarpus* [318]. *Dypsis* is one of the more advanced and reduced genera. It is a spineless Arecoid with very small flowers on slender inflorescences, monoecious with the flowers in the usual triads of two male and a central female, but the male have merely three small stamens with or without as many staminodes. The small red berries are asymmetrically developed with the stigma displaced basally, and the one seed has non-ruminate endosperm.

Four species with slender stems less than three feet high, have small unsplit leaves except for the bifid apex (figure 125). One of them has a simple spike-like inflorescence (*D. longipes*); two have the inflorescence once branched (*D. humberti, D. louvelii*); and the other has the

301

inflorescence twice branched. Several larger species have the leaf split imperfectly into compound leaflets with three to ten folds (midribs) per leaflet. The most divided leaves have about six or seven pairs of leaflets composed of two or three folds, rarely one; and so even these are imperfectly split; their inflorescences are larger.

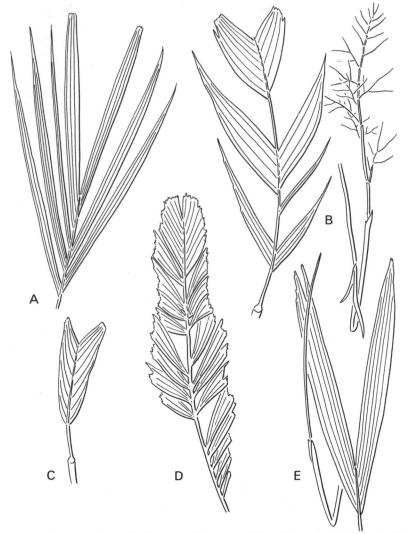

Figure 125. Leaves of the Madagascan *Dypsis* and *Neophloga*. A, *D. linearis* with compound leaflets, × ⅓. B, *D. forficifolia* with few pairs of compound leaflets, and much branched inflorescence, × ¼. C, *D. forficifolia* var. *reducta* with unsplit frond, × ¼. D, *N. thiryana* with fish-tail leaflets, × ⅓. E, *D. longipes* with simple bifid frond and unbranched inflorescence, × ⅓. (After Jumelle, 1945.)

Here is a series that could be taken to represent the evolution of large palms from small 'liliaceous' beginnings in isolated Madagascar, but in all points of inflorescence, flower, and fruit they are advanced and reduced. We come upon the species *D. forficifolia* and find that it has a variety *reducta*, growing in the upper montane limit of the species at six hundred metres. It is a small plant with simple leaves and small inflorescences. We learn, at once, that this is a juvenile state that has become fertile in spite of being vegetatively under-developed. We find in *Dypsis* the clue, again, to the finality, not the beginning, of palm evolution, which has been to evolve the small neotenic under-growth habit. The explanation accords with the advancement of *Dypsis* in other ways. The unsplit leaves in all cases, whether seedling or adult, appear to have merely eight to ten folds on each side. Bigger leaves add more folds, up to twenty-four, by basal growth and liberate these by normal, though compound, splitting. We must look for a bigger leafed ancestor of *Dypsis* in the Madagascan flora.

The genus *Neophloga*, with twenty-nine species confined to Madagascar, is described as closely allied and is said to differ only in having larger male flowers with six fertile stamens. This is exactly what would be expected, and we find that *Neophloga* also has a number of progressively neotenic species with compound leaflets and, finally, the simple unsplit leaf. One species *N. thiryana*, however, is particularly interesting because it has fish-tail leaflets to indicate that the once pinnate leaves of the group are simplified from the doubly pinnate. *Neophloga*, thus, stands clearly as the ancestor to *Dypsis*, and we may wonder if the species of *Neophloga* may not have turned into species of *Dypsis* on several different lines of evolution. We begin to wonder what is a phyletic genus among palms, and to suspect herbarium categories.

Close to *Neophloga* and, perhaps, not entirely distinct is *Chrysalidocarpus* with about twenty species, eighteen in Madagascar, two in the Comoro Islands, and a species in Pemba Island. They have taller and more robust trunks with large leaves, usually completely split into leaflets; one species *C. decipiens* is a bottle-palm with swollen basal part of the trunk. Here is the genus of yet larger palms, contesting with trees, that have led through *Neophloga* by neoteny to *Dypsis*. We can continue the analysis of the Madagascan palms and discover that with comparatively few large and robust kinds there have developed many reduced undergrowth species all in the Arecoid tribe Dypsideae, peculiar to the island. So far as palms go, there is nothing primitive about this tribe comparable with the lemurs of Madagascar, and it is clear that the ancestral Dypsideae probably disappeared from the island long before the lemurs got there.

The Dypsid palms parallel *Areca* and numerous other genera of its subfamily, such as *Chamaedorea*, *Geonoma*, and *Pinanga*, and show that the small, simple, undergrowth palm is not primitive, as so often assumed, but large palms reduced to seedling stature. The Dypsid series happens to be particularly complete. It offers an exceptionally rich field for evolutionary research, morphological, ecological, and genetical. But, alas!, the primeval forest of Madagascar has been most extensively destroyed and no one knows how many of its palms may have survived.

### Elaeis

The African oil palm *E. guineensis* is second only to the coconut in the world's supply of palm-oil (p. 296). It is the only palm, however, to which an entire journal is dedicated [319]. Though of ancient status, undoubtedly, in village life of West Africa, its introduction into world commerce is recent and began with the abolition of slavery. For fifty years the produce of the wild palms was exported and cultivation, which is now expanding all through the humid tropics, did not begin till around 1860. It inhabits swamps and lowland throughout Africa, even Madagascar, but it has not the preference for light coastal soils. Thus its cultivation can be extended inland in Asia and America where it is less profitable to plant coconuts. It is, moreover, easier to harvest. It gives a quicker return, for palms come into bearing by the fourth or fifth year from seed; and the oil is readily extractable by machinery. Nevertheless it has its own problems. To extract the big fruit-bunches, the spiny leaf-stalks must be cut away. Thus the plantations are uniquely trimmed, the chopped-off leaf-bases on the thick trunks displaying the spirals of leaf-arrangement. Tall wild palms are climbed in the native manner (p. 335). Tall palms on estates need ladders, for the bunches cannot be extracted on long hooks in the way that coconuts may be cut off; and, of course, monkeys cannot be used.

*Elaeis* is a Cocoid genus. It agrees with *Cocos* and its allies in the absence of epidermal spines on the trunk, leaf-sheaths, and spathes, which characterize the Bactrid palms, but it differs in the unisexual inflorescences on the spikes of which the flowers are set in depressions, and in the union of the stamens of the male flower into a tube.

Furthermore the branches of the male inflorescence end in sterile spine-like tips and the lower reduced leaflets on the leaf are turned into spikes through the loss of their small blades.

In nearly all respects *E. guineensis* differs from *C. nucifera*. To compare them feature by feature is as good an exercise in elementary botany as it is for the advanced student of palms, the biochemist of palm-products, or the domestic user of palm-oil, meaning African palm-oil, compared with coconut-oil. Both are solitary palms reaching a height of eighty to a hundred feet, with many pinnate leaves in the crown, but no one should confuse them even from a distance. The leaves of the oil-palm have more leaflets (100–160 pairs) and in the middle part of the frond every other leaflet is strongly deflexed: hence the oil-palm never has the elegant pectinate crown of the coconut. The leaves, too, are not shed so cleanly and the trunk of the oil-palm is more or less stubbed with their remnants. Then, the oil-palm opens a new leaf every fortnight, not once monthly as the coconut palm, though seedlings of the oil-palm up to six months old are said to develop the leaves once a month. Correspondingly an old leaf turns yellow to orange and falls off every two weeks. The total age of the oil-palm leaf is given as three and a half to four years, compared with an estimate of five years for the coconut (p. 44). The male inflorescences alternate with the female in their development. A male phase of about three months sees only male inflorescences developed singly from each leaf-axil in succession. Then follows a female phase, which may last for six months, before the return to the male. Actually every inflorescence is initially bisexual but at a very early stage either the ovaries or the stamens abort in the flower primordia so as to produce the unisexual flowers. The rhythm seems unassociated with external conditions and there are freak palms which are wholly male or female. Thus, the oil-palm is tending, like the sugar palm *Arenga*, towards the dioecious habit of the date palms *Phoenix*. The male inflorescence in young palms has about fifty thousand flowers, and the number increases to 140,000 by the tenth year; the female inflorescence similarly increases its flowers from 3,500 to 5,000. The coconut has rarely more than eight to twenty female flowers per inflorescence.

The fruit of the oil-palm is a drupe one and a half inches long, with pulpy, red or black wall or pericarp and a small, pointed stone. The three germ-pores or eyes are set near the rounded apex and not at the base as in the coconut. Palm oil is obtained both from the pulpy pericarp and from the endosperm or kernel within the stone. Thus what the oil-palm loses in size compared with the coconut, it makes up by numbers and a double source of oil. The fruit ripens in five to six months, or half the time required for the coconut, and those of a bunch ripen more or less uniformly. Seed-germination may occur in two months, but is often delayed for four to six months and seems very much more uncertain than in the coconut, though there is a greater percentage of seeds with two and three embryos. In both palms, dry weather reduces the fruit-supply.

There are by no means as many varieties of the oil-palm as there are of the coconut, which doubtless reflects the much shorter period of cultivation; the longer and more intensively a plant is cultivated the more numerous in general are its varieties. There are genetic differences in leaf-arrangement and one variety is said to bear more or less unsplit leaves like those of the American *Manicaria*. The four important varieties in cultivation differ in the relative thickness of pericarp and stone: one has practically no stone and transgresses, therefore, the ruling character of the Cocoid palms in general.

The two genera which defy the rule that palm genera are restricted to the Old or New World are *Raphia* (p. 329) and *Elaeis*. Both have species in Africa and America. *Cocos* in its wide sense could be added to join Asia or Australasia with America, and there is also the relation between the South American *Jubaea* and the South African *Jubaeopsis*. Perhaps the African Arecoid genera *Podococcus* and *Sclerosperma* should be added, if related to the American *Geonoma*. Nevertheless, *Raphia* and *Elaeis* are unique in relating Brazil and the Guianas with West Africa. Many other flowering plants do this [320], but there is something peculiar about these palms. In the first place they seem to differ fundamentally in their origins. *Raphia* is related with the Lepidocaryoid palms of the Old World, *Elaeis* with the Cocoid palms of the New World, and there is the Amazon genus *Barcella* closely akin to *Elaeis*. Secondly, whereas *Raphia* has many African species, it has but one in tropical America (p. 329). *Elaeis* has one species in America and one in Africa. The American *E. melanococca* has been separated as a distinct genus *Corozo*, but the small differences in flower are scarcely worthy of this rank and the making of two genera merely obscures the problem of distribution and origin [321]. The American species tends to affect the American way of growth in the allies of *Cocos* in that the trunk is weak or weakly supported and leans; it may even become horizontal and develop adventitious roots along its length in the manner of the soboliferous or rhizomatous species of the *Cocos* alliance. It is not the habit of Old World palms. Thirdly, it must be concluded that *Raphia* sent a species to America and *Elaeis* a species to Africa.

The theory of continental drift, whereby Brazil loosened and separated from West Africa would neatly explain the problem. It absolutely fails, however, to explain why all the other genera of American and African palms were not similarly affected. It also, fails to explain why the separation affected two species that are very extensively employed in village life, *R. taedigera* in America, *E. guineensis* in Africa. Both are wine-palms; both in fibre, leaf, and timber make villages; *Elaeis* supplies the oil and grease. It is impossible to neglect the probability of pre-Columbean, African sailors carrying *Raphia taedigera* to America and *Elaeis* to Africa. Certainly both are now extremely widespread on their respective continents, and *E. guineensis* differs in many respects from *E. melanococca* but the coconut, betel, and peach palms are also immensely widespread as the result of human activity (p. 282). It is a strange reflection on our knowledge of palms that either the enormous forces of continental drift or the whims of human drift may be invoked to explain just these two peculiar instances of transatlantic distribution.

## Geonoma

'The humble but graceful palms composing this genus often grow beneath the shade of the Mauritias, Attaleas, and other lofty palms, and bear about the same relation to them as the Hazels of our European woods do to the giant Oaks' [322]. No other palm genus has specialized so successfully in the forest undergrowth, to which its species, well over two hundred, are practically confined. It is rivalled by *Chamaedorea* of similar habit and also confined to the American tropics, and in Asia *Pinanga* would be its counterpart or *Licuala*, though neither genus seems to have had the same evolutionary capacity. If one wanted to study thoroughly the minutiae of palm-evolution into simplified, neotenic, almost herbaceous forms, *Geonoma* should be the choice. It offers a range in size from stems fifteen to twenty feet high down to a foot or so and a corresponding simplification of leaf and inflorescence to the undivided state. The little flowers are highly peculiar, but practically nothing is known of their biology and the same may be said of fruit and seedling. They

307

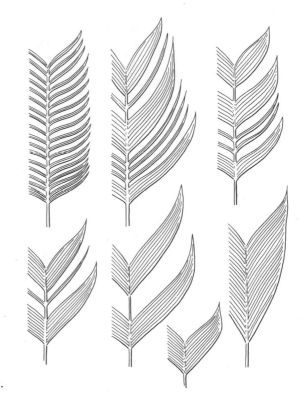

Figure 126. Leaves of *Geonoma* to show the various compounding of the leaflets in different species, all with 17–20 pairs of leaflets and folds except the smallest with 10–11 pairs; × $\frac{1}{10}$ (after Barbosa Rodriguez, 1903).

become, in fact, so much like small aroids that they have been considered a connecting link between the two families, but the aroids lack entirely the plicate leaf through which the progress of *Geonoma* must be read. Spruce, with his usual perspicacity, noted that the number of leaflets on a leaf varied greatly with the species, yet the total number of veins in the whole leaf remained unchanged; in other words, the leaf develops to the same extent throughout a large group of species, if not in the whole genus, but variously loses its power of splitting in a surprising variety of ways (figure 126).

Concerning the female flower, Spruce noted that 'it is a common thing for small beetles to deposit an egg in the nascent ovary; and as the larva develops, the staminal tube swells below and becomes ovoid or lageniform.' Whether this is incidental to pollination or a part of it remains to be discovered. Some species flower from every leaf-axil after the juvenile stage; others in aroid manner flower intermittently at every second or third leaf.

# Hyphaene

This Borassoid genus has several points of similarity with *Phoenix* (p. 322). It has been stranded in the dryer parts of tropical and subtropical Africa, the Middle East, and western India. It also reaches Madagascar. It consists, also, of a very uncertain number of species, variously estimated between twelve and twenty-eight, though probably less because they may alter much in appearance according to the circumstances in which they grow. Restricted in nature to savanna-land and semi-desert, they can thrive in cultivation in the rain-forest climate. Here the doum-palm, *H. thebaica*, accustomed to the merciless sun of upper Egypt and the Sudan, luxuriates almost unrecognizably, and can form a trunk thirty feet high in twenty years, while in very dry poor soils it has not only much smaller leaves than usual, but smaller fruits [323]. Besides the date-palm *Phoenix dactylifera*, the doum-palm is the only other Egyptian palm to have been cultivated since time immemorial for its edible and drug-providing fruits, and it has become even more strikingly incorporated into early Egyptian civilization.

Like most trees of Ancient Egypt, the doum-palm was considered sacred. It was the symbol of male strength. Several representations showing how the palm was worshipped by a man kneeling under the tree are known from different tombs at Thebes. The God of Science, Thout, was represented in Ancient Egypt by the Ibis and Baboon. As the baboons frequently fed on doum fruits and lived in the crown of the palms, the doum became Thout's special tree . . . very often the baboon, Thout's sacred animal, and the doum-palm are pictured together . . . nineteen scenes with doums and monkeys . . . As a rule the baboons are seen climbing the trees and gathering the fruits [324].

The large brown, smooth fruits, about three inches long and two wide, contain a sweet juicy pulp that tastes like gingerbread and is diuretic; this pulp is also made into a syrup or cakes. The stone surrounds the very hard white endosperm which is used as vegetable ivory for buttons, needles, carvings and so on. The style of the fruit is placed at the base because only one of the three carpels of the ovary swells into a fruit, the other two with the style remaining abortive.

Botanical interest centres on the dichotomy of the trunk which distinguishes most species, though several are said to be consistently unbranched (p. 85). Basal suckers are not developed, unless in the Madagascan *H. shatan*. It is remarkable that a group with such ancient form of branching should be also the largest genus of a subfamily distinguished by its relict distribution (p. 237). Apart from the forking trunk, the genus can be recognized by the comparatively short costapalmate leaves with strongly arched blade.

## Licuala

It is always a pleasure in the dense and perplexing forest to find a genus that is easily recognized. *Licuala* soon becomes an old friend in the vast and varied region between Burma and Bougainville Island. It is a Coryphoid palm, distinguished by the wedge-shaped leaflets; they are compound leaflets widened to the abrupt toothed apex. There are about eighty species. Some form thickets up to twenty feet high, chiefly in the tidal swamps, but, as the genus ascends the hills, stemless species appear, some robust, others small, and it has the distinction of being the only fan-palm that has evolved a great number of undergrowth palmlets. When the forest is cleared, the thickets of *Licuala* may be left, and they catch the eye with their striking foliage and long sprays of pink, orange, and red berries. It is an amenable genus, even though the leaf-stalks are thorny, and worthy of field-study in order to trace its evolution, but a word of caution is needed. The very fibrous stems, caused by the break-up of the leaf-sheaths, are good nesting ground for pig-ticks, which may swarm in hundreds on to arms and legs. When this happens with intolerable itching, there is no remedy but to start a bonfire with dry leaves, strip, and smoke clothes and body; and be careful, then, that Anacardiaceous leaves have not been gathered in the fire! *L. grandis*, of New Britain, is one of the rare examples of a fan-palm with almost orbicular unsplit leaves [325].

## Livistona

This genus accompanies and, in places, overshadows *Licuala* in its distribution. It has about twenty species, for there is no diversification into the minor habitats of the forest. They are lofty, solitary palms with robust yet elegant trunks, coated below the crown with the fibrous leaf-sheaths, but with tapered leaflets to their fan-leaves; and they differ from *Licuala* in various floral details. The temptation is to conclude that *Livistona* is the progenitor of *Licuala*, as *Chrysalidocarpus* to *Dypsis* in the Madagascan flora, but the association may be superficial. So far as they have been examined, the species of *Livistona* have a diploid chromosome number of twenty-six; the number is either sixteen or twenty-eight in *Licuala*. What this difference signifies is unknown, but *Livistona* agrees with the palms of the *Chamaerops-Pritchardia* alliance (p. 329), whereas *Licuala* is excluded and, with *Washingtonia* (2n = 24) sets a problem. Beccari and others have considered *Livistona* as the tropical Asian ally of the American *Brahea* and *Erythaea*, and this brings in the American *Sabal* and *Copernicia*, with the same chromosome number. Clearly there is need for much more research before we can appreciate either these figures, the value of the genera, or their biogeography.

The great height of the palms has excluded them from the ecological studies that have been made in the eastern tropics. We know little of their habits, except in the case of the relict *L. mariae*, stranded in a few sunken river-beds in the heart of Australia, where they form the Palm Valley of the Finke River in the MacDonnell Ranges, west of Alice Springs (p. 247). As ornamental palms, Livistonas excel in the combination of elegant fan-leaves and open bunches of orange, red, and purple fruits. The large, tough, bright brown, and beautifully woven fibrous bandages which wrap the leaf-bases are natural fabric that must have led the way to weaving in India and China.

## Lodoicea

On two small islands of the Seychelles group in the Indian Ocean, far off the course of mammalian and human evolution, where *Calamus* never reached, there dwells the vegetable goliath known as the double coconut because its enormous fruit, when split open, resembles two coconuts joined as Siamese twins. Botanically it has been misnamed, *Lodoicea maldivica*. The nuts, bouncing down hill and splashing into the sea, have for millennia been washed up with its other dead on the shores of the Maldive Islands, and from thence they became known to Indians and, so, to Europeans. Fables arose about this origin and imagined that gigantic kelps or marine palms, even the Garden of Eden, were the source of the nuts, but the fictions were dispelled when Mahé de La Bourdonnais (1699–1753) saw the living palm in 1743 on his 'Isle of Palms', which is now known as Praslin. Others attribute the discovery to his compatriot du Roslan when in 1770 he found it on two other little islands nearby, Curieuse and Round [326].

There are about thirty-three islands, as granite mountain tops of pre-Cambrian age, emerging from the Indian Ocean to form the Seychelles group [327]. Praslin is eight miles long, one to three wide. Curieuse, just to the north, is two miles by one. Round Island, off

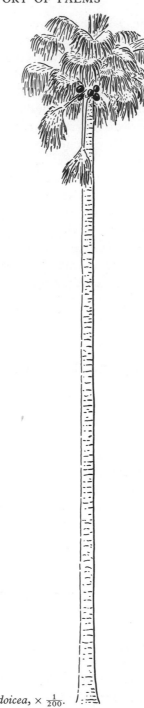

Figure 127. *Lodoicea*, $\times \frac{1}{200}$.

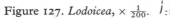

the east tip of Praslin is less than half a mile wide. On Praslin and Curieuse the palms thrive from the valleys and headlands to the hill-tops of several hundred feet, though developing their greatest stature in the valleys. Many have been destroyed by man, but there are two national reserves on Praslin amounting to more than five thousand palms. They are extinct on Round Island which carries only the traces of the trunk-bottoms. It is the habit of these huge palms to develop at the very base a kind of socket in which they fit into the deep, red, laterite soil of the decomposed granite. The socket has the form of a shallow, stout bowl one and a half to two and a half feet wide and six to ten inches deep, made of extremely dense lignified ground-tissue, like the shell of the coconut, and perforated where the roots issue as strands half to one inch thick. These sockets are scattered over Round Island. Neither the palm nor a socket has been found on other islands of the group.

The giant survives on two remote little islands. The fruits, thirty to forty lbs., even fifty, in weight cannot travel uphill and, with a specific gravity of 1·2, sink in water. Hence they sprout in the valleys and on hillsides, where they are caught up, while the palms on the ridges must have descended from parents on higher ridges that have disappeared. Botanically we build up the vista of the old Gondwana tableland between south-east Africa and India, where over one part there was an immense forest of *Lodoicea*, dropping its Brobding-nagian apples and sheltering the lemurs. But what and where were its ancestors?

As a Borassoid palm, the immediate ally seems to be *Borassus* itself, but the single nut of *Lodoicea* is very different from the relatively small, three nuts in the fruit of *Borassus*. The only other Borassoid genus that has the tendency to divide the growing nut into lobes is *Borassodendron* with a single species in north Malaya. It has three nuts to the fruit as in *Borassus*, but each is partially divided internally by seven or eight ridges. Both these genera have the male flowers reduced to six stamens, while *Lodoicea* has fourteen or more and is placed for this reason by some near to the Mascarene *Latania*, (branched male inflorescences, one to three small nuts in the fruit). Yet anatomically, *Lodoicea* comes nearer to *Borassodendron* [328]. The conclusion must be that *Lodoicea* is both an extreme relic of very ancient palm geography and a summit of palm evolution around which, at distances of one to three thousand miles, there are other descendants of its ancestry. The massive, unbranched male and

313

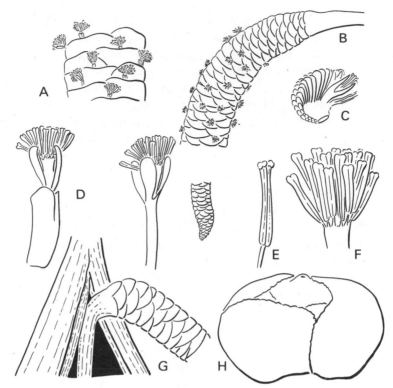

Figure 128. *Lodoicea*. A, part of a male spike with open flowers, × ¼. B, base of a male inflorescence, × ⅛. C, cluster of male flowers as a spikelet in the axil of a bract, × ½. D, male flowers, × 1½. E, stamen, × 8. F, stamen cluster, × 5. G, male spike emerging through the split leaf-base, × ⅛. H, female flower, × ½. (A, D, E, after Bailey, 1942; B, C, F–H, after Hooker, 1827.)

female spikes, borne on separate trees, and the one immense seed derived from an ovary with three ovules cannot be considered primitive any more than the immense costapalmate leaves; but the female flower is the most massive in the plant world and may have inherited this size from the durian-like ancestry of palms. It is necessary to think back to the progenitors of *Phoenix*, *Hyphaene*, *Caryota*, and the Lepidocaryoid palms, the range of which lies to west, north, and east of the outpost of *Lodoicea*.

The size of this palm may be conveyed in these points:–
Trunk up to one hundred feet in height, about one foot thick throughout its length, except the base; estimated at one to several centuries old.

Leaf-stalk eight to twenty feet long, to thirty feet in saplings;

blade ten to sixteen feet long, six to eight feet wide; at first developing twelve leaves in the young crown, the leaves opening at intervals of nine months, (giving the total leaf-age as eighteen years, or nine years of photosynthetic activity).

Male and female spikes four to six feet long, three to four inches thick, emerging through the split leaf-bases; female flowers two inches wide, five to thirteen per spike; palms beginning to flower at twenty to forty years of age.

Fruit eighteen inches long, several in a cluster; full-sized after twelve months, but not maturing till six years old; weight thirty to forty (−50) lbs., or about that of a bunch of coconuts.

Germination after about a year on the ground; seedling remaining attached to the nut for three to four years; cotyledon stalk three to twelve feet long.

## Metroxylon

The landscape of the sago palms, which make this Lepidocaryoid genus, is one of the most fantastic and Palaeozoic that can greet the eye. They are hapaxanthic palms with enormous terminal inflorescences, in the manner of *Corypha*, but they produce these inflorescences two to four times as frequently, and their leaves are pinnate. Furthermore, as suckering palms, they build up gigantic swards that invade the derelict sago-villages. Seven or eight species have been recognized in eastern Malaysia and Polynesia, from the Moluccas to Fiji, but another is now added which was formerly given a separate genus *Coelococcus*. It is a solitary palm without suckers and it is not hapaxanthic but has the usual succession of lateral inflorescences developed from below upwards. This anomalous species is the Caroline ivory-nut palm, *M. amicorum* of Micronesia. It is not a sago-palm but one that supplies vegetable ivory from the endosperm of the large seeds. All the species, however, are inadequately known because their parts are much too big for ordinary systematic procedure in the herbarium. They require to be studied in the field and compared in cultivation in a tropical botanical garden: there, it is to be hoped, *M. amicorum* may be hybridized with a normal hapaxanthic species. It is not really certain whether the inflorescence is truly terminal in the hapaxanthic species or falsely so in that it may arise from the axil of a subterminal and imperfectly developed leaf [328a]. Even whether the far eastern species may or may not produce suckers is also uncertain. The genus should supply the critical evidence to decide which method

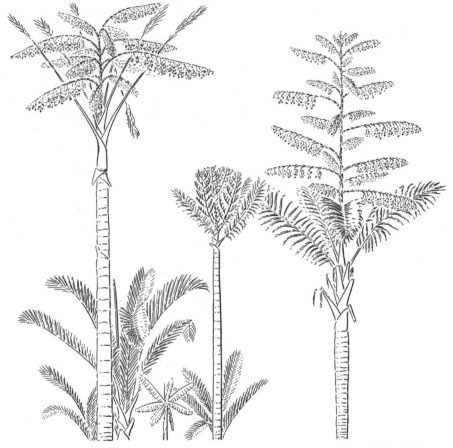

Figure 129. *Metroxylon* with terminal inflorescences. Left, *M. rumphii* developing suckers; centre, the New Guinea species (? *M. oxybracteatum*) with erect inflorescence branches; right, *M. salomonense* of the Solomon Islands, hapaxanthic without suckers; × $\frac{1}{200}$.

of flowering, the terminal and hapaxanthic or the lateral, is primitive and which mode of growth, the solitary or the tufted.

*M. sagus* with smooth leaf-bases and *M. rumphii* with spiny are the most commonly cultivated in villages. They are wild in the lowland swamps of New Guinea and New Britain but whether they are native or introduced to the Moluccas is unknown, though a third species *M. squarrosum* is said to occur there; they are certainly not native in western Malaysia. Eastwards there are *M. bougainvillei* (Bougainville Island), *M. salomonense* (Solomon Islands) which is scarcely distinct, *M. warburgii* (New Hebrides), *M. vitiense* (Fiji), *M. upolense* (Samoa), and the Caroline *M. amicorum* [329]. Unlike the New Guinea and Moluccan species which inhabit lowland swamps and have eighteen vertical series of scales on the oblong fruits, the more easterly species grow on hillsides and have twenty-four to twenty-eight vertical series of scales on their more or less globose fruits. Now this insular distribution does not accord with the origin of so central and important a genus as *Metroxylon* in the Lepidocaryoid subfamily. Island-hopping, as it is sometimes called, concerns the distribution of species but not the making of a palm genus and, even if it is supposed to have arisen in Cretaceous New Guinea or the Melanesian foreland [330], there has still to be explained how the stock of the genus got there.

By far the most Lepidocaryoid palms are rattans (chapter 9). The tree-genera are the fan-leafed *Mauritia* and its allies in tropical America, and the pinnate-leafed genera *Raphia* (Africa), *Eugeissona* and *Salacca* (south-east Asia, west Malaysia), *Pigafetta* (Sumatra, Celebes), and *Metroxylon*. The most derived of these are the dioecious fan-leafed American genera, but they are said to be more nearly related anatomically with *Metroxylon*. *Pigafetta* and *Salacca* are dioecious and, thus, more advanced than *Metroxylon*. *Raphia*, geographically so distant from *Metroxylon*, differs in its ruminate endosperm, in the arrangement of the flowers having the female flowers in the lower part of the spikes, the male flowers in the upper part, and in its lateral inflorescences. *Metroxylon* has a female, or bisexual flower, and a male flower in pairs throughout the spikes, in much the same manner that the dioecious *Calamus* has a female and a neuter flower in the female spikes. The most central position, geographically and structurally, is occupied by the very problematic *Eugeissona* (p. 180). For the origin of *Metroxylon* it is necessary to think of the intermediate between it and the ancestor of *Eugeissona*. Thus, *Metroxylon* takes one back to the continental Asian origin of the subfamily, where *Pholidocarpus* and *Teysmannia* are Coryphoid relics (p. 176).

Sago is the starch extracted from the stems where it has been stored as the excess of vegetative growth preparatory to the hapaxanthic flowering. The stout trunks take about fifteen years to reach the flowering stage, when they are about thirty feet high and almost as many inches thick; in *M. salomonense* the age may be twenty years [331]. They must be cut down two or three years before the inflorescence has begun to form and drain away the starch, if the

317

maximum amount of sago is to be won. Villagers become skilled in estimating the right age and, according to Burkill, they may make experimental borings into the trunk to determine its state of development [332]. Sometimes the terminal bud is cut off to ensure no loss of starch into the inflorescence. There are, also, rare trunks which are naturally sterile and accumulate exceptional amounts of starch. The yield from ordinary palms varies from 250–650 pounds per trunk; that from naturally sterile trunks is 900 pounds; and exceptional yielders are said to give up to 1,200 pounds. Barrau estimates the yield from an acre with twenty-five trunks that are worth felling at 6,250–8,750 pounds of crude starch; allowing thirty to forty per cent of weight for the water content, this is the equivalent of seven to ten million calories in food-value. 'The huge Metroxylon forests of New Guinea represent enormous potential resources in starch' [333].

The best account of sago-life is that related by Wallace from the island of Ceram, a brief extract of which is given on p. 33 [334]. The filled trunk is cleaned of its leaves and split open. The interior is chopped, gouged, and scraped out, and the bits are pounded in water to enable the starch grains to escape from the cells. The pulp is washed, kneaded, and washed again. It may be used immediately or, after drying with moderate heat, it can be kept as sago-flour. The refuse begins to decay at once and generates a foul, sour putrefaction. Poor quality sago is tainted in this way. The better quality is made by the Chinese method which scrapes the filled trunks from the outside and obviates the decomposition which sets in as soon as the trunk is split open and a large extent of tissue is exposed to the air. Pearl sago of varying size is made according to the degree of agitation given to the vessel in which the starch-grains are settling and rolling together. Most of the sago to be had now, however, in shops is derived from the root of the Euphorbiaceous tapioca-plant *Manihot*.

Sago-leaves produce the best attap, or palm thatch, which is serviceable for seven or more years. The trunk and leaf-stalks can be used as timber; the granaries of rice-fields are often built from sago-palms. Strangely enough, with so much good food in the trunk, the cabbage 'is bad food . . . by eating much of it dropsy and diarrhoea are caused' [335].

## Chapter 14

# Generic Notes
Nipa – Phoenix – Pritchardia – Raphia – Roystonea – Sabal –
How to climb

### Nipa

The nipa palm, which is the sole species of its genus, has been mentioned frequently in the preceding pages. It needs mentioning again and again. It is an advanced palm (p. 251) that has existed since the Cretaceous period with so little variation as to be the record of, perhaps, a single species over one hundred million years in spite of its migrations with the Tethys Sea (p. 250); and in this satisfactory state it occupies still to the exclusion of all other palms in south east Asia and Australasia the brackish tidal zone of the primitive riverine habitat. It shows how flowering plants conquered the land in their final form long before animals, for nipa dominates in pure stands miles of river-bank on all the major rivers in its vast geographical range. It extends from Ceylon and the Bay of Bengal to the Philippines, Carolines, Solomons, and Queensland; that it is not in Fiji, Samoa, or New Caledonia may be a matter of habitat. Over this range it is almost without structural variation; there are said to be two kinds in Malaya differing merely in the tilt of the leaflets. To suggest that there may be a rate of evolution applicable to plants, far less to living organisms in general, is absurd in the light of this ancient, yet modern, most widely distributed palm which must have been represented by millions of individuals coming and going century by century for a million centuries. How long, then, did it take to evolve? The origin of palms, cognate with the origin of flowering plants, has shattering antiquity; the genetic code has an impregnable stolidity. There are no dwarf, slender, neotenic nipa-allies, none with small undivided leaves, none with simplified inflorescences, no fan-leafed derivatives, and no indication of the usual trends in palms. If spines, an aerial trunk, a terminal paniculate inflorescence with bisexual flowers, and

319

scaly fruits are restored to *Nipa* on the principle of palm evolution, the result would be something like the stout sago-palms of the problematic genus *Eugeissona*, centred in the hinterland of the nipa rivers of western Maylasia. An affinity between *Nipa* and the Lepidocaryoid palm is borne out by the strong resemblance of their spiny pollen grains.

Griffith, in his lonely meditations, pondered the nature of *Nipa* [336]. The branching inflorescence with many large bracts, the compact male spikes, the dense head of female flowers with much reduced perianth, the short stout stigma on the ovary with one ovule, and the compact head of nuts, are all so remarkably like *Pandanus* that it is really the pinnate leaf that decides the issue whether *Nipa* is palm or pandan. What, then, if the pandan-leaf is derived from a spiny pinnate-leaf of palm-type? Are the pandans, belonging to the Old World and predominantly Malaysian like nipa, related to its ancestors or a parallel and, if so, from what? How does the genetic code of *Pandanus* differ from that of *Nipa*? Both are stolidly consistent, though *Pandanus* has the terminal inflorescence while *Nipa* has the lateral. The pandan stem is commonly erect, tree-like, and branching but there are many stemless, tufted species suckering in the manner of *Nipa*. Into this mystification comes *Sararanga* with its branched, extended inflorescence to show, as the pre-pandan, the origin of the condensed heads of *Pandanus*. Yet, this lengthened inflorescence is merely the paniculate palm-inflorescence which must have preceded the compact state of *Nipa*. The two run parallel and what a wonderful hybrid may be raised between *Nipa* and *Sararanga*!

The soft muddy banks in the brackish, tidal portions of rivers are the habitat of the nipa palm. It does not front the sea as the mangrove trees do, and it does not extend into the fresh-water tidal swamps. It may grow with the mangrove tree *Sonneratia* but more generally its stands lack any overshadowing canopy. Thus they can be recognized easily and studied from the air. Probably the wide coast of Sarawak offers the best opportunities. Here it was that the first white Raja observed that the nipa palm always grows on banks that are steep, where the section of the river or stream is U-shaped, and boats may come close alongside. It does not grow on the shelving banks preferred by the mangrove trees and pandans. On the steep banks the germinating nut is stranded, to root and slowly build up the rosette of large leaves up to twenty-five feet long. Their bases are expanded into broad, thick, pedestals which, permeated with large air-spaces, float the rosette on the semi-liquid mud while the roots, also permeated with air-channels, anchor it.

The rosette begins to flower at four years of age when it begins also to branch and produce side rosettes. An old plant may be surrounded with a dozen such rosettes. How they die or intersperse themselves is not known, but there are often sufficient gaps between the rosettes for a narrow canoe to pass at high tide, and at low tide there can be seen small aroids (*Aglaonema*), creeping plants (*Herpestis*), and the mangrove *Acanthus* growing on the intervening mud. If the bank is being undercut, the rosettes subside into the river and are carried away as floating islets to die in the salt water and eventually to disintegrate where they are washed up in the estuary or on the neighbouring parts of the coast. Despite the copious supply of water where nipa grows, it is far from being a delicate marsh plant. Its stomata seem particularly inactive [337], but there is no knowledge of the water-relations of nipa [338].

When the inflorescences are nearly ready to open, the spathes turn a peculiar warm, terra-cotta red which recalls so strongly the colour of rubber hot-water bottles that one is tempted to feel if they are also hot. We have not measured the temperature, but they are distinctly hot to the cheek and, when the flowers open, they smell exactly like rubber hot-water bottles. This tremendous physiological activity, in part respiratory, of massive and actively growing inflorescences is well known in the case of some aroids where, indeed, the high temperature is part of the attraction to the insects, but nothing seems to be known of the pollination of nipa.

According to Blume [339], the fruits remain attached to the inflorescence heads for several years, but it is not my experience and, if the inflorescence stalks are cut, the fruits soon drop off as the stalk dries out, for which reason it is impossible to make intact dried specimens.

The young nipa inflorescence is tapped for the sugary juice that will flow from it. When the fruit is beginning to form and the inflorescence stalk to curve, this stalk is pommelled for several days with a stick. Then the bruised part is cut across and a collecting vessel attached below the cut end. A thin slice is removed daily to open a clean unfermented surface for the flow which may then be continued for two to three months, but it is said that the flow diminishes when the stalk is cut down to the region where the nodes of the lower spathes are becoming crowded. The sugary juice soon ferments into nipa-wine and this, in turn, goes in a few days into vinegar. The juice is either evaporated to produce the brown molasses-like nipa sugar, usually sold in thick discs, or it is distilled, after fermentation, to produce arrack. It is estimated that an acre of nipa-palms will provide 3,200 gallons of sugary liquid or twenty-eight hundredweight of sugar. At one time there was a proposal to make power-alcohol for internal combustion engines from the vast number of nipa palms in Borneo, but the petroleum industry would not consent [340].

The adult leaves are cut for palm-thatching of high quality, yet not so durable as that from the sago-palms *Metroxylon*. The unopened, but nearly full-grown leaves, are cut to make cigarette-papers which are stripped from the surface-tissue of the leaflets. The endosperm of the immature fruits is soft and edible, like that of the coconut. The trimmed leaflets are also used for basketry, matting, and hats. The adult leaves, cut off at the very base, are tied in bundles and used as floats in the sea to attract fish; the stout leaf-bases, containing many air-spaces, act as the floats to the submerged leaves. Thus the nipa, with its many uses, suffers greatly as mature leaves, young leaves, and inflorescences are drained away. Near villages its appearance is often debilitated but most nipa-regions are little worked, if at all, and so long as this is so, it is false to assume that the world has insufficient food. There is enormous, untapped, photosynthetic wealth in the nipa beds.

Brown treacly nipa sugar and white aromatic coconut milk from the grated endosperm poured on sago-puddings made from the sago of *Metroxylon*, make the 'three-palm pudding' which should terminate every curry repast.

## Phoenix

This genus contains the date-palm *P. dactylifera*, perhaps the most historic of all palms. It has also great botanical interest. It is the only pinnate-leafed genus with pointed and induplicate leaflets. They are leathery, spiky at the tip, reduced to spikes towards the leaf-base, often glaucous (or grey-green with a waxy bloom, like the fierce-eyed Athena), and without a midrib. Thus, near at hand, *Phoenix* is the easiest of palms to distinguish. From a distance it can be recognized from the rough trunk, covered with persistent leaf-bases, and the large crown of many, stiff, spreading leaves. The female flowers are primitively apocarpous, and all the species are dioecious. The fleshy fruit is stoneless, for the 'stone' is the seed (p. 183). The alliance of the genus is with the fan-leafed Coryphoid palms, both in respect of the induplicate leaflet and in microscopic structure, as if *Phoenix* were the modified survivor of their apocarpous, drupaceous, and pinnate-leafed ancestors. If the leaf of *Phoenix* were shortened into the fan-shape, the genus would closely resemble *Chamaerops* and its Asiatic ally *Trachycarpus* which border the northern boundary of the natural range of *Phoenix* from West Africa to China. If this is the true interpretation of *Phoenix*, then it follows that the modern Coryphoid genera may have descended along several distinct lines from the ancestral and extinct subfamily. Reports of hybrids between *Phoenix* and *Chamaerops* are, however, fabulous [341].

Ten or twelve species can be distinguished, but this does not mean that every *Phoenix* palm can be ascribed exactly to one of them. The species are spread at intervals and in certain habitats over the great range of distribution. Where they meet, they seem to intergrade by hybridization. It is well known from the records of botanical gardens, where several species are cultivated and their seeds are raised, that they will hybridize. The pollen is blown by wind and the effect on these dioecious plants is promiscuous. The chromosomes have been found in all the species that have been studied to be remarkably alike in size and shape, and constant in number ($2n = 36$) so that there is no structural barrier to their pairing in meiosis to form pollen-grains or egg-cells [342]. Even the Canary Island species *P. canariensis*, most readily distinguished by its very stout trunk and huge crown of up to two hundred leaves which are not glaucous, and so isolated geographically, can hybridize with others, when grown with them, and its pollen can set the fruit on the date-palm. All who have studied the genus carefully agree that specific limits are hard to draw [343]. Here is a genus of ancient mien, broken up over its ancient range into numerous species, yet despecifying when the plants are re-assembled.

The date-palm flowers in February and March in North Africa at the beginning of the hot, dry season. It needs a temperature over $65°$ F, and rain is inimical because it destroys pollen, stigmas, and young fruit. The same requirement holds, it seems, with the wild species of India and Ceylon where under monsoon conditions they flower with one exception, from December to March during the dry winter. *Phoenix* is a seasonal genus and this may be the decisive factor in its distribution affecting even the widespread African *P. reclinata*, and that which halts its species at the rain forest. The estuarine *P. paludosa* of Bengal proceeds down the west coast of the Malay

Peninsula to Selangor where the thunderstorms obliterate the effect of the monsoon. The exception is the so-called wild date-palm *P. sylvestris* of India. It flowers in the hot wet season and fruits in the dry winter; it is now so much planted that its natural range is uncertain, but it seems to have been the greater part of central India from the foothills of the Himalayas southwards.

Specific differences are found in size of trunk and leaf, relative lengths of calyx and corolla, size and colour of fruit, size and shape of seed, and embryo-position (figure 103). But, with experience, it is not difficult to distinguish the species by their habit, shape of crown, tilt of leaf, and so on. The possible extent of variation, however, is shown by the fact that there are hundreds of varieties of the date-palm. It is the tallest. It can reach over eighty feet high and live well over a century, the greatest part of this time in good bearing. *P. canariensis* is the most massive. In contrast there are short-stemmed and stemless species which sucker freely and build close tufts; they resemble greatly the small sapling states of the larger species; for instance *P. acaulis* (north India, Burma), *P. humilis* (India, south China), *P. pusilla* (south India, Ceylon), and the dwarf *P. arabica*, recognized by Burret on his Arabian journey as allied with *P. caespitosa* of Somaliland [344]. Most of the species are well described by Blatter and illustrated by McCurrach.

Phoenix, meaning purple or red, was the Greek name for a person of Phoenicia where the Tyrian purple was supposed to have been first won from the poisonous shell fish *Murex*. The Phoenicians possessed the date-palm with its red-brown to purple fruits and the name was transferred in Greek to the palm. Herodotus distinguished the male and female trees but, in a way of grammar, had the habit of making the female masculine. Thus *Phoenix*, the palm-genus, is not the fiery bird that never dies. The specific epithet *dactylifera* means finger-bearing, from the finger-like appearance of the fruits, and the Greek word dactylus was transferred to the date-fruit. Our word date comes from this source and both words are said to be cognate with the Hebrew dachel or finger [344a]. Sanskrit had no word for the palm or its fruit, wherefore it is argued that ancient India did not have the date-palm. Since it has never been found wild but only in or about cultivation from West Africa to India, its origin is problematic. It is known to have been in the Middle East since 5000 BC [345].

The date-palm was sanctified to Apollo by the Greeks. The waving frond became the emblem of their victories. It passed to the winners of the public games, and to the triumphs and arena of Rome. It welcomed the Holy Entry to Jerusalem and it survives in the Feast of the Tabernacles from the time when the tents in the desert were made from palm leaves. Coins of Tyre and Sidon were designed with the palm tree, as happens now with postage stamps [346]; 'to commemorate the conquering of the Jews and the destruction of Jerusalem by Titus, a coin was struck by Vespasian, representing the figure of a weeping woman sitting under a palm tree' [347]. Jericho was the city of palms. The fir of the north and the phoenix of the Middle East are woven into Christianity, but the Far East in bustling economy has provided us with another and more durable leaf, the cycad's, which usurps the palm by our bitter monuments [348].

In India, which is the headquarters of the genus and perhaps, therefore, near its source, there occurs *P. sylvestris* which is very like the date-palm and is generally supposed to have been its progenitor. There are difficulties. The fruit of *P. sylvestris* is dry and astringent; yet so are some dates. The flower differs in small specific ways, and the leaflets are not placed so obliquely on the leaf-axis. More important is the fact that *P. sylvestris* is a solitary palm, unlike most species of the genus, and in contrast to the date-palm in which the suckers, produced after six or more years of growth, are the chief means of propagation. Since one male date-palm is enough to pollinate a hundred female palms, propagation by seed which will give fifty per cent of male plants is wasteful; they cannot be recognized until they begin to flower at seven or eight years of age; the suckers from female trees begin to bear dates at five years. Seed, too, may not come true because of cross-pollination with inferior varieties. It has been argued that domestication would soon select for suckering and so alter the solitary habit of the progenitor, but it is one thing to select a tendency and another to start it. The property of suckering is one of the evolutionary accomplishments of the palms.

The most telling fact against this theory is physiological. *P. sylvestris* is a rain-palm. It can grow with Himalayan pines at five thousand feet. The date-palm needs dry weather to flower, fruit, and propagate itself although it, too, needs an abundant supply of underground water to maintain activity. It can withstand drought, as it can withstand frost, but it will not flower under these conditions. Thus it marks the oases as the outlets of the vast subterranean water-reserves in North Africa. It may be that the large bract covers and protects the inflorescence from rain in India, where insects may be the agent of pollination. It has been suggested, in the absence of any detailed knowledge of the working of *P. sylvestris*, that the date-palm was its adaptation under the conditions of early domestication to the drier climate where civilization was beginning, and thus the date-palm spread from the Middle East across Africa, improving, and settling in greatest number in the Nile Valley. Here it became deified in the early Egyptian dynasties. Temples were made of its trunks and these columns were replaced, as architecture progressed, by stone and granite capped with carved leaves in imitation of the origin of the column; even fences of date-leaves became a motif. Egypt has built up the greatest date-industry. It possesses over five million trees, and this is only half of the number that there were; neglect, war, politics, and the encroaching desert have done away with so many.

The climate of the arid zone from Pakistan to Senegal seems never to have been so bad as it is now. There is much evidence that over-population with deforestation, fire, and over-grazing, especially by goats, has removed a vast savannah, if not a forest belt, out of which has evolved the man-made Sahara. It is not clear that in its distant, prehistoric days Mesopotamia was so inhospitable and suited, therefore, to the progressive evolution of the date-palm from *P. sylvestris*. Undoubted seeds of this species have been found in Egyptian deposits, dated about 14,000BC. [349] Therefore, it seems

Figure 130. East African cave painting representing elephants eating *Phoenix* palms; perhaps the oldest representation of palm natural history (after Fosbrooke, 1951).

rather that *P. sylvestris* has receded with civilization and that the origin of the date-palm may be African. A second suggestion took the African *P. reclinata* as the progenitor. It is a tufted, suckering palm, of shorter stature than the date, and with dry, astringent fruits as *P. sylvestris* but 'the green bunches of fruit, if immersed for twelve hours in water, suddenly assume a rich scarlet hue, and the astringent pulp becomes sweet' [350]. One would like to know more about the hybrids between *P. reclinata* and *P. sylvestris*. The origin of the date-palm is as insoluble as ever and will remain so until there are minds commensurate with the contributions that palms have made to civilization.

The wild date-palm *P. sylvestris* provides mainly a source of palm sugar; its use for toddy and arrack has diminished. The sugar is obtained not from the inflorescence but from the sap which flows out of wounds inflicted on the active part of the trunk within the crown. The tapper first cuts away enough leaves on one side of the stem to expose a clean white surface measuring about twelve inches each way. He then makes a V-shaped incision at the foot of this surface, about three inches wide and half an inch deep. A bamboo spout is put at the base of the V and the sap flows along it into a collecting vessel. The process is mainly nocturnal, the flow declining at sunrise to a minimum at noon or 1 p.m. Every evening for about six days the cut is deepened slightly to renew the flow. After a week a new cut is opened above the first and so on until by the end of the tapping season during the winter months December to March the whole of the exposed surface has been cut out to a depth of three or four inches. A new tapping panel is opened next season above the first on the opposite side of the trunk. Tapping can be continued for many years, even up to forty, and the trunk in consequence acquires a curious zig-zag appearance from the alternate notching. Tapping is usually on the east and west sides of the trunk, the explanation being that the oblique rays of the sun heat the surface and stimulate the flow. Records of the sap collected from single trees vary from four to nineteen litres per day or 250–1,100 litres per tree per season [351].

The date-palm is tapped for the same purpose but so drastically that the stem is killed. The whole central bud is cut out and the sap flows upwards into the central cavity so excavated, whence it is removed. 'Three or four quarts of sap may be obtained daily from a single palm for ten days or a fortnight, after which the quantity lessens, until, at the end of six weeks or two months, the stem is

X.

exhausted, becomes dry, and is used for firewood' [352]. It seems that the date-palm cannot be tapped in the same way as *P. sylvestris*, and that flow in the date-palm is an expression of root-pressure, or the upward flow of sap consequent on the absorption of water by the roots: if not it is purely secretory. The subject has been too great for plant-physiology.

## Pritchardia

Alone among palms in the distant Hawaiian Islands and in some inexplicable way beyond the grasp of our understanding, as if we stood in an intellectual prison and knew that a highway ran without, there thrives the Coryphoid genus *Pritchardia*. With the aspect of *Livistona*, *Sabal*, or *Thrinax*, the unbranched fan-leafed palms of *Pritchardia* have prospered and varied, yet never succumbed to reduction into underground forms; they carry the individuality of *Corypha*, not the tufted habit of *Licuala* and *Chamaerops*. About twenty species have been described, limited in the characteristic manner of insular distribution so that a species occurs only on one island [353]. The larger Hawaii and Oahu are said to have five and six species respectively, Molokai and Kauai four each, and Mawi three. Yet there is doubt whether they are genetically isolated species that cannot interbreed, or merely populations of one or two species isolated by stretches of ocean, mountain ridges, and deep valleys, so as merely to be prevented from interbreeding [354]. They are said to be pollinated by bees, wasps, and other small insects, and to fruit abundantly. Since their ancestor arrived, the offspring has obviously been dispersed through island-making within the whole group which has been subject continually to volcanic action during its existence. If forested originally, the terrain was dissected by deep ravines which would have hastened the isolation of the palms into self-breeding pockets. What remain now on the deforested slopes, ravaged by man and domesticated animals, are only a small part of the number which must have existed formerly. The differences between the so-called species are small peculiarities in leaf and fruit, pronounced more from herbarium study, perhaps, than reality. If the palms were not such tardy objects for research, they would provide an excellent example for enquiry into the micro-evolution of species, similar to the problem of *Sabal* in the Caribbean area, or the continental *Phoenix*.

*Pritchardia* has also two species in Fiji and two in the Tuamotu Islands east of Tahiti. Its presence in Hawaii, therefore, is a

Polynesian problem of dispersal between volcanic islands. It has been suggested that pigeons may have been the agent, but this explanation of island distribution does not explain how the genus reached its Pacific isolation. Beccari related it with the Cuban bottle palm *Colpothrinax wrightii*. The main difference between them is that the dry corolla of *Pritchardia* falls before the stamens open, whereas this structure is rather thick and fleshy in *Colpothrinax* and persistent; there are minor differences in the number of spathes on the inflorescence and in seed structure. Burret agreed with Beccari to call the Cuban palm *Pritchardia wrightii*. Then Beccari associated with *Pritchardia* the Asian and Australasian *Licuala* and *Livistona*, and the American *Brahea*, *Copernicia*, *Erythea*, and *Washingtonia*. He advanced a theory of a land-bridge in the north Pacific between tropical America and Australasia to account for this alliance. However, recent studies on the chromosome numbers in these genera show that the problem is more complicated (p. 311). As with all palm problems, we are still just at the beginning of their unfolding.

## Raphia

The tangled, treacherous, and almost impenetrable swamp forests, which rendered the lowland rivers of the tropics so majestically beautiful and may still be seen, though rarely unmutilated, are the homes of the grand palms. *Metroxylon*, *Nipa*, *Oncosperma* and the peeping *Licuala*, bound up with the whipped rattans of the *Calamus* alliance, distinguish the east. *Mauritia*, *Manicaria* and many Cocoid genera, bound up with the Cocoid *Desmoncus*, distinguish the west. Central Africa is a strange combination. It introduces the problematic Arecoid palms *Podococcus* and *Sclerosperma*, the oil palm *Elaeis*, and this genus *Raphia*, and they are bound up with a few species of *Calamus* and the special African rattans which have the habit of *Desmoncus* (p. 208). Then, to promote the link from east to west, a species of *Elaeis* (*E. melanococca*) and a species of *Raphia* (*R. taedigera*) are at home in the swamps of tropical America. *Nipa* and *Calamus* failed to cross the Atlantic from the east, *Mauritia* and the *Cocos* alliance from the west, but these genera did; they pose one of the unsolved riddles of palm geography.

*Raphia* is the most distinguished African contribution to palms. There are said to be about twenty species, but they are so massive that our knowledge of them is fragmentary and we wait their study by an African botanist. The larger have stout trunks up to forty feet high and pinnate leaves fifty to seventy feet long; they have, in fact, the largest leaves in the world. A stemless species *R. humilis*, is a dwarf with leaves six to ten feet long. *R. sassandrensis* is said to have a creeping trunk. Most appear to be solitary palms but some are tufted in the manner of the sago palms. Thus, *Raphia* has exploited in the usual palm way the African swamp forest.

Figure 131. *Raphia hookeri,* × $\frac{1}{200}$.

The greatest interest centres on the very massive inflorescence. The accounts in the books are conflicting, for they suggest that it is axillary in some species and terminal in others, the trunks of which die down after flowering [355]. The genus seems to come, therefore, in this respect between the fan-leafed American *Mauritia* with axillary inflorescences and the hapaxanthic, pinnate-leafed eastern *Metroxylon* with terminal inflorescence. *Raphia* may hold the clue to decide which is the primitive state. The inflorescences emerge from among the leaves as enormous worms covered with spathes, and they branch into enormous centipedes with the bracts set regularly in two rows as if they were trousers to the legs; the whole construction may be twelve feet long and hang menacingly overhead.

Here is one of the problems which crop up on almost every page of a palm book, and the answers lie far and wide. I may add, almost in postscript as I write, information received about *R. gigantea* in West Africa [356]. It is a tufted species. Each trunk ends with three to five inflorescences produced from the axils of as many reduced leaves, and so it appears to be terminal (plate 18). The uppermost inflorescence is situated so near the true apex of the stem that this, now arrested in growth, is pushed to one side and the last inflorescence appears to be truly terminal. The inflorescences are practically contemporary, though they flower after each other from below upwards in the sequence of their production, and after flowering the trunk dies, to be reproduced by a basal sucker. Each inflorescence emerges through the median nerve of the bract-like leaf which subtends it, and reaches nine or ten feet long. If the production of inflorescences was restricted to the uppermost, then there would be the condition as it appears in *Metroxylon*. If, instead, many leaves produced axillary inflorescences, there would be the condition of *Mauritia* and *Pigafetta*. The Madagascan *R. ruffia* seems to be truly hapaxanthic without suckers. Are there species which are not hapaxanthic, but have a succession of lateral inflorescences?

Palm wine is made from the sap obtained from the African *R. vinifera* and its very close American ally *R. taedigera*. The method of extraction is that adopted for *Phoenix sylvestris*, and consists of cutting out the inflorescence to get at the trunk. Raffia-fibre, bast or bass, is obtained by stripping the fibrous tissue from the upperside of young leaflets. Piassava, or African bass, is derived from the vascular bundles of the leaf-stalk and sheath when these have been retted in water. The seeds of some species are edible when young, whereas those of others are used as fish-poisons [357].

## Roystonea

The royal palms which comprise this genus, formerly known as *Oreodoxa*, are among the largest of Arecoid palms. They come from Central America and the Caribbean region [358]. Twelve species are recognized but intermediates occur which may have arisen through hybridization where the species are cultivated. As ornamentals they are often planted in parks and gardens, and their smooth lofty trunks lend themselves to avenues, those of Rio de Janeiro being among the stateliest. Cuba has four species, including the well-known *R. regia*. Jamaica has two. Trinidad, Porto Rico, and Haiti have each a single species restricted to the island. Then, as continental representatives, there is a species *R. elata* in Florida and another in Venezuela. The distribution is typically Caribbean, and relates Florida with Venezuela, but not the Guianas and Brazil [359]. The geographical differentiation, island by island as with *Pritchardia* in Hawaii, may be as incomplete and so permit hybridization when the species are re-assembled. The massive trunks, which give out a characteristic and fully aqueous sound when slapped, taper slightly from the base where it is swollen by the emergent roots, and enlarge gradually upwards to contract rather sharply below the crown shaft of dark green tubular leaf-bases. They show the delayed thickening of the stem, deferred until the leaves have been shed and often, though erroneously, called secondary thickening.

In all except *R. oleracea* of Trinidad, the leaflets are set in four rows. Every second or third leaflet on each side of the leaf-axis is

Figure 132. Royal palms; left, *Roystonea oleracea* with the leaflets in two rows; right, *R. regia* with the leaflets set in four rows to give the bushy effect; × $\frac{1}{200}$.

stood up or, rather, less displayed by its pulvinus, and its distal half droops down towards the others. In *R. oleracea* the leaflets are set regularly in two ranks; hence this palm, which is the loftiest of all the species, attaining 120 feet, is the most easily recognized from its pectinate crown.

The small purple fruits of *R. regia*, half an inch long, develop in enormous bunches, fifty to sixty pounds in weight, below the crown shaft. In an agricultural manner the oily fruit-wall is used in Cuba to fatten hogs. There ensues a skilful method of cutting the bunches before they are fully ripe, to prevent the fruits falling one by one. Professional climbers, or trepadores, ascend the lofty trunks by means of a pair of ropes. Each has a loop round the trunk and a hanging stirrup. With his foot in one and his thigh in the other, the trepador see-saws his weight from right to left and works the loops upwards with his hands. Arrived at the top he severs the bunch with a stout knife and rides it down an inclined rope from round his waist to his assistant on the ground [360]. The method is an African one and an imported stage in the evolution of palm-climbing (p. 335).

## Sabal

The interest of this Central American genus of fan-palm lies in the north temperate extension of its species, the dwarfing and decumbent habit which several develop, and its relations with surrounding genera. Twenty-five species are recognized but the distinctions between some of them seem rather fine and more of the nature of geographical variations [361]. Their distribution is from Colombia and Venezuela (one species), Panama (one), British Honduras (two), Guatemala (one), Mexico (five), and the South-East United States from south Virginia to Florida (three), to Cuba (two), and Bermuda, Jamaica, Hispaniola, Porto Rico, Bahama Island, St Bartholomew Island, and Trinidad (one species each); the origin of three species is unknown. They have unbranched trunks up to one hundred feet high, clean or more or less covered with persistent leaf-bases, much branched panicled and long-stalked inflorescences of bisexual flowers producing one-seeded berries of small size, and non-ruminate endosperm. They resemble *Copernicia* (ruminate endosperm, Caribbean and South American) and *Washingtonia* (with a stone in the fruit, Mexico, California). The leaves on the larger species are costapalmate as in these two genera, but the leaf-axis curves down conspicuously to give the leaves an arched appearance very much as in the

333

Borassoid *Hyphaene*.

Most species inhabit swampy and sandy coastal regions where they have given rise to practically stemless kinds. These, such as the bush palmetto *S. minor*, appear so different from the tall kinds that they were made into two genera. The small kinds have truly palmate leaves, or the rachis is so short that they are practically palmate, with the leaflets separate almost to the base; the leaf-stalks are unsplit at the base, and the seedling stems have the curious faculty of growing downwards into the ground as they enlarge. There is, however, much evidence to suggest that this is the seedling-sapling state of all the species and that the larger, on growing trunks into the air, become costapalmate with less divided leaves but with split leaf-base. Indeed, it has been found that some species, such as *S. minor*, though commonly without a trunk or with only creeping stems, may develop trunks to ten or more feet high and begin to assume the form of the taller species; such forms have been described as distinct species. Similarly it has been observed that lofty species, as *S. palmetto*, may begin to flower and fruit when merely one to two feet and emerging from the sapling form. Hence, as Bailey suggested for *S. minor*, the short species seem to be neotenic derivatives persisting in their dwarf sapling state, adaptable to swampy riversides, as the nipa-palm of the Old World, or to coastal sand-dunes, for which there seems to be no counterpart among the palms of the Old World (p. 246). Thus, the genus provides another instance of the main way in which palm species have evolved by persisting in the youthful state with short stature fit for other ecological niches. The decumbent stems, producing abundant adventitious roots, are typical of dune and marsh plants. What is puzzling is to know if these prostrate stems remain unbranched like the aerial trunks, or whether they ramify by means of suckers. When we read of vast extents occupied by thickets of these dwarf palms, it is never explained if each crown has grown from one seed or if they are the product of branching in the manner of *Nipa*, *Phoenix* and the creeping pandans. It would, indeed, be remarkable if these species of *Sabal* represented the unbranched pachycaul contribution to dune and marsh vegetation. The saw-palmetto, *Serenoa*, is a branching palm of similar habitats and, though of close resemblance with *Sabal*, its fruit has the more or less apical stigma found in *Acoelorrhaphe* (*Paurotis*), *Brahea*, and *Erythea*, not the basal stigma of *Sabal* [362]. The affinity of *Serenoa* within the complex of American Coryphoid palms is far from clear.

## How to Climb

To gather fruit before it falls and to tap, villagers must climb. To study what is going on in the palm crown, scientists must ascend. The latest method, combining a small platform, table, and gearing, is the palm bicycle [363]. A metal framework encircles the trunk and is held in position by two horizontal rollers pressed to opposite sides of the trunk, one above the other, by stout springs. The weight of the scientist on the platform is also distributed to the rollers and improves

Figure 133. Climbing the palm. Upper figures from left to right; the African on the oil palm; Rumphius' Amboinese on the coconut; the Tamil on the coconut; a Bornean Dusun on the coconut; a coconut monkey. Lower figures from left to right; the Brazilian climbing the coconut in the improved African way; Singhalese rope-work. (After Rumphius, Lau, and Hodge.)

335

their contact but, as the construction under load weighs 250 pounds, there is a safety brake for complete security. Chains connect the rollers to a wheel with a handle on the right of the operator; he turns the handle, engages the rollers, and causes them to ride, somewhat bumpily, up or down the trunk. Thus the ladder has been superseded, though it is still necessary for rough trunks as in the oil-palm estates. Most climbing, however, is still carried out by the human animal.

Primitively he climbs as a monkey. Partly embracing the trunk with outstretched arms and hands pressed to it, he works his way up by squatting, straightening, squatting and so on: with heavy body he cannot hop neatly upwards with feet close together. Then, with shorter arms and longer legs, he prefers to walk. With curved back and straddled legs on either side of the trunk, he steps upwards pausing now and then to squat in monkey fashion. Others, less skilful, clasp, heave, and perch with feet, to repeat the process which readily degenerates into clumsy swarming. The long-legged Tamil of Madras puts his feet sideways and walks up in bandy-legged fashion. He notches with knife or axe trunks which are habitually climbed and takes enormous strides impossible for men of lesser stature.

Sagaciously the human climber introduces a short length of rope to brace either shoulders or feet. If the rope passes round the shoulders, it is worked up the trunk by the arms as the legs are straightened. If it passes round the feet, they brace it against the trunk . and the arms are used for steadying. The foot-brace seems to be popular in Asia, the shoulder-brace in Africa. America has lagged behind until the African introduced his improved method with hanging loops. Rarely the two braces are worked together, for it seems rather difficult to couple the manipulation with the foot-work.

The African improvement turns the horizontal braces into two stirrups, one for the thigh and the other for the foot. There are now two ropes, made primitively of palm or bark fibre as before; each is fitted to the stature of the climber and has a loop at either end. One rope loops the trunk and a thigh just above the knee. The other loops the trunk below the first and makes a stirrup for the opposite foot. By putting the weight on one or other leg, the unstretched loop can be moved up the trunk. Holding the neck of each trunk loop, then, with either hand and see-sawing the body from one to other purchase on thigh or foot, the ropes are moved alternatively upwards, and the strain on the bowed back is removed. Thus the oil palm *Elaeis* is climbed in Africa, the coconut palm in Brazil, and the royal palm *Roystonea* in Cuba [364].

In parts of Ceylon, where coconut palms are tapped extensively for toddy to be distilled into arrack, adjacent palms are connected by an elaborate cat-walk from crown to crown [365]. Ladders are constructed on the trunks cheaply and ingeniously by tying partly split leaf-stalks to them, the split fibrous stalk making the rope which attaches the unsplit leaf-base as the step. Coir-ropes, made from the husk of the coconut, are passed from crown to crown and twisted round the tops of the trunks; one serves as a foot-rope and two as guide-ropes for the hands. Along these the skilled toddy-collector passes until his collecting gourd is full; he lets it down to an assistant on the ground who tips it into the collecting tub and returns the empty.

In Lower Burma, Thailand, Malaya, Sumatra, and, perhaps, the Nicobar and Andaman Islands, where the pig-tailed monkey *Macaca nemestrina* is wild, there is quite a different method of collecting coconuts. A monkey is employed of such intelligence, much beyond that of its congeners, that it is deemed to have affinity with the African baboon. Young males, a year old, are trapped in the forest. They are taught by word of command to twist the nuts from the inflorescences, which they learn to do with one hand and the opposing foot. If the nut sticks, the twist is reversed by changing limbs as often as may be necessary. As it crashes to the ground, the monkey jumps up and shakes a frond in excitement. So the man stands below and shouts to the monkey which he holds by a thin cord attached to a copper collar round its neck. He must keep the cord from entangling and he must guard against the falling objects which the monkey delights in knocking down. It is taught, also, to jump from crown to crown where the palms are close enough, and to obviate the need to descend and re-ascend. All these accomplishments intrigue the monkey as much as they assist the man. A good monkey, clever, strong, and fearless, is worth five to ten pounds, but the financial transaction is easier than the change of master. Such a monkey, four or five years in age, may collect forty to fifty nuts in a morning. As a Malay once sighed, it was more use to him than his children [366].

Here is an opportunity for modern cinematography to make a film of how palms are climbed, and how they are tapped, which would be entertaining and, in this fast changing world, documentary.

## Chapter 15

# Palm Classification

THE USE of a classification is obviously to enable those interested in a set of objects to identify them and apply to them names of international acceptance. By this means we can all hope by the spoken and written words of a classification to intend the same things. But there is a deep and extensive background to biological classification, which has been employed repeatedly throughout this book. By its very classes, biological classification assimilates knowledge. The names *Borassus* and *Phoenix*, or Lepidocaryoid and Arecoid palms, betoken far more than a string of specific or generic names which they cover. There is a conceptual or philosophic background to this kind of classification which leads to much misapprehension.

Whatever the manner in which life arose, whether in one or a few or many forms, it is certain that ever since its beginning it has been diversifying exponentially. Novelty has renovated and enlarged the environment, which has grown fitter for more life. The content of living nature has been increasing, and we enjoy a crest of evolution. It is the staggering specificity of living things which forces the biologist to classify. Throughout his researches he compares, but he cannot think of all and sundry at once and deal with them in their multitudes. The numbers must be reduced to manageable proportions. He has developed the system of genera, promulgated by Linnaeus, and extended this into a hierarchy of increasing dignity, with the intention that the name of a higher class denotes all the significant properties of the lower classes over which it reigns. A high class is not a king that rules but a book that contains. The billions of individual plants are marshalled into several hundred thousand species, these into thousands of genera, these again into fewer tribes and fewer families to be counted in hundreds, and so on through orders and cohorts until there are but a dozen or so divisions of the plant kingdom.

This hierarchy, accepted by international agreement, becomes the

338

staircase of botany, as the animal hierarchy in zoology. The trouble is that, as it is printed in book after book and repeated in lectures to students, it comes to be accepted as a creed. Philosophers come to the building and review its construction and all its appurtenances in the way of herbariums, museums, gardens, and libraries. They wonder what it all implies in the universe of thought, what it signifies to civilization, and how it should be improved. Some approve and limit themselves to minor alterations. The procrustean would have the rooms, at least on one floor, of one size; genera or families should be uniform. Others would be accommodating and fit adjustable partitions; genera and families should be elastic. Others would introduce electronic apparatus to get rid of ageing specialists, whose lives have been devoted to the solution of certain problems; and turn the whole of classification into a cypher. And, yet, there are others who will concede the usefulness of means to identify and recognize, but deny reality to any class of the hierarchy. There is uncertainty and, when this appears, it is necessary to return to the beginning and re-discover the basis.

It is here that palm classification comes in. Its material outstrips conventional methods and cannot be compressed either into herbarium cabinets or into herbarium notions. Palms must be studied in their immensity in nature. They cannot be deduced in a metropolis. What, therefore, is a genus, tribe, subfamily or even a species of palm? It is absurd to suppose that the criteria of herb, ferns, or bacteria can be applied to these massive plants. They must be sought, found, and studied in nature. The hugeness of palms restores the lesson, so easily forgotten, that biological classification deals not with figment but with living things which were before man.

As botanists, we turn to the familiar comparison with the tree of life. Its robust trunk, singular and filled with possibilities, breaks into limbs and branches of diminishing thickness and competence until a multitude of twigs, mostly deprived of further growth, and in innumerable working leaves of short existence. The leaves of a twig may be thought of as the individuals of a species. A cluster of twigs from a branchlet corresponds with a genus; an array of branchlets make a tribe; branches make families, and their union into limbs the orders, classes, or divisions of the stirp or trunk: for in this airy analogy roots do not count. But the limbs were once twigs. As they grew, some were dropped. As more twigs were produced to enlarge the crown, others and even branches were shed, while leaves have

339

always been falling. So individuals die; species die; genera, tribes, and classes become extinct. Occasionally a new twig sprouts from a dormant source and grows into its genera and species; and the lower its origin on the tree, the greater may be its contribution to the new order. Indeed, the trunk may die and a cluster of subsidiary stems, as coppice shoots, may take its place. This is the picture of palm-classification. The ancestral palm family must be deduced, not in armchair, but from the ramifications all over the tropics.

A big alliance of plants has, therefore, very many species, many genera, and successively fewer, but still many, major ranks. Beneath the tree are fallen leaves, twigs, branches, variously dismembered and fragmented. If we would reconstruct the whole it must be done in stages for it has been by this very dismemberment that the tree has taken shape; its discarded or fossil parts cannot simply be put back. Yet as we reconstruct, we find twigs becoming branches, twigs dying with few leaves left, twigs dead but still attached, moribund branchlets and, even, branches. We cannot make a sharp distinction between living and dead or branch and twig, but the final state of the tree is set out in this array, as we can follow in the ranks of classification. We learn that it is the shedding or extinction of parts which has isolated the remaining into the clear categories of branches and branchlets, but that the difficulty in distinguishing smaller branchlets and twigs into discrete units lies in their continued growth or evolution. So the limits of genera and species are often uncertain and cannot be resolved until many minds have decided on the best practical solution; that is, what is most suitable for biology. There have been too few minds concerned with palms. We list two hundred genera and two and a half thousand species, but who knows? Who perceives the limits of the branchlets of the palm branch of the tree of life? Who knows how many tribes, subfamilies, or families should be recognized and how many have become extinct? The treatment is tentative. We respect, though we must weigh and consider, the contribution of the palm-pioneers and specialists. They went over the world to find palms and without this service we should have no adequate outline of the palm branch.

These men did not find one or a few kinds of palm, such as the date, coconut, talipot, and betel palms. In their journeys through the forests they came upon a multitude, which lead them to recognize similar individuals which they called in the usual manner species. They related these species into genera and, when Martius had returned from Brazil, the relationship of genera into tribes began to appear. As the genera multiplied, the tribes multiplied and were aggregated into subfamilies in the old family concept of Palmae. We learn another lesson that it was through big groups that the hierarchy of classification was conceived. *Areca*, *Bactris*, *Chamaedorea*, *Geonoma*, and *Pinanga*, or *Calamus* and its allies were the vigorous shoots with vigorous twigs giving the outline to palm classification. The small and isolated genera as *Phoenix*, *Borassus*, *Nipa*, and *Phytelephas*, without close allies, could make no such detailed contribution, though they could be fitted on to the whole.

Big genera and big families are formidable tasks. Their study demands years of experience, much leisure, and years of comparison. Monographers prefer to leave them. But our predecessors tackled them and with herculean labour built the classification which we must use, even though we perceive many faults. Rectification must come from greater labour. The character of a genus is derived from the properties which its species have in common; the more species the better will be the character of the genus, as Griffith required. One species cannot give a generic character, nor can one genus give a tribal character, nor one tribe that of a family. Yet we find, especially among palms, the anachronism of many genera with one species and, even, subfamilies limited to one genus. This is the artificial result of the system of classification which has been laid on. Consider what different ideas of Leguminosae would be given if, instead of many thousand species, there were one phyllodic *Acacia*, or one apetalous *Saraca*, a clover, or a practically leafless *Lathyrus*. Yet, that is all that *Nipa* can supply for its so-called subfamily.

The nipa palm is a common species represented by billions of individuals among which no one has detected a second species. It differs in so many ways from other palms that it cannot be grouped with their majority. To give it an international name we are obliged to follow the system of binomial nomenclature; that is, it must have a generic name and a specific epithet. So the genus *Nipa* is decreed, not found, and the subfamily *Nipoideae* is decreed, not found, for *Nipa* cannot be attached to any other subfamily though it is clearly a palm in the family Palmae. Thus it is classified out artificially. Now we do not know at what level of evolution the ancestors of *Nipa* acquired these peculiarities, for they are extinct and the traces of *Nipites* add no information in this respect. The capitate inflorescence supposes an ancestor with extended spicate or paniculate inflores-

341

cence, as *Sararanga* is to the screw-pines *Pandanus*, but we do not make two subfamilies of Pandanaceae on this account. A close ancestor of *Nipa* may have had the extended inflorescence and, in accordance, a normal perianth, in which case *Nipa* could be fitted into the subfamily Arecoideae. The same reasoning could be applied to *Phytelephas* to dispose of its subfamily Phytelephanoideae. *Phoenix* with a dozen species is the only genus in the subfamily Phoenicoideae, which is an artefact even if *Phoenix* is a respectable genus. However, the ancestor of *Phoenix* might coincide with that of the subfamily Coryphoideae and the ancestors of both might coincide with those of Borassoideae and Caryotoideae to make a unit contrasting with the remainder of the palms. We could, in fact, make merely two subfamilies according to the leaf-character whether induplicate or reduplicate, though we scarcely know enough about this intricate feature to value it so highly. Several monographers of the palms make the Cocoid and Arecoid subfamilies as tribes of a bigger subfamily Ceroxyloideae and associate with it or place in it the Caryotoideae with induplicate leaf. We must conclude that there are many great uncertainties in the accepted classification of palms; they arise from lack of theory or understanding as well as from lack of information.

The classification, just considered, is called the phyletic, evolutionary, or natural. It allies species into genera, genera into tribes, and tribes into families because their common properties are explicable on the theory of evolution as the heritage from a common ancestor. The result is not perfect, as we have just seen, but it is the goal of biological comparison to produce a classification following as nearly as possible the evolutionary tree with the taxa demarcated through extinction of ancestors. It should give the genetic relationships of the organisms and, thereby, enable facts from other disciplines such as physiology, biochemistry, cyto-genetics, and pathology to be organized in evolutionary sequence.

There are, however, many other ways in which living things can be classified, for instance by their usefulness, their distribution on sea and land or over continents, their colours or smells, their size and shape, and so on. These ways are called artificial or unnatural, because none is necessarily peculiar to one evolutionary direction. No botanist would consider as scientific a major distinction into trees and herbs, poisonous and non-poisonous, or free-living and parasitic, though these features may be peculiar to certain evolutionary lines. Artificial classification tends to cut across evolutionary classification by selecting levels of advancement attained by different lines of evolution in parallel; so it is often called grading. Now it happens that first attempts at a natural classification are nearly always grades, especially when the subject matter is not well understood. More knowledge re-orientates and a later, improved classification sorts the parallel from the phyletic. Linnaeus's system, counting styles and stamens, is forgotten and only that part of Ray's is remembered which counts cotyledons. Palm-classification is young compared with that of well studied groups such as the orchids and the grasses, and it may hold numerous grades. The induplicate *versus* the reduplicate may be such, perhaps also the palmate *versus* the pinnate leaf, because the palmate is surely derived from the pinnate. Both these kinds occur in the Lepidocaryoid palms which appear to be a natural subfamily, well-defined by the remarkable loricate fruit. In this group and, particularly in its great alliance of rattans centred on *Calamus*, as we have pointed out in chapter 9, one should look for the direction of palm-evolution and, thus, the way in which to classify naturally. The real difference between the natural and the artificial methods of classification is that the natural improves with more knowledge whereas the artificial deteriorates.

Artificial classification is most useful in making diagnostic keys to identification. The purpose, now, is not to relate but to separate. Making such keys is an important part of the monographer's work; they compel him to explain succinctly his method. Actually contrasting keys are easier to make and to use than the natural keys for they employ as much as possible superficial characters, while the natural must probe deeply. The monographer tends, therefore, to the diagnostic and to the magnification of differences. He tends to become a splitter who carves up large groups into small, substituting several genera or species where there was one. He works usually with preserved material. With palms he has only bits and, perhaps, some plants in a glasshouse. He cannot consider natural variation because he does not know the living plants, and he is, thus, unaware of evolutionary display. He eschews the evolutionary implications of his work. He prefers, even, to divide his material geographically in order to avoid the difficulties of a world synthesis. By introducing more names, he perplexes the subject until it drops out of general botany. Thus the tribe Areceae, containing the majority of palms, passes now the comprehension of all but two or three specialists. This is a misfortune because, if the group is natural, it should be comparable

Y

with the Lepidocaryoid palms and, by checking on the parallel evolution within the whole family, improve its natural classification. As it is, the student loses himself in details of perianth, stamens, ovule, seeds, and embryos. They certainly supply information for they make the herbarium material, but there is no explanation why these features should suddenly be employed for generic differences or what has been their part in palm evolution. The Arecoid genus loses character, as Griffith complained, and the general botanist gives up. Many genera are suspect of the rank attributed to them, and this is important when estimating the status of palms in world vegetation and plant geography. Much of the insular distribution of genera ascribed to palms becomes suspect, for no subject suffers so much from poor classification than plant geography. Islands and continents can be joined or initiated in many ways and there is a fit for nearly every classification, but there will be only one fit for the natural which describes plant-evolution; the others are wrong. The revision of the Arecoid palms should be an exhilarating opening for research. The alternative to splitting may be lumping. It, too, may be bad. But the contrasts have their values. Research calls for the utmost refinement; it needs splitting which is nowhere more evident than in pathology where disease may prefer varieties, subvarieties, or even maldeveloped individuals. But the result is a specialist language. General botany, dealing with the whole domain of plants, cannot be bothered with minutiae; it needs fewer, major ideas and prefers lumping. The reason why a knowledge of world taxonomy is dropping out of botany is simply because the specialists have over-elaborated it. We need two classifications, the synthetic and the analytic. The ranks they accord to groups of species will not be comparable and a notation will have to be devised to distinguish the two systems. The naturalist amidst the riches of the palm-scene will prefer the synthetic.

What reality can be ascribed to a taxon or unit of classification? Some biologists deny the reality of any above the rank of species. This is usually taken to mean the assemblage of individuals propagating their kind. The individuals are real, for they have been found, and the properties that they transmit to their offspring, enabling them to grow in their particular way, are real for they are the cytoplasmic and nuclear particularities of their protoplasm. There is not one genetic code, but a code for every species. Some of these particularities, however, are not specific but common to many species; they are the generic characters, which are not encountered as discrete bodies in nature, being inside the living cells. Similarly some of these generic characters are common to several genera as the tribal characters. It is not the rank or taxon which has reality, but the protoplasmic structure which evinces it. We may know nothing as yet about the generic genetic code or that of higher taxonomic rank, but these higher codes make up all the genetic code of a living organism except its specific detail. This is a problem for advancing biochemistry and biophysics which, in unravelling the complexity of cell-constituents, will be guided by the natural classification developed from the explicit manifestation or functional expansion of the molecular structure. All taxa, therefore, have a protoplasmic basis and are real. A pollen-grain carries taxonomic properties of every rank but we cannot perceive them until it has been developed into an adult. Plant biochemists should be able, nevertheless, to classify pollen-grains as well as any cell of the plant-body. This is looking far ahead. Palm-genetics has only just begun but we may expect advances from the breeding programmes of the coconut and oil-palm research stations and from horticultural establishments specializing in ornamental palms. A knowledge of the palm genetic code will be needed to evaluate that of the monocotyledons.

The palm family is recognizable because there are no plants which link it with other families of monocotyledons. These ancestors must have become extinct. Likewise the extinction of the intermediate ancestors enables the subfamilies to be recognized, and the tribes and genera. The reasons for extinction must have been various. The ancestors may have been beaten in the struggle for existence as better kinds were evolved; improvement in root, leaf, stem, flower, fruit, seed, and seedling establishment may have enabled the new palms to grow better and shade out their forebears. But this takes a long time, for the new palms must spread throughout the region inhabited by their forebears. Thus forebears may persist through some geographical isolation in places that later palms could not reach. Then some catastrophe may occur through sudden climatic change, earthquake, flood, or eruption to exterminate them. An increase in animal activity may react on the palms, which have much to offer as food, and lead to their extermination. Diseases may, also, have become so epidemic as to exterminate them, though palms do not seem now to be prone to such. Nevertheless, there are many accidental ways in which species may disappear, besides the ruthless advance of evolution. The isolation of genera and higher ranks, which enables

345

their classification to be developed in a hierarchy, is the outcome of all sorts of misfortune acting through geological time since the beginning of the Cretaceous period, if not earlier. Furthermore, it cannot be supposed that the Cretaceous groups of palms had all advanced at exactly the same evolutionary rate; some might have gone further than others, and some might have suffered more extinction than others. It follows that higher taxa such as genera and tribes cannot be equal in number of species or in definition; they must be accepted as they are discovered.

Classification must be morphological and based on structure, not merely because structure offers the readiest assessment, but because through its structure the plant enters the environment and takes effect. Griffith must have meant that a good genus should have a distinct effect. *Phoenix* in its subarid life is such. So is *Calamus* or *Desmoncus* in hooking through the trees. *Pinanga* and *Licuala* are good effects in the Asian forests, *Chamaedorea*, *Geonoma*, and *Bactris* in the American. *Mauritia*, *Metroxylon*, and *Raphia* are Lepidocaryoid effects in their continents. The *Attalea-Scheelea* landscape is peculiar to America, but we begin to doubt whether it represents more than one genus. The separation of genera from *Cocos*, *Iriartea*, or *Chrysalidocarpus* depends on intricate details of flower, fruit, and seed, the meaning of which is neither understood nor consistently handled in generic distinctions. We may expect that many genera of Arecoid, Cocoid, and, perhaps, Coryphoid palms will be telescoped as their field-study progresses.

The outline of palm classification, given in the following pages, is that which is now adopted as most convenient [367]. It is being revised and it will suffer more revision, especially as anatomical and chromosomal knowledge increases [368]. To apprehend the chief groups is the main step in the study of form-making and of the geographical display wrought by time, space, and form in the domain of palms.

### Family PALMAE (Arecaceae)

Stems solid, without secondary thickening, slender to massive, generally unbranched above ground. Leaves spirally arranged, in a few cases distichous, pinnate or palmate, plicate in bud, splitting along the folds into leaflets, in some cases unsplit.

Inflorescences terminal or lateral, multi-bracteate, often with large spathes, much branched, varying to simple or capitate. Flowers generally sessile, bisexual or unisexual, radially symmetrical or the male flowers subasymmetric. Perianth with calyx and corolla each of 3 segments, mostly rather thick and sepaloid. Stamens commonly 6, varying to many or to 3. Ovary apocarpous with 3 carpels to syncarpous with 3 loculi, varying 4–10 in *Phytelephas*. Ovule solitary in each carpel or loculus, anatropous with the micropyle descending, varying orthotropous, axile or basal; integuments 2 or 1.

Fruit indehiscent, fleshy and drupaceous or fibrous and nut-like, often with hard endocarp, small to very large; perianth persistent. Seeds with massive hard, often ruminate endosperm; seed-coat not matured.

Subfamilies 9. Genera *c.* 227. Species *c.* 2,600. Chromosomes with diploid number 16, 24, 26, 28, 32, 36.

Tropical, subtropical, and a few warm temperate.

### Subfamily Phoenicoideae

Leaves once pinnate, often with a terminal leaflet; leaflets pointed, induplicate, without midrib, reduced to spines in the lower part of the leaf-axis: bases sheathing, fibrous.

Dioecious. Inflorescence axillary, with a prominent spathe, much branched. Flowers unisexual, arranged singly along the inflorescence branches. Male flowers with the calyx as a shortly toothed cup: petals valvate; stamens 6; pistillode minute or none. Female flowers with the petals overlapping; staminodes 6; ovary apocarpous.

Fruit 1–2 (–3) per flower, drupaceous, but without stone, endocarp papery. Seeds oblong, grooved on one side; endosperm not ruminate.

Africa, continental Asia. Genus 1 (*Phoenix*). Species *c.* 12. Chromosome diploid number 36.

Anatomically near to the Coryphoid palms and probably related with their apocarpous, pinnate-leafed ancestors.

### Subfamily Coryphoideae

Leaves palmate or costapalmate, induplicate, often with spiny leaf-stalks or sheaths.

Monoecious. Inflorescence terminal or axillary. Flowers bisexual or unisexual, singly or paired or in triads: petals valvate: stamens generally 6. Ovary apocarpous or variously syncarpous.

Fruits more or less drupaceous, generally smooth, without or with a thin stone. Seeds rarely with ruminate endosperm.

America, Mediterranean region, and North Africa, Asia, Australasia. Genera *c.* 33. Species *c.* 330. Chromosome diploid number 16, 28, 36.

Except the six Borassoid and three Lepidocaryoid genera, all other fan-palms belong to this subfamilly.

### Subfamily Borassoideae

Differing from Coryphoideae in being dioecious with the female flowers in some genera much larger than the male, the inflorescences with very thick axis and covered in the male with large imbricate bracts; seeds generally with a hard stone; leaves always costapalmate; trunks not suckering.

Male flowers solitary, in triads, or more numerous in clusters, each cluster to a bract, petals overlapping: stamens six to many; pistillode minute. Female flowers sessile or stalked; petals overlapping; staminodes usually in a short ring; ovary syncarpous, usually trilocular. Fruit medium-size to very large, 1–3 seeds, smooth, fibrous or fleshy; endocarp as a single stone or as a stone round each seed; endosperm ruminate or not, in some cases hollow.

Africa, Asia. Genera 6. Species variously estimated at 22 to 43. Chromosome diploid number 32, 36.

Anatomically this subfamily is related with the *Sabal* alliance of the Coryphoid palms. The genera are well marked and can be distinguished by the following key.

1. Male and female flowers small, similar. Stigma and sterile carpels at the base of the 1-seeded fruit. Stamens 6

    2. Stems often dichotomous. Endosperm not ruminate ........... *Hyphaene*

    2. Stems unbranched. Endosperm ruminate ................... *Medemia*

1. Male flowers small, solitary or clustered in pits beneath the bracts, opening one at a time. Female flowers much larger, solitary. Stigma at the apex of the fruit

    3. Stamens 6

        4. Male flowers numerous in a cluster. Seed-stones without internal flanges. Leaf-stalks spiny ................................... *Borassus*

        4. Male flowers solitary. Seed-stones with 7–8 internal flanges. Leaf-stalks unarmed ..................................... *Borassodendron*

    3. Stamens numerous

        5. Fruit the size of a plum, with 1–3 seed-stones ................. *Latania*

        5. Fruit very large with bilobed stone ....................... *Lodoicea*

## Subfamily Caryotoideae

Unarmed, pinnate-leafed, with terminal leaflet; leaflets induplicate, fish-tailed or toothed along the margin to the broad or obtuse apex: leaf-sheaths fibrous.

Monoecious, hapaxanthic, with lateral inflorescences opening from the top of the trunk downwards. Flowers unisexual, usually in triads with a central female. Male flowers with six to many stamens; pistillode none. Female flowers with valvate petals; staminodes six or none; ovary with 2–3 cavities.

Fruit 1–3 seeded, smooth, drupaceous with a thin endocarp stone or none. Endosperm ruminate or not.

Asia, Australasia. Genera 3. Species *c.* 38. Chromosome diploid number 32.

This subfamily occupies a perplexing central position. The induplicate leaflets place it with the three foregoing subfamilies, but the flowers and general habit place it with the following. Thus it has, often, been classed with Arecoid and Cocoid palms in the former subfamily Ceroxyloideae. Anatomically it combines the characters of induplicate and reduplicate palms. The central position agrees with the primitive form of the doubly pinnate leaf of Caryota.

The three genera can be distinguished as follows.

1. Leaves doubly pinnate with wedge-shaped leaflets. Inflorescences bisexual. Stamens numerous. Endosperm ruminate .................... *Caryota*

1. Leaves once pinnate; leaflets oblong or wedge-shaped. Inflorescences (?) always unisexual. Endosperm not ruminate

    2. Stamens 6 ............................................. *Wallichia*

    2. Stamens numerous ....................................... *Arenga*

## Subfamily Lepidocaryoideae

Leaves pinnate or palmate with reduplicate leaflets. Ovary syncarpous, scaly. Fruit covered with imbricating scales (not spines or warts) usually set in whorls. Arborescent or climbing.

    Pantropic. Genera *c.* 25. Species *c.* 500. Chromosome diploid number 32 (*Calamus*).

    This subfamily, made up largely by the true rattans, is at once uniform in its scaly fruit and immensely varied in all other respects. It could be separated as a family of its own, within which practically all kinds of palm diversification occur except that of the capitate female inflorescence. There is, however, the problematic *Eugeissona* that seems to relate the subfamily with the Cocoid palms (p. 180).

    The genera may be keyed as follows.

1. Climbing ......................................... rattans (p. 223).

1. Not climbing

    2. Inflorescences terminal; flowering stems hapaxanthic. Leaves pinnate

        3. Fruit with stony endocarp and small scales not in distinct whorls. Flowers bisexual, solitary ................................... *Eugeissona*

        3. Fruit without a stone, the scales large and in distinct whorls. Flowers paired, bisexual and male in spikelets ........................ *Metroxylon*

    2. Inflorescences axillary

        4. Leaves palmate. America ......... *Mauritia, Mauritiella, Lepidocaryum*

        4. Leaves pinnate

            5. Flowers distichous in flattened spikes

                6. Monoecious, stout palms with very long leaves. Endosperm ruminate. Africa, America ............................... *Raphia*

                6. Dioecious, rather short palms, very spiny. Asia ........ *Calamus* pr.p.

            5. Flowers spirally arranged in cylindric spikes

                7. Short, tufted palms. Dioecious ........................ *Salacca*

                7. Tall palms, not tufted

                    8. Dioecious ...................................... *Pigafetta*

                    8. Monoecious ............................. *Metroxylon* pr.p.

349

## Subfamily Cocoideae

Leaves pinnate with reduplicate leaflets; sheaths not forming a crown shaft. Monoecious or, in a few cases dioecious. Inflorescences axillary with unisexual flowers generally in triads, but varying with male flowers distal and female flowers proximal, or the inflorescences unisexual. Ovary syncarpous. Fruit drupaceous or fibrous, smooth or in some cases spinous, but without reflexed scales; always with a woody or stony endocarp provided with three germ-pores.

America, Africa, and as *Cocos nucifera* in Asia and Australasia. Genera 27. Species 600. Chromosome diploid number 32.

## Subfamily Arecoideae

As Cocoideae but the fruit without the stone-like endocarp or, if with a thinly woody or fibrous endocarp, then without the three germ-pores: ovary syncarpous or in some cases more or less apocarpous: fruit smooth or in a few cases with pyramidal warts: leaves often with tubular bases set in a crown-shaft.

Pantropic. Genera *c.* 130. Species *c.* 1,100. Chromosome diploid number 26, 32, 36.

It was the custom to combine the Arecoid and Cocoid palms into one subfamily Ceroxyloideae, the two groups then being tribes of this subfamily. On anatomical grounds, Tomlinson distinguishes the Bactrid spiny palms sharply from the other Cocoid palms and finds that the first have resemblances with *Chamaedorea* and *Iriartea* in the Arecoid group [369]. It is, however, impossible yet to know whether these are phyletic agreements or parallel resemblances.

## Subfamily Nipoideae

Leaves pinnate with reduplicate leaflets, unarmed. Monoecious. Inflorescences axillary, consisting of a central globose head of female flowers surrounded by short spikes of male flowers, multibracteate. Male flowers with three anthers on a single column; pistillode none. Female flowers with small perianth; staminodes none; ovary unilocular; stigma sessile. Nuts in large globose heads, angled and ribbed; fibrous with firmer, woody endocarp: endosperm not ruminate.

Asia, Australasia. Genus 1 (*Nipa*). Species 1. Chromosome diploid number 16.

This subfamily and the next have been grouped as Palmae Anomalae because of the head of female flowers and fruits. Except that they are reduplicately pinnate-leafed palms of Ceroxyloid appearance, they have little else in common and appear as two extreme advances in the fundamentally different geographical regions of palms.

## Subfamily Phytelephantoideae

Leaves pinnate with reduplicate leaflets, unarmed. Dioecious, with axillary inflorescences. Male inflorescences more or less thickly cylindric, often very long: perianth with 6–9 lobes, much reduced; stamens 36–1,000 or more; pistillode none. Female flowers in multibracteate heads; perianth with 3–4 sepals and 5–10 petals; staminodes numerous; ovary with 4–10 loculi; style filiform with 4–10 long stigmas. Fruits in large heads, each fruit 4–10 seeded; fruit wall tuberculate with pyramidal warts, with fibrous or fleshy inner tissue and no woody endocarp; endosperm not ruminate.

350

America. Genus 1 (*Phytelephas*). Species 10. Chromosomes ?
This genus has been divided into four and given a family of its own [370].

## Key to the subfamilies of palms

1. Leaflets induplicate, V-shaped in cross-section, the midrib (when present) prominent on the underside

   2. Leaves pinnate, usually with a terminal leaflet

      3. Leaflets pointed, the lower as spines. Dioecious. Apocarpous . . *Phoenicoideae*

      3. Leaflets fish-tail shape or toothed. Monoecious. Syncarpous . . *Caryotoideae*

   2. Leaves palmate

      4. Monoecious. Inflorescence often much branched. Ovary apocarpous or syncarpous. Leaves palmate or costapalmate . . . . . . . . . *Coryphoideae*

      4. Dioecious. Inflorescences usually with few or no branches. Syncarpous. Leaves costapalmate . . . . . . . . . . . . . . . . . . . . . . . . . . . . *Borassoideae*

1. Leaflets reduplicate, Λ-shaped in cross-section, the midrib prominent on the upperside

   5. Fruit covered with recurved, often flattened and whorled, scales. Leaves pinnate or palmate . . . . . . . . . . . . . . . . . . . . . . . . . . . . *Lepidocaryoideae*

   5. Fruit without such scales, smooth or warted or spinous. Inflorescences lateral. Leaves pinnate

      6. Female inflorescence capitate. Unarmed

         7. Monoecious, stemless. Ovary unilocular. Fruit 1-seeded . . . *Nipoideae*

         7. Dioecious, with a trunk. Ovary multilocular. Fruit warted, many-seeded
            *Phytelephantoideae*

      6. Female inflorescence elongate, or the elongate inflorescences bisexual. Spinous or not

         8. Fruit with a stone supplied with germ-pores . . . . . . . . . . . . . *Cocoideae*

         8. Fruit without a stone or, if a thin stone, or fibrous endocarp, then without germ-pores. Often with a crown-shaft . . . . . . . . . . . . . . *Arecoideae*

# Appendix A

**A key to the commoner fan palms**

1. Tufted or stemless

   2. Leaf very large, diamond-shaped, not split into leaflets. South-East Asian forests .......................................... *Teysmannia*

   2. Leaf divided into leaflets or, if undivided, then orbicular

      3. Leaflets narrowly wedge-shaped, broader to the tip, or the leaf undivided
                                                   *Licuala*

      3. Leaflets pointed

         4. Creeping palms with truly palmate leaves, deeply divided into leaflets. South-east USA

            5. Leaf-stalk with toothed edges ......................... *Serenoa*

            5. Leaf-stalk with smooth edges ...................... *Sabal minor*

         4. Erect palms

            6. Stems slender, up to 1 inch thick. Leaves deeply divided into leaflets
                                                  *Rhapis*

            6. Stems stouter

               7. Tropical ................................. *Acoelorraphe*

               7. Temperate

                  8. Leaf-stalk strongly spiny. Mediterranean ........ *Chamaerops*

                  8. Leaf-stalk slightly spiny. Sino-Himalaya, Japan .. *Trachycarpus*

1. Trunks solitary

   9. Trunk repeatedly forked ................................. *Hyphaene*

   9. Trunk unbranched

      10. Immense palms, sterile until the development of the huge terminal panicle
                                                  *Corypha*

         11. Leaf-stalk with strongly spiny edge. Blade shorter than the stalk.. *C. elata*

11. Leaf-stalk with small spines. Blade about as long as the stalk
*C. umbraculifera*

10. Inflorescences lateral

12. Tropical America. Fruit scaly. Leaflets reduplicate ......... *Mauritia*

12. Fruit smooth. Leaflets induplicate

13. Trunk covered with persistent dead leaves .......... *Washingtonia*

14. Leaf-stalk reddish brown; leaflets bright green ...... *W. robusta*

14. Leaf-stalk green; leaflets grey-green ............. *W. filifera*

13. Trunk smooth or with persistent leaf-bases only

15. Leaf-bases with conspicuous brown fibrous sheath

16. Leaf-stalks spiny ......................... *Livistona*

16. Leaf-stalks smooth

17. Trunk massive, over 1 ft. thick, leaves stiff, with many leaflets
*Pritchardia*

17. Trunk rather slender. Leaflets few, rather drooping .. *Thrinax*

15. Leaf-bases without conspicuous fibrous sheaths

18. Inflorescences not or sparsely branched. Fruits large. Very massive palm ............................ *Borassus*

18. Inflorescences much branched

19. Fruits 1–2 in. wide. Young leaves often with red stalk, edges, or veins ................................ *Latania*

19. Fruits smaller. Leaves strongly arched with prominent midrib
*Sabal*

## A key to the commoner pinnate-leafed palms

1. Leaves undivided on opening, but often tattering into leaflets

2. Stemless. Leaf diamond-shaped, not splitting. South-East Asia .. *Teysmannia*

2. Trunk well developed. Leaves tattering

3. Without spines, but the fruits warted. Leaves 15–30 ft. long. Tropical America
*Manicaria*

3. Trunks and leaf-stalks spiny, at least when young. Leaves smaller. Seychelles palms, often cultivated

4. Trunk with stilt-roots ............................ *Verschaffeltia*

4. Without stilt-roots ............................ *Phoenicophorium*

1. Leaves splitting into leaflets on opening

353

5. Leaves doubly pinnate with fish-tail leaflets ................. *Caryota*

5. Leaves once pinnate

  6. Climbing palms

    7. Fruits fleshy, not covered with scales. Leaflets turned into hooks at the whip-end of the leaf. America ..................... *Desmoncus*

    7. Fruits covered with scales. Africa, Asia ............. rattans (p. 223)

  6. Not climbing

    8. Leaflets with toothed, truncate, or rounded tips

      9. Very spiny. Leaflets of fish-tail form .................. *Aiphanes*

      9. Not spiny

        10. Tall, stilt-rooted. Tropical America ................ *Iriartea*

        10. Leaf-sheath strongly fibrous ....................... *Arenga*

        10. Leaf-base tubular, as a crownshaft

          11. Often tufted, rather small. Seed ruminate ....... *Ptychosperma*

          11. Tall, solitary. Seed not ruminate ................. *Veitchia*

    8. Leaflets pointed

      12. Inflorescence terminal, immense. Stem usually suckering. Fruits scaly. Leaf-sheaths usually spiny ..................... *Metroxylon*

    12. Inflorescences axillary

      13. Spiny, or the lower leaflets as spines

        14. Fruits scaly. Leaf-sheaths spiny. Usually solitary

          15. Fruits round; seed not ruminate .... *Metroxylon amicorum*

          15. Fruits more or less oblong; seed ruminate. Trunk short compared with the very long leaves ........... *Raphia*

        14. Fruits not scaly, but pulpy

          16. Lower leaflets as spines

            17. Leaflets induplicate. Tufted or not. Flowers in panicles
                  *Phoenix*

            17. Leaflets reduplicate. Solitary. Flowers in large, compact heads ................................... *Elaeis*

              18. Erect. Africa or cultivated ............ *E. guineensis*

              18. Oblique or horizontal. Tropical America .. *E. melanococca*

          16. Stem and leaf-sheath with black spines. Mostly tufted

            19. With a crownshaft of tubular leaf-bases. Fruits without a stone. Tropical Asia ................ *Oncosperma*

19. Without a crownshaft. Fruits with a thick stone. America

 20. Stone with equatorial germ-pores ........ *Acrocomia*

 20. Stone with germ-pores in the upper half

  21. Germ-pores with star-like radiating fibres . *Astrocaryum*

  21. Without such star-like fibres

   22. Tall. Fruit triangular ovoid, reddish yellow. Stone with band-like fibres ...... *Gulielma gasipaes*

   22. Rather short and slender. Fruit round. Stone without such fibres ...................... *Bactris*

13. Unarmed palms .................... see the next section **A**

**A**. Unarmed; pinnate, with pointed leaflets. Fruits not scaly. Inflorescences lateral

1. Without a crownshaft

 2. Small, slender, tufted. Tropical America

  3. Flowers sunk in sockets on simple or sparingly branched inflorescences
                  *Geonoma*

  3. Flowers not sunk in sockets ........................ *Chamaedorea*

 2. Massive

  4. Stemless, tufted, estuarine. Asia, Australasia ................... *Nipa*

  4. Tall or, if stemless, not estuarine

   5. Fruit-stone with equatorial germ-pores. Trunk very massive .... *Jubaea*

   5. Germ-pores basal. Leaf-bases often fibrous

    6. Fruits at the base of bisexual inflorescences ................ *Cocos*

     7. Nut very large. Leaflets in two rows ............... *C. nucifera*

     7. Nut 1 in. wide. Leaflets appearing in several rows, arching and drooping
               *C. romanzoffiana (Arecastrum)*

    6. Fruits in large bunches on female inflorescences.. *Attalea* etc. (p. 283)

1. Stem with a crownshaft; leaf-bases tubular, not fibrous

 8. Leaf-sheath and stalk red ........................ *Cyrtostachys lakka*

 8. Not red

  9. Trunks very massive, solitary

   10. Trunk rather short, bottle-shaped .................... *Mascarena*

   10. Trunk lofty ....................................... *Roystonea*

    11. Leaflets in two rows; fronds flat .................... *R. oleracea*

355

11. Leaflets in four rows, arching and drooping; frond bushy; trunk often broadening upwards ............................ *R. regia*

9. Trunks relatively slender, solitary or tufted

12. Tufted

13. Leaflets with several midribs, variously compounded. Inflorescences turning red and set with black fruits throughout their length
*Pinanga*

13. Leaflets with one midrib ..................... *Chrysalidocarpus*

14. Leaf-sheaths and stalks yellow. Leaflets –60 pairs, rather stiff, erect; stem often with a short branch ............... *C. lutescens*

14. Leaflets –90 pairs, arched and drooping. Stouter palm, not yellowish
*C. madagascariensis*

12. Solitary

15. Leaflets with several midribs. Fruit at the base of the inflorescence branches, rather large, orange red ............. *Areca catechu*

15. Leaflets with one midrib

16. Leaflets conspicuously drooping .............. *Rhopaloblaste*

16. Leaf-axis and leaflets elegantly arched. Fruit rather large, orange
*Actinorhytis*

16. Without such character

17. Crownshaft conspicuous ................. *Archontophoenix*

18. Leaf-axis twisting the leaflets into a vertical plane, rather silvery grey beneath ......................... *A. alexandrae*

18. Not so ........................... *A. cunninghamiana*

17. Crownshaft often imperfect. America ............. *Euterpe*

# Appendix B

Alphabetical index of current genera of palms, together with their distribution, number of species, and diploid chromosome number (heavy type in brackets). *A*, Arecoid; *B*, Borassoid; *Ca*, Caryotoid; *Coc*, Cocoid; *Cor*, Coryphoid; *L*, Lepidocaryoid.

| | | | |
|---|---|---|---|
| Acanthococos | Paraguay, Brazil | *Coc* | 1 |
| Acanthophoenix | Mauritius, Réunion | *A* | 2 |
| Acoelorrhaphe | (=*Paurotis*) Florida, Mexico to British Honduras, Cuba, Bahamas | *Cor* | 1 |
| Acrocomia | Mexico to Argentina, Trinidad, Jamaica, Cuba, Antilles | *Coc* | 15–25 |
| Actinokentia | New Caledonia | *A* | 1 |
| Actinorhytis | Malaya to Solomon Isl. | *A* | 2 |
| Aiphanes | (=*Martinezia*) Colombia, Venezuela, Ecuador, Brazil, Antilles, Barbados, Puerto Rico | *Coc* | 30 (**32**) |
| Allagoptera | (=*Diplothemium*) Brazil, Paraguay | *Coc* | 5 |
| Ancistrophyllum | West Africa | *L* | 3 |
| Antongilia | Madagascar | *A* | 1 |
| Archontophoenix | Queensland | *A* | 2 |
| Areca | Ceylon, India to Solomon Isl., Queensland | *A* | 54 (**32**) |
| Arecastrum | (=*Cocos* pr.p) Brazil, Paraguay, Uruguay, N. Argentina | *Coc* | 1 (**32**) |
| Arenga | Burma, Formosa, to Australia, New Guinea | *Ca* | 20 (**32**) |
| Aricuriroba | (=*Cocos* pr.p.) Brazil | *Coc* | 3 |
| Asterogyne | British Honduras to Colombia | *A* | 3 |
| Astrocaryum | Tr. America | *Coc* | 45 |
| Attalea | Mexico to Colombia, Venezuela, Brazil, Haiti | *Coc* | 25 (**32**) |
| Bactris | Mexico to Argentina | *Coc* | 150 |
| Balaka | Fiji, Samoa | *A* | 20 |
| Barbosa | Brazil | *Coc* | 1 |
| Barcella | Brazil | *Coc* | 1 |
| Basselinia | New Caledonia | *A* | 10 |
| Beccariophoenix | Madagascar | *A* | 1 |
| Bejaudia | Indo-China | *L* | 1 |
| Bentinckia | Travancore, Nicobar Isl. | *A* | 2 |
| Borassodendron | Perak | *B* | 1 |

357

| | | | |
|---|---|---|---|
| Borassus | Africa, Madagascar, India, Ceylon to Indo-China, Java, New Guinea, ? Queensland | B | 4–7 (**36**) |
| Brahea | Mexico, Guatemala | Cor | 7 |
| Brassiophoenix | New Guinea | A | 1 |
| Brongniartikentia | New Caledonia | A | 1 |
| Burretiokentia | New Caledonia | A | 2 |
| Butia | (= *Cocos* pr.p.) Tr. America | Coc | 13 (**32**) |
| Calamus | Africa, Asia, Australasia to Fiji | L | 250–300 (**28**) |
| Calospathe | Perak | L | 2 |
| Calyptrocalyx | Moluccas, New Guinea | A | 18 |
| Calyptrogyne | Mexico to Costa Rica, Peru, Brazil | A | 6–9 |
| Calyptronoma | Colombia, Peru, Brazil, Antilles | A | 4 |
| Campecarpus | New Caledonia | A | 1 |
| Carpentaria | Queensland (dubious genus) | A | 1 |
| Carpoxylon | New Hebrides | A | 1 |
| Caryota | Ceylon, India to New Guinea, Queensland | Ca | 12 (**32**) |
| Catoblastus | Costa Rica to Bolivia | A | 6–10 |
| Catostigma | Colombia | A | 8 |
| Ceratolobus | Malaya, Java, Sumatra, Borneo | L | 6 |
| Ceroxylon | Andes | A | 15 |
| Chamaedorea | Mexico to Bolivia, Brazil | A | 80 (**26**) |
| Chamaerops | Mediterranean to Persia | Cor | 1 |
| Chambeyronia | New Caledonia | A | 2 |
| Chelyocarpus | Andean, Central America | Cor | 3 |
| Chrysalidocarpus | Madagascar (18), Comoro Isl. (2), Pemba (1) | A | 22 (**32**) |
| Chrysallido-sperma | (= *Cocos* pr.p.) Peru | Coc | 1 |
| Chuniophoenix | Indo-China | Cor | 1 |
| Clinosperma | New Caledonia | A | 1 |
| Clinostigma | (= *Bentinckiopois, Clinostigmopsis, Exorrhiza*) Bonin Isl., Caroline Isl., New Hebrides, Fiji, Samoa | A | 14 |
| Coccothrinax | Florida, Caribbean Isl. | Cor | 22 |
| Cocos | (as *C. nucifera*) ? West Pacific, Indian Ocean | Coc | 1 (**32**) |
| Colpothrinax | Cuba | Cor | 1 |
| Copernicia | Brazil, Paraguay, Argentina, Colombia, Venezuela, Cuba, Hispaniola | Cor | 23 (**36**) |
| Cornera | Malaya, Borneo | L | 3 |
| Corypha | India, Ceylon, Malaysia, Queensland | Cor | 6–8 (**36**) |
| Cryosophila | (= *Acanthorhiza*) Mexico to Colombia | Cor | 8 |
| Cyphophoenix | New Caledonia, Caroline Isl. (?) | A | 1–2 |
| Cyphosperma | New Caledonia | A | 1 |
| Cyrtostachys | Malaya to Solomon Isl. | A | 11 |
| Daemonorops | Assam, Indo-China to Philippine and Aru Isl. | L | 85 |
| Dasystachys | Guatemala | A | 1 |
| Deckenia | Seychelles | A | 1 |
| Desmoncus | Mexico to Brazil | Coc | 47 |

| | | | |
|---|---|---|---|
| Dictyocaryum | Costa Rica to Bolivia | *A* | 5 |
| Dictyosperma | Mauritius, Rodrigues | *A* | 2 (**32**) |
| Dolichokentia | New Caledonia | *A* | 1 |
| Drymophloeus | (=*Coleospadix*) Moluccas, New Guinea, Fiji, Samoa | *A* | 10 |
| Dypsis | Madagascar | *A* | 10–20 (**36**) |
| Elaeis | Tr. America, Africa, Madagascar | *Coc* | 2 (**32**) |
| Eleiodoxa | India, Siam, Malaya | *L* | 1 |
| Eremospatha | West Africa | *L* | 3 |
| Erythea | Mexico | *Cor* | 7 |
| Eugeissona | Malaya, Sumatra, Borneo | *L* | 6 |
| Euterpe | Guatemala to Brazil, Caribbean Isl. | *A* | 43 |
| Gaussia | Puerto Rico, Cuba | *A* | 2 |
| Geonoma | Tr. America | *A* | 200 |
| Gigliola | Borneo | *A* | 2 |
| Goniocladus | Fiji | *A* | 1 |
| Goniosperma | Fiji | *A* | 2 |
| Gronophyllum | Celebes to New Guinea | *A* | 8 |
| Gulielma | Costa Rica to Bolivia, Brazil | *Coc* | 7 |
| Gulubia | (–*Gulubiopsis*) Moluccas to New Hebrides, North Australia, Palau | *A* | 11 |
| Haitiella | Haiti | *Cor* | 1 |
| Hedyscepe | Lord Howe Isl. | *A* | 1 |
| Hemithrinax | Cuba | *Cor* | 2 |
| Heterospathe | Philippine Isl., Palau, Marianne Isl., New Guinea, Solomon Isl. | *A* | 18 (**32**) |
| Howeia | Lord Howe Isl. | *A* | 2 (**32**) |
| Hydriastele | New Guinea, North Australia | *A* | 3 |
| Hyophorbe | Mauritius, Réunion | *A* | 2 |
| Hyospathe | Tropical South America | *A* | 6 |
| Hyphaene | Africa, Madagascar, to West India | *B* | 10–28 |
| Iguanura | Malaya, Sumatra, Borneo | *A* | 20 |
| Iriartea | Costa Rica to Bolivia, Brazil | *A* | 7 |
| Iriartella | Colombia to Peru, Venezuela, British Guiana | *A* | 2 |
| Jessenia | South America | *A* | 5 |
| Johannesteijsmannia | see *Teysmannia* | | |
| Juania | Juan Fernandez | *A* | 1 |
| Jubaea | Chile | *Coc* | 1 |
| Jubaeopsis | South Africa | *Coc* | 1 |
| Kajewskia | New Hebrides | *A* | 1 |
| Kalbreyera | Colombia | *A* | 1 |
| Kentia | New Guinea, North Australia | *A* | 6 (**32**) |
| Kentiopsis | New Caledonia | *A* | 1 |
| Korthalsia | Lower Burma, Andaman and Nicobar Isl., Thailand to New Guinea | *L* | 30 |

z

| | | | |
|---|---|---|---|
| Laccospadix | New Guinea, Queensland | *A* | 2 |
| Latania | Mascarene Isl. | *B* | 3 (**32**) |
| Leopoldinia | South America | *A* | 4 |
| Lepidocaryum | South America | *L* | 8 |
| Lepidorrhachis | Lord Howe Isl. | *A* | 1 |
| Leptophoenix | New Guinea | *A* | 1 |
| Liberbaileya | Malaya | *Cor* | 1 |
| Licuala | Burma, South China to Solomon Isl., Queensland | *Cor* | 80 (**16, 28**) |
| Linospadix | New Guinea, North Australia | *A* | 12 |
| Livistona | Assam, China to New Guinea, Australia | *Cor* | 20 (**36**) |
| Lodoicea | Seychelles | *B* | 1 |
| Louvelia | Madagascar | *A* | 3 |
| Loxococcus | Ceylon | *A* | 1 |
| Manicaria | Guatemala to Brazil | *A* | 3–4 |
| Markleya | Brazil | *Coc* | 1 |
| Mascarena | Mauritius, Rodriguez | *A* | 3 |
| Masoala | Madagascar | *A* | 1 |
| Mauritia | South America | *L* | 6 |
| Mauritiella | Brazil, Colombia | *L* | 10 |
| Maxburretia | Malaya | *Cor* | 1 |
| Maximiliana | South America | *Coc* | 10 |
| Medemia | ( = *Bismarkia*) East Africa, Madagascar | *B* | 3 |
| Metasocratea | Colombia | *A* | 2 |
| Metroxylon | Moluccas, Caroline Isl. to Fiji | *L* | 7–9 |
| Microcoelum | ( = *Cocos* pr.p.) Brazil | *Coc* | 2 |
| Myrialepis | Thailand, Indochina, Malaya | *L* | 1 |
| Nannorrhops | Arabia, Afghanistan, West Pakistan, N.W. India | *Cor* | 4 |
| Nenga | Burma, Indo-China, Thailand, Malaya, Sumatra, Java | *A* | 4 |
| Nengella | New Guinea | *A* | 7 |
| Neodypsis | Madagascar | *A* | 14 |
| Neonicholsonia | Costa Rica, Panama | *A* | 1 |
| Neophloga | Madagascar | *A* | 30 |
| Neoveitchia | Fiji | *A* | 1 |
| Nephrosperma | Seychelles | *A* | 1 (**32**) |
| Normanbya | Queensland | *A* | 1 |
| Nipa | ( = *Nypa*) Ceylon to Solomon Isl., Queensland | | 1 (**16**) |
| Oenocarpus | South America | *A* | 16 |
| Oncocalamus | West Africa | *L* | 2 |
| Oncosperma | Ceylon, Malaysia | *A* | 5 (**32**) |
| Opsiandra | Guatemala | *A* | 1 |
| Orania | Malaysia, Queensland | *A* | 16 |
| Orbignya | South America | *Coc* | 20 |
| Paragulubia | Solomon Isl. | *A* | 1 |

| | | | |
|---|---|---|---|
| Parajubaea | Ecuador, Bolivia | *Coc* | 2 |
| Paralinospadix | New Guinea | *A* | 21 |
| Parascheelea | Colombia | *Coc* | 1 |
| Pelagodoxa | Marquesas Isl., ? New Caledonia | *A* | 1–2 |
| Phloga | Madagascar | *A* | 2 |
| Phoenicophorium | (= *Stevensonia*) Seychelles | *A* | 1 |
| Phoenix | Canary Isl., Africa, Madagascar, Asia to China, Formosa, Hainan, Batan Isl., Malaya | | 12 (**36**) |
| Pholidocarpus | Malaya, Borneo, Sumatra, Celebes | *Cor* | 5 |
| Pholidostachys | Costa Rica | *A* | 1 |
| Physokentia | New Hebrides | *A* | 1 |
| Phytelephas | Tr. America | | 10 |
| Pigafetta | Sumatra, Celebes | *L* | 5 |
| Pinanga | Indo-Malaysia | *A* | 115 |
| Plectocomia | Sikkim to Indo-China, Malaya, Sumatra, Java, Borneo, Philippine Isl. | *L* | 12 |
| Plectocomiopsis | Burma, Indo-China, Malaya, Sumatra, Borneo | *L* | 6 |
| Podococcus | Africa | *A* | 2 |
| Polyandrococos | South America | *Coc* | 1 |
| Prestoea | Guatemala, Panama, Grenada, Trinidad | *A* | 4 |
| Pritchardia | Hawaii, Fiji, Paumotu Isl. | *Cor* | 12–30 (**36**) |
| Pritchardiopsis | New Caledonia ? | *Cor* | 1 |
| Pseudophoenix | Florida, Jamaica, Hispaniola, Cuba, Bahamas | *A* | 5 |
| Ptychandra | Moluccas, New Guinea | *A* | 5 |
| Ptychococcus | New Guinea to Solomon Isl. | *A* | 8 |
| Ptychoraphis | Malaya, Nicobar Isl. | *A* | 3 |
| Ptychosperma | Key Isl., New Guinea to Solomon Isl., Palau, Ponape, Queensland | *A* | 41 (**32**) |
| Pyrenoglyphis | Guatemala to Bolivia, Brazil | *Coc* | 28 |
| Raphia | Tr. America, Africa, Madagascar | *L* | 20 |
| Ravenea | Madagascar, Comoro Isl. | *A* | 9 |
| Rehderophoenix | Solomon Isl. | *A* | 1 |
| Reinhardtia | Mexico to Colombia | *A* | 12 |
| Rhapidophyllum | South Carolina to Florida | *Cor* | 1 |
| Rhapis | China, Indo-China, Japan | *Cor* | 9 (**36**) |
| Rhopaloblaste | Moluccas, Philippines, New Guinea | *A* | 9 |
| Rhopalostylis | Norfolk Isl., New Zealand, Kermadec Isl. | *A* | 3 |
| Rhyticocos | (= *Cocos* pr.p.) Martinique, Dominica, Guadeloupe | *Coc* | 1 |
| Rooseveltia | Cocos Isl. (Panama) | *A* | 1 |
| Roscheria | Seychelles | *A* | 1 |
| Roystonea | Venezuela, Florida, Caribbean Isl. | *A* | 12 (**36**) |
| Sabal | N. Carolina to Colombia, Caribbean Isl., Bermuda | *Cor* | 25 (**36**) |
| Salacca | (= *Zalacca*) Assam to Indo-China, Malaya, Sumatra, Java, Borneo, Philippines | *L* | 14 |
| Scheelea | Mexico to Brazil, chiefly Andean | *Coc* | 40 |

z*

| | | | |
|---|---|---|---|
| Schizospatha | New Guinea | *A* | 1 |
| Sclerosperma | West Africa | *A* | 3 |
| Schippia | Br. Honduras | *Cor* | 1 |
| Serenoa | South-east United States of America | *Cor* | 1 |
| Sindroa | Madagascar | *A* | 1 |
| Siphokentia | Moluccas | *A* | 2 |
| Socratea | Panama | *A* | 5 |
| Solfia | Samoa | *A* | 1 |
| Sommieria | New Guinea | *A* | 3 |
| Strongylocaryum | Solomon Isl. | *A* | 3 |
| Syagrus | (= *Cocos* pr.p.) South America | *Coc* | 39 |
| Synechanthus | Mexico to Ecuador | *A* | 6 |
| Taenianthera | South America | *A* | 11 |
| Taveunia | Fiji | *A* | 1 |
| Tessmanniodoxa | Brazil | *Cor* | 2 |
| Teysmannia | West Malaysia | *Cor* | 1 |
| Thrinax | Florida, Caribbean Isl. | *Cor* | 10 (**36**) |
| Trachycarpus | Himalayas, Assam, Burma, Indo-China, China, Japan | *Cor* | 5–6 (**36**) |
| Trithrinax | Brazil, Argentina | *Cor* | 5 |
| Veitchia | (= *Vitiphoenix*) Philippines, New Hebrides, New Caledonia, Fiji | *A* | 18 |
| Verschaffeltia | Seychelles | *A* | 1 |
| Vonitra | Madagascar | *A* | 4 |
| Wallichia | Assam, Burma, Thailand, Indo-China | *Ca* | 6 |
| Washingtonia | California, Arizona, Mexico | *Cor* | 2 (**24**) |
| Welfia | Central America | *A* | 3 |
| Wendlandiella | Peru | *A* | 3 |
| Wettinia | Costa Rica to Bolivia | *A* | 2 |
| Wettiniicarpus | Colombia | *A* | 5 |
| Wissmannia | North-east Africa, Arabia | *Cor* | 1 |
| Yuyba | Brazil, Surinam, Trinidad | *Coc* | 25 |
| Zalacella | Indo-China | *L* | 1 |
| Zombia | Haiti | *Cor* | 1 |

# Glossary

*acropetal* with apical growth, the parts developing in succession from the apex of the structure backwards; with the youngest parts near the apex.

*apocarpous* with the carpels free from each other.

*aroid* of the family Araceae *e.g.* the arum lily.

*axillary* placed in, or arising from, a leaf-axil.

*basipetal* with basal growth, the parts developing in succession from the base of the structure towards the apex; with the youngest parts near the base.

*bract* a reduced leaf on the inflorescence.

*cabbage* the bud of a palm.

*cambium* the internal layer of dividing cells that produces secondary xylem and phloem.

*carpel* the part of the flower that bears the ovules, and corresponds with a single leaf.

*compound* referring to a leaf, with two or more separate leaflets in place of a single lamina; referring to palm leaflets, composed of more than one fold.

*costapalmate* a palmate leaf with the stalk prolonged as a midrib into the blade.

*cotyledon* a seed leaf.

*dichotomy* the division of a growing point into two.

*dicotyledon* a flowering plant with two cotyledons.

*dioecious* with male and female flowers on separate plants.

*distichous* with the leaves, branches, or flowers in two alternating rows; staggered.

*drupe* a fleshy indehiscent fruit with a stone enclosing the one or two seeds.

*durian* of the genus *Durio*.

*endosperm* the sterile storage tissue of the seed.

*epidermis* the surface layer of cells.

*epiphyte* a plant that grows on another, but not parasitically.

*formicarian* relating to ants.

*germ-pores* soft regions in the stone or hard wall of a fruit, permitting outgrowth of the seedling.

*hapaxanthic* reproducing once only at the end of the plant's life; or with this behaviour for each stem of a cluster.

*hastula* see ligule.

*imbricate* with the parts overlapping.

*induplicate* referring to palm leaves splitting into leaflets along the upper edges of the folds.

*internode* the lengthened part of the stem between successive leaves; the lengthened part of the leaf-stalk or axis between successive leaflets.

*leptocaul* with thin or slender primary stem.

*ligule* in pinnate-leafed palms, the outgrowth of the leaf-sheath on the side opposite to the leaf-stalk; in palmate-leafed palms, the outgrowth or hastula from the top of the leaf-stalk.

*Malaysia* the biogeographical region from Malaya to New Britain, embracing the Malay Archipelago.

363

*meristem* the growing region with cell-division.

*micropyle* the opening of the integuments of the ovule.

*monocotyledon* with one cotyledon.

*monoecious* with male and female flowers on the same plant, or the flowers themselves bisexual.

*monopodial* with persistent main axis.

*multilocular* an ovary (or fruit) with the ovules set in numerous separate cavities.

*multistaminate* a flower with numerous stamens.

*myrmecophilous* inviting ants.

*neoteny* the process of fulfilling a function in an imperfect or young state.

*ovule* the small body in the ovary that becomes, on fertilization, the seed.

*pachycaul* with thick or massive primary stem.

*palmate* with the leaflets radiating, as the fingers of a hand.

*panicle* a much-branched inflorescence.

*perianth* the reduced leaves (sepals, petals) external to the stamens and ovary.

*phloem* the tissue of the vascular bundle that conducts organic food material.

*phyllode* a leaf-stalk flattened as a leaf-lamina.

*phyllotaxis* the manner of leaf-arrangement on a stem.

*pinnate* with the leaflets set along the stalk, or axis, of a compound leaf.

*pistillode* the sterile and, often, rudimentary ovary in a male flower.

*pleonanthic* reproducing (flowering) repeatedly during the plant's life, generally with axillary inflorescences.

*plicate* with the leaf-lamina folded in bud.

*praemorse* with ragged end to the leaf or leaflets, as if bitten off.

*pulvinus* the cushion of inflating cells at the base of leaflets, spines, or inflorescence branches.

*rachis* the axis of the pinnate leaf bearing the leaflets.

*raphids* microscopic needle-shaped crystals inside cells, usually in bundles.

*reduplicate* referring to palm leaves splitting into leaflets along the lower edges of the folds.

*simple* a leaf with single lamina, not divided into leaflets.

*soboliferous* with horizontal stems turning into erect stems.

*spathe* the large bract or bracts subtending an inflorescence or its main branches.

*spathels* diminutive spathes subtending the smaller branches of an inflorescence.

*staminode* sterile, often rudimentary, stamens in a female flower.

*supra-axillary* produced from a stem or leaf-sheath above a leaf-axil.

*syncarpous* with the ovary as a single box containing cavities, usually three to six in palms.

*trimerous* with the parts in threes.

*unilocular* with a single cavity; referring to a syncarpous ovary reduced to one cavity.

*valvate* with the parts fitting edge to edge, not imbricate.

*vascular bundle* the conducting strand composed of xylem and phloem.

*whorl* a circle of structures (as leaves, petals, stamens) arising at one level on the stem.

*xylem* the lignified water-conducting tissue.

# Chapter References

## Chapter 1

1 HILL (1952), SCHERY (1954).
2 HEGNAUER (1963)
3 *Principes (Journal of the Palm Society*, Miami); LEDIN (1961)
4 HUTCHINSON (1959), LAWRENCE (1951), WILLIS (1948). For palms, MCCURRACH (1960)
5 DAHLGREN and GLASSMAN (1961-3)
6 CORNER (1964), 110, 155
7 NEES VON ESENBECK, quoted by SEEMANN (1856), 12
8 CORNER (1964), 216-23
9 ENGLER (1930), CHEADLE (1953), FAHN (1954), HOLTTUM (1955), TOMLINSON (1964a)
10 Pandanaceae, see 4. Also WARBURG (1900), MARTELLI and PICHI-SERMOLLI (1951), VAUGHAN and WIEHE (1953), VAN STEENIS (1954)
11 CORNER (1964), 154
12 See 7. Also VAN STEENIS (1954), STONE (1961)
12a Recently there were found by the Royal Society Expedition to the Solomon Islands two species of pandan with lateral inflorescences. They were borne among the leaves or on the bare stem below the crown of leaves. It seems that this is the habit also in a few species from the Philippine Islands and New Guinea. They have yet to be studied in detail and appraised.
13 *Sedges* (Cyperaceae), see 4. *Microdracoides*, see HUTCHINSON and DALZIEL (1936)
14 Banana trees (Musaceae), see 4. Also SCHUMAN (1900), ENGLER (1930), SIMMONDS (1959), TOMLINSON (1959)
15 *Montrichardia*, see ENGLER, A. (1911) *Das Pflanzenreich* Bd. IV, 23C (Araceae – Lasioideae), 121 Leipzig, Wilhelm Engelmann
16 Bamboos (Gramineae) see 4 and 6. Also, CORNER (1964), 158, 271
17 See 4. Also, ENGLER (1930), FAHN (1961)
18 ENGLER (1930)
19 Rushes (Juncaceae), see 4 and ENGLER (1930). For *Prionium*, see *Curtis's Botanical Magazine* (1868) t. 5722 London, L. Reeve & Co.
20 ENGLER (1930), MEZ (1933); also ENGLER (1911), *Vegetation der Ende* 12 taf II b.
21 See 4. Also, HOLTTUM (1953)
22 See 4, and ENGLER (1930)
23 CORNER (1964), chapters 7 and 15

## Chapter 2

24 BURKHILL (1953), 849
25 RUMPHIUS (1741-55)
26 DE WIT (1952), 104, STEENIS-KRUSEMAN, V. (1950)

365

27 *ibid* 110
28 MERRILL (1917)
29 LINNAEUS (1753)
30 VERDOORN (1945)
31 JACQUIN (1763)
32 See HUMBOLDT; MARTIUS (1860),
   AGASSIZ (1869); SPRUCE (1908)
   Vol. I, XII 'In Humboldt's
   country'; STEARN (1960); and
   *idem* (1959) 'Alexander von
   Humboldt and plant geography'
   *New Scientist* 957-9
33 HUMBOLDT (1849b) Vol. 2, 20
34 *idem* (1850) Vol. I, 300 (For
   comparison with man, apparently
   without palms, see the essays in
   the symposium edited by
   ELLIOTT (1964))
35 *idem* (1852) Vol. 3, 9
36 *ibid*, 73
37 HUMBOLDT, BONPLAND, and
   KUNTH (1815)
38 CANDOLLE (1856-7)
39 SPIX and MARTIUS (1824-31)
40 MARTIUS, EICHLER, and URBAN
   (1840-1906)
41 VAN STEENIS-KRUSEMAN (1950);
   DE WIT (1949) p. CIV
42 BLUME (1836-47)
43 BURKILL (1956), 58-71; VAN

STEENIS-KRUSEMAN (1950), 201,
604
44 GRIFFITH (1847-54)
45 BURKILL (1957), 771
46 GRIFFITH (1848) Posthumous
   Papers II, p. XXVIII
47 *ibid* Posthumous Papers II, p. XXV
48 WALLACE (1853), 9-11
49 SPRUCE (1871)
50 VAN STEENIS-KRUSEMAN (1950),
   VAN STEENIS (1952), REED (1942)
51 BECCARI (1908, 1911, 1918)
52 BECCARI and PICHI-SERMOLLI
   (1955)
53 BECCARI (1908) *Calamus*, I
54 *idem* (1904), 114
55 *ibid*, 406; *idem* (1884)
56 *ibid*, 254, footnote
57 *idem* (1913)
58 *idem* (1904), 392, figure 51
59 BONDAR (1941)
60 DRUDE (1889); BURRET and
   POTZTAL (1953-6)
61 See VELHO SOBRINHO, J. F.,
   *Dicionário Bio-Bibliográfico
   Brasileiro*; HOEHNE, F. C. (1941)
   *O Jardim Botânico de São Paulo*,
   São Paulo, Instituto Botânico
62 BECCARI (1916)
63 BONDAR (1941)

## Chapter 3

64 ASHIDA (1958), HOLTTUM (1959)
65 SURRE and ZILLER (1963)
66 VENKATANARAYA (1957)
67 See the correspondence in the
   *Indian Forester* 35 (1909), 394-5
   (JACKSON, A. B.), 632-4 (HOLE,
   R. S.); 36 (1910), 362-4, 687
   (LUSHINGTON, A. W.), 575-8
   (McCRIE, C. M.), 688
   (DONALD, J.)
68 DUROCHER, YVON (1947),
   THISELTON-DYER (1910)
69 See 67
70 See the illustrations in
   McCURRACH (1960); READ (1961)

71 See EICHLER (1885), EAMES
   (1953), PERIASAMY (1962)
72 PERIASAMY (1962),
   VENKATANARAYA (1957).
   There have been several mistaken
   accounts of the folds arising from
   splits in the leaf-tissue. They are
   based on misinterpretations of
   oblique sections.
73 COPELAND (1905),
   VENKATANARAYA (1957)
74 BRANNER (1884), 480
75 TOMLINSON (1962a)
76 *idem* (1964b)
77 HUMBOLDT (1852) Vol. 2, 387

78 This palm has been called *Johannesteijsmannia*, because the name *Teysmannia*, after the Dutch botanist Teysmann, is antedated by the same name for another plant. However, they are unlikely to be confused and all the references in palm-literature for a hundred years refer to *Teysmannia*.
See MOORE, H. E. (1961), *Principes* **5**, 116

## Chapter 4

79 CORNER (1964), 110, figure 37
80 BRANNER (1884)
81 BLATTER (1926), 180
82 SCHOUTE (1909)
83 BARBOSA RODRIGUES (1903) Vol. 1 82–5, and Vol. 2; MORRIS (1892); MARTIUS (1823–56) Vol. 1.
For the palmyra palm, FERGUSON (1850)
84 PETCH (1915)
85 BONDAR (1964); BARBOSA RODRIGUES (1903)
86 BONDAR (1964), RAWITSCHER (1946, 1948)
87 COOK and DOYLE (1913), MOORE (1963
88 WALLACE (1853), 36
89 MOORE, H. E. (1962) *Principes* **6** 90–6
90 SPRUCE (1871)
91 TOMLINSON (1961a), 12
92 BECCARI (1904), 114
93 BALL (1941)
94 HELM (1937), BALL (1941). German botanists distinguish the apical meristem as the 'Vegetationspunkt', the subapical mass of tissue as the 'Vegetationskegel'.
95 SCHOUTE (1912)
96 TOMLINSON (1961a), 23
97 See 67, for the palmyra palm.

Also SMITH (1963), TACKHOLM (1950), SURRE and ZILLER (1963)
98 MOHL (1849), TOMLINSON (1961a)
99 KAUL (1960)
100 BRANNER (1884). The study of the course of vascular bundles must be resumed with this work before one. After reading the first six pages of this dogmatic essay, one should study it backwards from the end paragraph by paragraph. Branner's assertion that anatomy follows the course of development seems reasonable but it does not follow that the course of development is that which he assumed. ZIMMERMAN and TOMLINSON (1965).
101 TOMLINSON (1961a), 71–3
102 SCHOLANDER *et al* (1961)
103 DAVIS (1961)
104 COPELAND (1906)
105 SCHOLANDER *et al* (1961)
106 BOSE (1929), 224–35
107 COPELAND (1906), SURRE and ZILLER (1963), DAVIS (1961)
108 WRIGHT (1951)
109 CORNER (1964) plate 33
110 RUDOLPH (1911), TOMLINSON (1962b)
111 LEON (1957), TOMLINSON (1962b), REES (1963)

## Chapter 5

112 Recently in the Solomon Islands I dissected several flowering trunks of the sago or leaf-palm *Metroxylon salomonense*. At the base of the huge terminal inflorescence I found a gradual transition from reduced foliage leaves to the comparatively small tubular

spathes. Perhaps such a transition occurs in all palms with terminal inflorescences.

112a See BAILEY (1963b), (1937), (1943), (1944)

113 For *Howeia*, see *idem* (1939); *Linospadix*, see HODGE, W. H. (1961) *Principes* **5**, 89–90

114 BLATTER (1926)

115 DOUGLAS and BIMANTORO (1957)

116 CORNER (1964), 273

117 Hapaxanthy and its alternative were first called monocarpy and polycarpy (DECANDOLLE, 1818, 1832). The terms are ambiguous for they imply one fruit, as in the crocus, and many fruits. ASA GRAY (*Structural Botany* pt 1, 33) in 1880 suggested monotocous and polytocous, but they have never been employed. WARMING in 1884 introduced hapaxanthy and pollacanthy though the better word is clearly pleonanthy. In his *Ecology of Plants* (1909), Warming ascribed the words to A. Braun and Kjellman respectively.

118 AUDUS (1959)

119 BONDAR (1964), 140

120 STANDLEY and STEYERMARK (1958)

121 GOODSPEED (s.d.)

122 SCHOMBURGK (1922), with many references to American palms in its vigorous pages

123 BOSE (1923), xiii

124 HOLTTUM (1955), CORNER (1954)

125 AITCHISON (1882), BECCARI (1931)

125a I have recently been able to determine by dissection of flowering trunks of *Metroxylon salomonense* in the Solomon Islands that the inflorescence is really terminal. The trunk tapers gradually through a region with smaller reduced leaves directly into the huge inflorescences. See reference 112.

126 FURTADO (1956), 37

127 SARKAR (1957)

128 BURRET (1953–6), MOORE (1963)

129 BUNTING, B., EATON, B. J. and GEORGI, C. D. V. (1927) The oil-palm in Malaya. *Malayan Agricultural Journal* **15**, 297

## Chapter 6

130 SARKAR (1956)

131 KNUTH (1909)

132 HOOKER (1856)

133 DOUGLAS and BIMANTORO (1957)

134 MOORE (see 89), FURTADO (1951)

135 CORNER (1964) figure 65c

136 MOORE (1957)

137 DRUDE (1877). This early work is fundamental for future investigations on the palm ovary and avule.

138 FURTADO (1964)

139 COSTERUS and SMITH (1916)

140 CORNER (1964) figure 76

## Chapter 7

141 WINTON (1901)

142 See p. 24 (HUMBOLDT)

143 LEACH (1948)

144 RIDLEY (1930). See also BURKILL (1958)

145 RIDLEY (1930), 356

146 BURKILL (1935) Vol. 1

147 STANDLEY and STEYERMARK (1958)

148 BOLIVAR-PIELTAIN (1950)

149 For the colours of fruits see the large works of MARTIUS and BARBOSA RODRIGUES.
150 SPRUCE (1906) Vol. 2, 223
151 WALLACE (1853), 24
152 *ibid*, 29
153 HUMBOLDT (1850), 161; WALLACE (1853), 94. See also 150.
154 WALLACE (1853), 15
155 GUPPY (1906), 330
156 BONDAR (1964), 22
157 GUPPY (1906), 436
158 CORNER (1964), xii
159 *idem* (1954)
160 For *Aiphanes*, see DUGAND (1944); for the other genera see the large works of MARTIUS and BARBOSA RODRIGUES
161 SPRUCE (1871)

162 BECCARI (1886), 90–2; BURRET (1956)
163 MIQUEL (1868) *Annales Musei Botanici Lugduno-Batavi* 4, 89, plates 2, 3. See also 78.
164 COOK (1910), BAILEY (1947b)
165 BURRET (1927)
166 BECCARI and PICHI-SERMOLLI (1955)
167 BURRET (1953–6)
168 SPRUCE (1871), 176
169 BURRET (1928a)
170 *idem* (1929b), BAILEY (1947a)
171 BECCARI (1931)
172 *idem* (1918), 197; *idem* (1913). See also GRIFFITH (1850) plate ccxx; MARTIUS (1850) Vol. 3, plates 179, 180
173 BECCARI (1918) plate 3

## Chapter 8

174 (BLUME (1836–47)
175 LOTHIAN (1959)
176 BURRET (1930a)
177 NETOLITZKY (1926)
178 MOORE (1957c)
179 SCHNARF (1933)
180 THISELTON-DYER (1910)
181 HEGNAUER (1963)
182 GATIN (1906)
183 BLATTER (1926), 220

184 CORNER (1964) figure 37
185 TOMLINSON (1960). Seedling and sapling leaves are called by this author *eophylls*, but the name does not carry the usual connotation of *eo* for the phyletic dawn.
186 BURRET (1930a)
187 BONDAR (1946)
188 COSTERUS and SMITH (1916)

## Chapter 9

189 BURKILL (1935), 1869
190 BAILEY (1947b), BURRET (1934), BAILEY and MOORE (1949)
191 COOK (1947)
192 BLUME (1847), BECCARI (1908, 1911, 1918), FURTADO (1951, 1953, 1955, 1956)
193 BECCARI (1908)
194 FURTADO (1956)
195 TOMLINSON (1964a)
196 *idem* (1962)

197 BECCARI (1884)
198 RIDLEY (1910)
199 BECCARI (1911)
200 HUMBOLDT (1849b) Vol. 1, 260
201 FURTADO (1951)
202 CORNER (1964) plate 33
203 FURTADO (1949)
204 BECCARI (1908)
205 FURTADO (1951)
206 TOMLINSON (1962)
207 BURKILL (1935)

**Chapter 10**

208 CROIZAT (1952, 1958), STEENIS (1963)
209 THORNE (1963)
210 CROIZAT (1952), 442–58
211 WULFF (1943), 173–99; RUNCORN (1962), 23–34; GOOD (1964) xxi
212 GOOD (1964)
213 RUNCORN (1962)
214 See, especially, ALAIN (1961), BAILEY (1942), BECCARI (monographs), BLAKE and ATTWOOD (1942), BLATTER (1926), BONDAR (1964), BURRET (monographs), CHRISTOPHERSEN (1955), CORDOBA and MEDINA (1951), DAHLGREN (1936), DRUDE (1895), DUGAND (1940), FURTADO (monographs), GAGNEPAIN (1937), GUILLAUMIN (1948, 1961), HUTCHINSON and DALZIEL (1936), JUMELLE (1945), LEON (1946), MOORE and FOSBERG (1956), PARHAM (1964), STANDLEY and STEYERMARK (1958).
215 TOMLINSON (1962)
216 CROIZAT (1958)
217 MENARD and HAMILTON (1963)
218 FURTADO (1941)
219 TOMLINSON (1962)
220 BAILEY (1933), 59
221 MOORE (1963), BONDAR (1941, 1964)
222 BARRY (1957), STORY (1959)
223 SKOTTSBERG (1953), 108, plates 60, 61; BECCARI and PICHI-SERMOLLI (1955)
224 JUMELLE (1945)
225 CORNER (1958); GOOD (1964) figures 25, 27
225a OAKLEY and MUIR-WOOD (1948)
226 BECCARI and PICHI-SERMOLLI (1955)
227 BAILEY (1942b)
228 ibid, KNUTH (1963)
229 BECCARI and PICHI-SERMOLLI

(1955)
230 LONCAREVIC (1964)
231 MOORE and FOSBERG (1956)
232 CROIZAT (1952) figure 93
233 CORNER (1958, 1963)
234 idem (1954b)
235 HODGE (1960)
236 BAILEY (1939)
237 MICHALOWSKI (1955)
238 SMALL (1926)
239 HODGE (1964)
240 CROIZAT (1952), 442–58; SMITH (1958)
241 LOTHIAN (1958–9)
242 MONOD (1955), TOMLINSON (1961b, 1962)
243 BURRET (1944)
244 CORDOBA y MEDINA (1951) 326–7
245 LEDIN, R. B., KIEM, S. C. and READ, R. W. (1959), *Principes* **3**, 23–33
246 McCURRACH (1960)
247 BAILEY (1942b)
248 MOORE and FOSBERG (1956)
249 GUPPY (1906)
250 HODGE (1960)
251 BLATTER (1926)
251a CORNER (1964) ix
252 NOÉ (1936), PRAKASH (1954), SITHOLEY (1954), GOTHAN (1964)
253 MARTIUS (1823–50) Vol. I
254 MAHABALÉ (1958), GREGUSS (1959), KAUL (1960), PRAKASH (1961), ZIMMERMANN (1962)
255 LADD, H. S. and BROWN, R. W. (1956), *National Geographic Magazine* **109**, 363 BROWN, R. W. (1956), *U.S. Geological Survey Prof. Paper* 274-H, 205–9
256 Reported at the Xth International Botanical Congress, held at Edinburgh 1964
257 CHANDLER (1964), 86–9
258 ARNOLD (1952), TRALAU (1964)

259 BEMMELEN, R. W. VAN (1949) *The Geology of Indonesia IA*, 358, figure 148

260 BERRY (1914)

261 PEARSON (1964)

## Chapter 11

262 MacLeod and Cobley (1961), 95-6

263 CORNER (1964) xi

264 EAMES (1953), TOMLINSON (1960)

265 ARBER (1925), v

266 CORNER (1964), 125-6

267 HUTCHINSON (1959)

268 CORNER (1964) figure 75

269 ZIMMERMANN (1959)

270 COSTERUS and SMITH (1916)

271 BONDAR (1964) 'It is in the schools that we should teach the new generations both to know and to love the palms, emphasizing their singular beauty and their multiple uses.'

272 HARLING (1958)

273 GRIFFITH (1856)

274 HIRMER (1920)

275 TROLL (1935)

275a For a similar picture of the Glossopteris flora of Gondwanaland, see EDNA P. PLUMSTEAD (1963), The influence of plants and environment on the developing animal life of karroo times, *South African Journal of Science* **59**, 147-52

## Chapter 12

276 FURTADO (1960)

277 BURKILL (1935)

278 FURTADO (1933)

279 BECCARI and PICHI- SERMOLLI (1955), 17

280 MOORE (1957)

281 BURRET (1934a)

282 GRIMBLE (1933-4)

283 BURKILL (1935)

284 See 283

285 See 283

286 SANDS (1926)

287 *Conselho Nacional de Geografia* (1949), 46; BONDAR (1964)

288 BURRET (1928b), BAILEY (1947b), BONDAR (1964)

289 CROIZAT (1958) Vol. I

290 FERGUSON (1850), BLATTER (1926)

291 BOSE (1923, xiii

292 BLATTER (1926), 193

293 BURKILL (1935)

294 BLATTER (1926)

295 See 365

296 McCURRACH (1960)

297 HUMBOLDT and BONPLAND (1808) plate I, 1-7

298 ANDRÉ (1878), BOMHARD (1936), BURRET (1929a), KARSTEN (1858-61)

299 MOORE (1963)

300 BECCARI (1916)

301 BONDAR (1941, 1964)

302 COOK (1939)

303 WALLACE (1853), 126

304 REYNE (1939)

305 BERRY (1926), COUPER (1952)

306 GUPPY (1906), COOK (1910), BECCARI (1917), RIDLEY (1930), BURKILL (1935), EDEN (1963)

307 DAVIS (1962)

308 AUDUS (1959), MAHESHWARI (1962)

309 COOK and DOYLE (1916)

310 FAO (1964)

311 CHILD (1964)

312 DAVIS (1962a, b)

**Chapter 13**

313 DAHLGREN and GLASSMAN
(1961–3)
314 *Conselho Nacional de Geografia*
(1949), 68
315 BECCARI (1931)
316 HODGE (1961)
317 DOUGLAS and BIMANTORO (1957)
318 JUMELLE (1945)
319 *Journal of the West African
Institute for Oil Palm Research*
(1953–64) Vols. I–V. See also,
BURKILL (1935), SURRE and
ZILLER (1963), HARTLEY (1964),
for accounts of the oil palm.
320 GOOD (1964), 438
321 BAILEY (1933)
322 SPRUCE (1871)
323 BLATTER (1926)
324 TÄCKHOLM and DRAV (1950), 281
325 BECCARI (1931), FURTADO (1940)

326 BLATTER (1926), BAILEY (1942a),
FITZGERALD (1946), HOOKER
(1827), DUROCHER YVON (1947),
JEFFRY (1963); SCHIMPER (1903),
233, f. 121
327 LONCAREVIC (1964)
328 TOMLINSON (1962)
328a See reference 125a for evidence
that the inflorescence is really
terminal in *Metroxylon
salomonense.*
329 MOORE and FOSBERG (1956),
BARRAU (1958, 1960), LEVER
(1964)
330 CROIZAT (1958)
331 BURRET (1936)
332 BURKILL (1935)
333 BARRAU (1958)
334 WALLACE (1869); GUPPY (1887),
82–3
335 BURKILL (1935)

**Chapter 14**

336 GRIFFITH (1847–54) *Posthumous
Papers III*, 168–75
337 CORNER (1964) figure 40
338 KARSTEN (1891)
339 BLUME (1836–47) Vol. 1, 71; Vol.
3, 73–80, t. 164, 165. See also, for
illustrations of *Nipa*, MARTIUS
(1823–50) Vol. 3; GRIFFITH,
*Icones Plantarum Asiaticarum III*,
t. 244–7; TRALAU (1964)
340 BURKILL (1935), LOOMIS (1956)
341 BARGAGLI-PETRUCCHI (1900)
*Malpighia* **14**, 306–60
342 BEAL (1937)
343 BECCARI (1890), HOOKER (1894),
DRUDE (1895), BLATTER (1926)
344 BURRET (1944)
344a CANDOLLE (1884)
345 THOMPSON (1949)
346 WEBER (1960)
347 SMITH (1878)
348 SKINNER (1911), MOLDENKE
(1952)

349 SWINGLE (1904); TÄCKHOLM and
DRAV (1950), 164–273
350 BLATTER (1926)
351 BOSE (1923) xiii
352 BLATTER (1926)
353 BECCARI and ROCK (1921)
354 ST JOHN (1957)
355 BECCARI (1910, 1910a)
356 A letter from Dr Francis Hallé,
Centre d'Adiopodoumé, Côte
d'Ivoire
357 BECCARI (1910), DALZIEL (1937)
358 BAILEY and MOORE (1949), 117
359 CROIZAT (1958) Vol. I
360 HODGE (1958)
361 BAILEY (1944)
362 MOORE (1951)
363 DAVIS (1961c)
364 *Conselho Nacional de Geografia*
(1947), 92; HODGE (1958),
HARTLEY (1964)
365 HODGE (1963)
366 For accounts of the coconut

monkey, see CORNER (1937)
*Annual Report of the Botanic
Gardens*, Singapore; *Zoo Life*

(1946) **1**, 89–92; *Proceedings of the
Royal Institution of Great Britain*
(1955) **36** 1–16

## Chapter 15

367 BURRET (1953–6), HUTCHINSON
(1959), MOORE and LEDIN (1961),
17–26; MOORE (1963c)
368 For anatomy, see TOMLINSON
(1962). For chromosome-studies,

see SHARMA and SARKAR (1956),
READ (1963).
369 TOMLINSON (1962)
370 SEEMANN (1854), HOOKER (1856),
SPRUCE (1871), COOK (1910, 1927)

# Bibliography

AGASSIZ, L. (1869) Address delivered on the centennial anniversary of the birth of Alexander von Humboldt (Boston Society of Natural History, Boston, Mass.)

AITCHISON, J. E. T. (1882) 'On the flora of the Kuram Valley, Afghanistan'. *Journal of the Linnean Society of Botany* **19**, 140-1, plate 26

ALAIN, BROTHER (1961) 'Palms of Cuba'. *Principes* **5**, 59-70

ANDRE, E. (1878) 'Les palmarès de Ceroxylon andicola en Colombie. *L'Illustration Horticole* **25**, 174-6

ARBER, AGNES (1925) *Monocotyledons* (Cambridge University Press. Reprinted 1961, J. Cramer: Weinheim)

ARKELL, W. J. (1956) *Jurassic geology of the world* (Oliver and Boyd Ltd: Edinburgh and London)

ARNOLD, C. A. (1952) 'A Nipa fruit from the Eocene of Texas'. *The Palaeobotanist* **1**, 73-8

ASHIDA, I. (1958) 'Kwan Koriba'. *The Botanical Magazine* **33**, 165-6

AUDUS, L. J. (1959) *Plant growth substances*. Ed. 2 (Leonard Hill Books Ltd, London)

BAILEY, F. M. (1913) *Comprehensive catalogue of Queensland plants* (Government Printer: Brisbane)

BAILEY, L. H. (1933) 'Certain palms of Panama'. *Gentes Herbarum* **3**, 33-116

—— (1936a) 'Arecastrum, Butia'. *Gentes Herbarum* **4**, 1-50

—— (1936b) 'Washingtonia'. *Gentes Herbarum* **4**, 53-82

—— (1937) 'Erythea'. *Gentes Herbarum* **4**, 85-118

—— (1939a) 'Howea cultorum'. *Gentes Herbarum* **4**, 189-98

—— (1939b) 'Zombia'. *Gentes Herbarum* **4**, 239-46

—— (1941) 'Acrocomia'. *Gentes Herbarum* **4**, 421-76

—— (1942a) 'Palmae Sechellarum'. *Gentes Herbarum* **6**, 3-48

—— (1942b) 'Palmae Mascarenarum'. *Gentes Herbarum* **6**, 51-104

—— (1943) 'Brahea et una Erythea'. *Gentes Herbarum* **6**, 177-97

—— (1944) 'Revision of the palmettoes'. *Gentes Herbarum* **6**, 367-459

—— (1946) 'The palm herbarium'. *Gentes Herbarum* **7**, 153-80

—— (1947a) 'Haitiella'. Contribution from the *Gray Herbarium of Harvard University* **165**, 5-9

—— (1947b) 'Palmae indigenae Trinitenses et Tobagenses'. *Gentes Herbarum* **7**, 353-445

—— and MOORE, H. E. (1949) 'Palms uncertain and new'. *Gentes Herbarum* **8**, 93-205

BAILLON, H. (1895) *Histoire des plantes*, Tome **13**, 244-404 (Librairie Hachette et Cie: Paris)

BALL, E. (1941) 'The development of the shoot apex and of the thickening meristem in *Phoenix canariensis* (Chaub.) with comparisons to *Washingtonia filifera* (Wats.) and *Trachycarpus excelsa* (Wendl.)'. *American Journal of Botany* **28**, 820–32

BARBOSA RODRIGUEZ, J. (1899) *Palmae novae paraguayenses* (Rio de Janeiro)

—— (1903) *Sertum palmarum Brasiliensium.* 2 vols. (Veuve Monnom: Brussels)

BARRAU, J. (1958) 'Subsistence agriculture in Melanesia'. *Bernice P. Bishop Museum Bulletin* **219**, 1–111

—— (1960) 'The sago palms'. *Principes* **4**, 44–53 (*Journal of the Palm Society*)

BARRY, D. (1957) 'The African relative of the Chilean Wine Palm'. *Principes* **2**, 180–2

BATES, H. W. (1910) *The naturalist on the River Amazons* (John Murray: London)

BEAL, J. M. (1937) 'Cytological studies in the genus *Phoenix*'. *Botanical Gazette* **99**, 400–7

BECCARI, O. (1884) 'Piante ospitatrici, ossia piante formicare della Malesia e della Papuasia'. *Malesia* **2**, 62–79

—— (1886) 'Nuovi studi sulle palme asiatiche'. *Malesia* **3**, 58–149

—— (1890) 'Rivista monographica delle specie del genere *Phoenix* (Linn.) *Malesia* **3**, 345–416

—— (1902) *Nelle foreste di Borneo*, Firenze, 2nd ed. (1921)

—— (1904) *Wanderings in the great forests of Borneo.* Translated by E. Gigliolo. Revised and edited by F. H. H. Guillemard (Archibald Constable and Co. Ltd: London)

——(1908) 'Asiatic palms—Lepidocaryeae, Part I, The species of *Calamus*'. *Annals of the Royal Botanic Garden, Calcutta* **11**, with Appendix (1913)

—— (1910a) 'Le palme del genere Raphia'. *L'Agricoltura Coloniale* **4**, 137–70

—— (1910b) 'Glaziova treubiana, nouvelle espèce de Cocoinée, avec observation sur le genre Cocos'. *Annales du Jardin Botanique de Buitenzorg*, Series 2, Supplement 3, 791–806

——(1910c) 'Contributo alla conoscenza delle Lepidocaryeae affricane'. *Webbia* **3**, 247–94

—— (1910d) 'Studio monografico del genere Raphia'. *Webbia* **3**, 37–130

—— (1911) 'Asiatic palms—Lepidocaryeae. Part II. The species of *Daemonorops*'. *Annals of the Royal Botanic Garden, Calcutta* **12**

—— (1913) 'Le palme del genere *Eugeissona* sono delle *Lepidocaryeae* o piuttosto delle *Cocoineae?*'. *Webbia* **4**, 190–202

—— (1916) *Il genere Cocos* (Linn.) *e palme affini* (Firenze)

—— (1917) 'The origin and dispersal of Cocos nucifera'. *Philipppine Journal of Science C*, Botany **12**, 27–43. Summary in *Principes* 7 (1963) 57–69

—— (1918) 'Asiatic palms—Lepidocaryeac. Part III. The species of the genera *Ceratolobus, Calospatha, Plectocomia, Plectocomiopsis, Myrialepis, Zalacca, Pigafetta, Korthalsia, Metroxylon, Eugeissona*'. *Annals of the Royal Botanic Garden, Calcutta* **12**

—— *Nuova Guinea, Selebes e Molucche*, Firenze

—— (1931) 'Asiatic palms—Corypheae'. Revised and edited by U. Martelli. *Annals of the Royal Botanic Garden, Calcutta* **13**

—— and PICHI-SERMOLLI, R. E. G. (1955) 'Subfamiliae *Arecoidarum palmae gerontogeae*'. *Webbia* **9**, 1–187

—— and ROCK, J. F. (1921) 'A monographic study of the genus *Pritchardia*'. *Memoirs of the Bernice Pauohi Bishop Museum* 8, 1-77

BERRY, E. W. (1914) 'Fruits of a date palm in the Tertiary deposits of East Texas'. *American Journal of Science*, ser. 4, 37, 403

—— (1926) 'Cocos and Phymatocaryon in the Pliocene of New Zealand'. *American Journal of Science*, ser. 5, 12, 181

BILLIARDIÈRE, H. LA (1819) 'Mémoire sur le palmier Nipa'. *Mémoires du Muséum National d'Histoire Naturelle* 5, 297

BLAKE, S. F. and ATWOOD, ALICE C. (1942) *Geographical guide to the floras of the world*. Part I. United States Department of Agriculture, Miscellaneous Publication n.401

BLATTER, E. (1926) *The palms of British India and Ceylon* (Oxford University Press: London)

BLUME, C. L. (1836-47) *Rumphia*, Vols I-III (C. G. Sulpke: Amsterdam)

BOLIVAR-PIELTAIN, C. (1950) *Informe sobre el Huallaga* (Organismo Coordinador de la Hileia Amazonica, Ministerio de Relaciones Exteriores: Lima)

BOMHARD, M. L. (1936) 'The wax palms'. *Annual Report*, Smithsonian Institution, publ. 3429, 303-24

BONDAR, G. (1941) 'Palmeiras do genero Cocos'. *Instituto Central de Fomento Econômico da Bahia, Boletim* 9, 1-53

—— (1964) 'Palmeiras do Brasil'. *Instituto de Botânico, Boletim* 2

BOSE, J. C. (1923) *The physiology of the ascent of sap* (Longmans, Green and Co.: London)

—— (1929) *Growth and tropic movements of plants* (Longmans, Green and Co.: London)

BRANNER, J. C. (1884) 'The course and growth of fibro-vascular bundles in palms'. *Proceedings of the American Philosophical Society* 21, 459-83

BURKILL, I. H. (1935) *A dictionary of the economic products of the Malay Peninsula.* 2 vols. (Crown Agents for the Colonies: London)

—— (1953) 'Chapters in the history of botany in India, I'. *Journal of the Bombay Natural History Society* 51, 846-78

—— (1956) 'Chapters in the history of botany in India, II'. *Journal of the Bombay Natural History Society* 54, 58-71

—— (1957) 'Chapters in the history of botany in India, V'. *Journal of the Bombay Natural History Society* 59, 771

—— (1958) Obituary—H. N. Ridley. *Proceedings of the Linnean Society of London* 169, 35-8

BURRET, M. (1927) 'Eine neue Art der Palmengattung *Pelagodoxa* (Becc.) aus der Südsee'. *Notizblatt des Botanischen Gartens und Museums zu Berlin-Dahlem* 10, 286-8

——(1928a) 'Die Palmengattungen *Chelyocarpus* (Dammer) und *Tessmanniophoenix* (Burret) nov. gen.' *Notizblatt des Botanischen Gartens und Museums zu Berlin-Dahlem* 10, 394-401

—— (1928b) 'Die Palmengattungen *Orbignya*, *Attalea*, *Scheelea* und *Maximiliana*'. *Notizblatt des Botanischen Gartens und Museums zu Berlin-Dahlem* 10, 493-543, 651-701

—— (1929a) 'Die Gattung *Ceroxylon*'. *Notizblatt des Botanischen Gartens und Museums zu Berlin-Dahlem* **10**, 841-53

—— (1929b) 'Palmae Cubenses et Domingenses a cl. E. L. Ekman 1914-28 lectae'. *Kungliga Svenska Vetenskapsakadamiens Handlingar*, ser. 3, **6**, n.7, 1-28

—— (1930a) 'Die Gattung *Euterpe*'. *Engler Botanische Jahrbücher* **63**, 49-76

—— (1930b) 'Geonomeae Americanae'. *Engler Botanische Jahrbücher* **63**, 123-270

—— (1934a) 'Bactris und verwandte Palmengattungen'. *Fedde's Repertorium Specierum Novarum Regni Vegetabilis* **34**, 167-253

—— (1934b) 'Desmoncus'. *Fedde's Repertorum Specierum Novarum Regni Vegetabilis* **36**, 197-221

—— (1936) 'Neue Palmen aus New Guinea III. Zugleich Palmen von dem Salomo-Inseln'. *Notizblatt des Botanischen Gartens und Museums zu Berlin-Dahlem* **13**, 65-101

—— (1938) 'Palmae Brasilienses'. *Notizblatt des Botanischen Gartens und Museums zu Berlin-Dahlem* **14**, 231-60

—— (1940) 'Indomalayische Palmen'. *Notizblatt des Botanischen Gartens und Museums zu Berlin-Dahlem* **15**, 164-210

—— (1944) 'Die Palme Arabiens'. *Engler Botanische Jahrbücher* **73**, 175-90

—— and POTZTAL, EVA (1953-6) 'Systematische Uebersicht über die Gruppen der Palmen'. *Willdenowia* **1**, 59-74, 350-85

CANDOLLE, A. DE (1856-7) 'Sketch of the life and writings of M. de Martius'. *Hooker's Journal of Botany and Kew Gardens Miscellany* **8**, 362-9; **9**, 6-10, 41-7

—— (1884) *Origin of cultivated plants* (Kegan Paul, Trench and Co.: London)

CHANDLER, MARJORIE E. J. (1964) *The Lower Tertiary Floras of Southern England IV* (British Museum, Natural History: London)

CHILD, R. (1964) *Coconuts* (Longmans: London)

CHRISTOPHERSEN, E. (1935) 'Flowering plants of Samoa'. *Bernice P. Bishop Museum Bulletin* **128**

CONSELIIO NACIONAL DE GEOGRAFIA (1949) *Tipos e aspectos do Brasil.* 5th Ed. (Rio de Janeiro)

COOK, O. F. (1910a) 'Relationship of the ivory palms'. *Contributions from U.S. National Herbarium* **13**, 133-41

—— (1910b) 'History of the coconut palm in America'. *Contributions from U.S. National Herbarium* **14**, 271-342. (1963) Summary in *Principes* **7**, 54-7

—— (1927) 'New genera and species of ivory palms from Colombia, Ecuador and Peru'. *Journal of the Washington Academy of Sciences* **17**, 218-30

—— (1939) 'A new palm from Cocos Island, collected on the Presidential Cruise of 1938'. *Smithsonian Miscellaneous Collections* **98**, n.7

—— (1947) 'Climbing and creeping palms in Mexico and Guatemala, related to household palms'. *National Horticultural Magazine* **26**, 215-31

—— and DOYLE, C. B. (1913) 'Three new genera of stilt palms (Iriartaceae) from Colombia, with a synoptical review of the family'. *Contributions from U.S. National Herbarium* **16**, 225-39

—— —— (1916) 'Germinating coconuts'. *Journal of Heredity* **7**, 146-57

COPELAND, E. B. (1906) 'On the water relations of the coconut palm. (*Cocos nucifera*)'. *Philippine Journal of Science* **1**, 5-58

CORDOBA, L. C. F. and MEDINA, F. O. (1951) *Estudio sobre la vegetacion y la flora forestal de las Canarias Occidentales* (Instituto Forestal de Investigaciones y Experiencias: Madrid)

CORNER, E. J. H. (1952) *Wayside Trees of Malaya*, 2nd ed. 2 vols. (Government Printer: Singapore)

—— (1954a) 'The durian theory extended—II. The arillate fruit and the compound leaf'. *Phytomorphology* **4**, 152–65

—— (1954b) *The evolution of tropical forest. Evolution as a process.* Ed. by J. S. Huxley, A. C. Hardy and E. B. Ford, 35–46 (Allen and Unwin: London)

—— (1958) 'An introduction to the distribution of Ficus'. *Reinwardtia* **4**, 15–45

—— (1963) 'Ficus in the Pacific Region'. *Pacific Basin Biogeography* 233–45

—— (1964) *The Life of plants* (Weidenfeld and Nicolson: London)

COSTERUS, J. C. and SMITH, J. J. (1916) 'Studies in tropical teratology'. *Annales du Jardin Botanique de Buitenzorg* ser. 2, **14**, 83–94

CROIZAT, L. (1952) *Manual of phytogeography* (W. Junk: The Hague)

—— (1958) *Panbiogeography* Vols 3 (published by the author: Caracas)

DAHLGREN, B. E. (1936) *Index of American palms.* Chicago Field Museum of Natural History, Botanical series **14**, 1–438

—— and GLASSMAN, S. F. (1961–3) 'A revision of the genus Copernicia'. *Gentes Herbarum* **9**, 1–232

DALZIEL, J. M. (1937) *Useful plants of West Tropical Africa* (Crown Agents for the Colonies: London)

DAVIS, T. A. (1961a) 'Importance des racines aériennes du cocotier'. *Oléagineux* **16**, 653–62

—— (1961b) 'High root-pressures in palms'. *Nature* **192** 277–8

—— (1961c) 'Climbing the coconut. New machine for climbing palms with smooth trunks'. *World Crops*

—— (1962a) 'Asymmetry and yield in coconut'. *Experientia* **18**, 321

—— (1962b) 'The non-inheritance of asymmetry in *Cocos nucifera*'. *Journal of Genetics* **58**, 43–50

—— (1962c) 'Vegetative propagation in the coconut'. *Nature* **196**, 905–6

DOUGLAS, J. and BIMANTORO, R. R. (1957) 'Identification of the Corypha palms which flowered in the Hortus Bogoriensis 1953–5'. *Annales Bogorienses* **2**, 137–48

DRUDE, O. (1881) 'Cyclanthaceae et Palmae'. *Martius, Flora Brasiliensis* **3**, Part 2 (Typographia regia: Munich)

—— (1887) 'Ausgewälte Beispiele zur Erläuterung der Fruchtbildung bei den Palmen'. *Botanische Zeitung* **35**, 600–39

—— (1889) 'Palmae'. *Engler, Natürlichen Pflanzenfamilien II*, 3 (Wilhelm Engelmann: Leipzig)

—— (1895) 'Die Palmenflora des tropischen Afrika'. *Engler Botanische Jahrbücher* **21**, 108–36

DUGAND, A. (1940) 'Palmas de Colombia'. *Caldasia* **1**, 20–84

—— (1944) 'Palmas nuevos o criticos Colombianos II'. *Caldasia* **2**, 442–58

DUROCHER, YVON F. (1947) 'Seychelles Botanical Treasure'. *La Revue Agricole de l'Ile Maurice* **26**, 69–87

EAMES, A. J. (1953) 'Neglected morphology of the palm leaf'. *Phytomorphology* **3**, 172–89

EDEN, R. A. (1963) 'The quest for the home of the coconut'. *South Pacific Bulletin*, July 1963, 39–42

EICHLER, A. G. (1885) *Zur Entwicklungsgeschichte der Palmenblätter*. (1886) Abhandlungen der Königlichen Akademie der Wissenschaften zu Berlin, Physikalisch-Mathematische Classe 1–24 (Berlin)

ELLIOTT, H. F. L. (1964) *The ecology of man in the tropical environment*. International Union for the Conservation of Nature, Publications new series n.4: Morge

ENGLER, A. (1908) *Die Pflanzenwelt Afrikas*. Vol. 2, 222–35 (Wilhelm Engelmann: Leipzig)

—— (1930) *Die natürlichen Pflanzenfamilien*, 2nd ed. Band 15a, Agavaceae (F. Pax and K. Hoffmann); Bromeliaceae (H. Harms); Juncaceae (F. Vierhapper); Liliaceae (K. Krause); Musaceae (H. Winkler); Velloziaceae (F. Pax). (Wilhelm Engelmann: Leipzig)

FAHN, A. (1961) 'The anatomical structure of Xanthorrhoeaceae and its taxonomic position'. *Recent Advances in Botany*, 155–60 (University of Toronto Press)

FAO (1964) *Production yearbook 1963* (Food and Agricultural Organisation of the United Nations: Rome)

FERGUSON, W. (1850) *The palmyra palm, embracing extracts from nearly every author that has noticed the tree* (Observer Press: Colombo)

FITZGERALD, V. (1946) 'On the vegetation of the Seychelles'. *Journal of Ecology* **28**, 465–83

FOSBROOKE, JANE (1951) 'A prehistoric picture gallery'. *East African Annual* 1950–1, 61–3

FURTADO, C. X. (1933) 'The limits of the genus *Areca* (Linn.) and its sections'. *Fedde's Repertorium Specierum novarum Regni vegetabilis* **33**, 217–39

—— (1940) 'Palmae Malesicae VIII—the genus *Licuala* in the Malay Peninsula'. *Gardens' Bulletin, Straits Settlements* **11**, 31–73

—— (1941) 'Palmae Malesicae IX—two new Coryphaceous genera in Malaya'. *Gardens' Bulletin, Straits Settlements* **11**, 236–43

—— (1949) 'Palmae Malesicae X—the Malayan species of Salacca'. *Gardens' Bulletin, Singapore* **12**, 378–403

—— (1951) 'Palmae Malesicae XI–XVI—*Korthalsia, Plectocomiopsis, Myrialepis, Plectocomia, Ceratolobus, Calospatha*'. *Gardens' Bulletin, Singapore* **13**, 300–65

—— (1953) 'The genus Daemonorops in Malaya'. *Gardens' Bulletin, Singapore* **14**, 49–147

—— (1955) 'Palmae Malesicae XVIII—two new *Calamoid* genera of Malaysia'. *Gardens' Bulletin, Singapore* **14**, 517–29

—— (1956) 'Palmae Malesicae XIX—the genus *Calamus* in the Malayan Peninsula'. *Gardens' Bulletin, Singapore* **15**, 32–265

—— (1960) 'The philological origin of Areca and Catechu'. *Principes* **4**, 26–31

—— (1964) 'The origin of the word "Cocos" '. *Gardens' Bulletin, Singapore* **20**, 295–312

GAGNEPAIN, F. (1937) 'Palmiers'. *Lecomte Flore générale de l'Indo-Chine* **6**, 946–1056 (Manon et Cie: Paris)

GATIN, C. L. (1906) 'Recherches anatomiques et chimiques sur la germination des palmiers'. *Annales des Sciences Naturelles*, ser. 9, **3**, 191–315 (Masson et Cie: Paris)

AA

GAUDICHAUD-BEAUPRE, C. (1840–8) 'Voyage au tour du monde sur la corvette La Bonite'. *Botanique Atlas* (Arthur Bertrand: Paris)

GOOD, R. (1964) *The geography of flowering plants*. 3rd ed. (Longmans: London)

GOODSPEED, T. H. (s.d.) *Plant hunters in the Andes* (Robert Hare Ltd: London)

GOTTIAN, W. and WEYLAND, H. (1964) *Lehrbuch der Palaeobotanik*. 2nd ed. (Akademie Verlag: Berlin)

GREGUSS, P. (1959) 'A palm trunk from the Lower Miocene Coal Basin of Salgotarjan'. *The Palaeobotanist* **8**, 19–21

GRIFFITH, W. (1847–54) *Notulae ad plantas asiaticas*. Posthumous papers arranged by John McClelland (Bishop's College Press: Calcutta)

—— (1850) *Palms of British East India*. Arranged by John McClelland (Charles A. Serrao: Calcutta)

GRIMBLE, A. (1933–4) 'The migrations of a pandanus people'. *Journal of the Polynesian Society* **42**, mem. 12, 1–84

GUILLAUMIN, A. (1948) *Flore de la Nouvelle Calédonie (Phanérogames)* (Office de la Recherche Scientifique Coloniale: Paris)

—— (1961) 'Les palmiers de la Nouvelle Calédonie'. *Journal d'Agriculture Tropical et de Botanique Appliquée* **8**, 57–64

GUPPY, H. B. (1887) *The Solomon Islands and their natives* (Swan, Sonnenschein, Lowrey and Co.: London)

—— (1906) *Observations of a naturalist in the Pacific between 1896 and 1899* (Macmillan & Co. Ltd: London)

HARLING, G. (1946) 'Studien über der Blutenbau und die Embryologie der familie Cyclanthaceae'. *Svensk Botanisk Tidskrift* **40**, 25–272

—— (1958) 'Monograph of the Cyclanthaceae'. *Acta Horti Bergiani* **18**, 1–428

HARTLEY, C. W. S. (1964) 'West African Institute for oil palm research'. *Principes* **8**, 92–107

HEGNAUER, R. (1963) *Chemotaxonomie der Pflanzen*. Band 2. Monocotyledoneae (Birkhäuser Verlag: Basel)

HELM, J. (1937) 'Das Erstarkungswachsthum der Palmen und einiger anderer Monocotylen'. *Planta* **26**, 319–64

HILL, A. F. (1952a) *Economic Botany* (McGraw-Hill Book Company, Inc.: New York)

HIRMER, M. (1920) 'Beitrage zur Morphologie und Entwickslungeschichte der Blatter einiger Palmen und Cyclanthaceen'. *Flora* **113**, 178–89

HODGE, W. H. (1958) 'The royal palm climbers of Cuba'. *Principes* **2**, 17–20

—— (1960) 'Bermuda's palmetto'. *Principes* **4**, 90–100

—— (1961) 'Nature's biggest bouquet'. *Principes* **5**, 125–34

—— (1963) 'Toddy collection in Ceylon'. *Principes* **7**, 70–9

—— (1964) 'A strand palm of south-east Brazil'. *Principes* **8**, 55–7

HOLTTUM, R. E. (1953) *Flora of Malaya*, Vol. 1, Orchids (Government Printing Office: Singapore)

—— (1955) 'Growth-habits of monocotyledons'. *Phytomorphology* **5**, 399–413

—— (1959) 'Kwan Koriba'. *Gardens' Bulletin, Singapore* **17**, 339–40

HOOKER, W. J. (1827) 'Lodoicea'. *Curtis's Botanical Magazine* **54**, t.2734–8

—— (1856) 'Phytelephas macrocarpa'. *Curtis's Botanical Magazine*, ser. 3, **12**, t.4913, 4914

HOOKER, J. D. (1879) 'Carludovica ensiformis'. Curtis's Botanical Magazine **35**, t.6418
—— (1889) 'Carludovica rotundifolia'. Curtis's Botanical Magazine **45**, t.7083
—— (1894) Flora of British India. Vol. 6 (L. Reeve and Co.: London)
HUMBOLDT, A. VON (1807) Essai sur la géographie des plantes (F. Schoell: Paris);
(1959) Sherborn Fund Facsimile I (Society for the Bibliography of Natural History,
British Museum of Natural History: London)
—— (1849a) Ansichten der Natur. 3rd ed. (Stuttgart); (1808) 1st ed.
—— (1849b) Aspects of nature. 2 vols. Translated by Mrs Sabine (Longman, Brown,
Green, and Longmans: London)
—— (1850) Views of nature. 2 vols. Translated by E. C. Otté and Henry G. Bohn
(Henry G. Bohn: London)
—— (1852) Travels to the equinoctial regions of America. 3 vols. Translated by
Thomasina Ross (Henry G. Bohn: London)
—— and BONPLAND, A. (1808) Plantae aequinoctiales. 2 vols (F. Schoell: Paris)
—— —— and KUNTH, C. S. (1815) Nova genera et species plantarum. Tomus 1,.
being Part 6 (Botany) of the voyage of Humboldt and Bonpland (Librairie Greque
—Latine—Allemande: Paris)
HUTCHINSON, J. (1959) The families of flowering plants. Vol. II. Monocotyledons (The
Clarendon Press: Oxford)
—— and DALZIEL, J. M. (1936) Flora of West Tropical Africa. Vol 2 (Crown Agents
for the Colonies: London)
JACQUIN, N. J. (1763) Selectarum stirpium americanarum historia (Officina Krau-
siana: Vienna)
JEFFREY, C. (1963) The botany of the Seychelles (Department of Technical Co-
operation: London)
JULIANO, J. B. (1926) 'Origin, development, and nature of the stony layer of the
coconut'. Philippine Journal of Science **30**, 187–200
—— and QUISUMBING, E. (1931) 'Morphology of the flower of Cocos nucifera'.
Philippine Journal of Science **45**, 449–58
JUMELLE, N. J. (1945) Flore de Madagascar et des Comores. Famille 30. Palmae
(Muséum National d'Histoire Naturelle: Paris)
KARSTEN, G. (1891) 'Ueber die Mangrove-Vegetation in Malayischen Archipel'.
Bibliotheca Botanica **22**, 1–71
KARSTEN, H. (1847) Die Vegetationsorgane der Palmen. Abhandlungen der König-
lichen Akademie der Wissenschaften zu Berlin; (1849) Physikalische Classe
(Berlin)
—— (1856) 'Plantae Columbianae'. Linnaea **28**, 251–5
—— (1858–61) Florae Columbiae. Vol. I (Ferdinand Duemmler: Berlin)
KAUL, K. N. (1960) 'The anatomy of the stem of palms and the problem of the
artificial genus Palmoxylon (Schenk)'. Bulletin of the National Botanic Gardens
**51**, 1–52, Lucknow
KERCHOVE DE DENTERGHEM, O. DE (1878) Les palmiers (J. Rothschild: Paris)
KIRKWOOD, J. E. and GIES, W. J. (1902) 'Chemical studies of the cocoanut with some
notes on the changes during germination'. Bulletin of the Torrey Botanical Club
**29**, 321–59
KNUTH, F. M. (1963) 'A visit to the Seychelles'. Principes **7**, 44–54

381

KNUTH, P. (1909) *Handbook of flower pollination*. Vol. 3, 486-7 (Clarendon Press: Oxford)

LAWRENCE, G. H. M. (1951) *Taxonomy of vascular plants* (The Macmillan Company: New York)

LEACH, R. (1948) *Amblypelta nut fall of coconut palms in the Solomon Islands.* Mimeograph, School of Agriculture, Cambridge

LEDIN R. BRUCE (1961) 'Cultivated palms'. *The American Horticultural Magazine* **40**, n.1

LEE, S. C. (1935) *Forest botany of China* (Commercial Press: Shanghai)

LEON, H. (1946) *Flora de Cuba*. Vol. I. Contribuciones Ocasionales del Museo de Historia Natural del Colegio de la Salle, n.8 (Cultural S.A.: La Habana)

LEON, N. J. DE (1957) 'Zombia antillarum'. *Principes* **1**, 148-50

LEVER, R. A. (1964) 'Ivory nut palms'. *World Crops* n.16 (Grampian Press Ltd: London)

LINNAEUS, C. (1753) *Species plantarum*. 2 vols. Facsimile edition with an introduction by W. T. Stearn, 1957 (The Ray Society: London)

LONCAREVIC, B. D. (1964) 'Geophysical studies in the Indian Ocean'. *Endeavour* **23**, 43-7

LOOMIS, H. F. (1956) 'The nipa palm of the orient'. *Principes* **1**, 41-5

LOTHIAN, T. R. N. (1958-9) 'The Livistonas of Australia'. *Principes* **2**, 92-4, **3**, 53-63

MACLEOD, ANNA M. and COBLEY, L. S. (1961) *Contemporary botanical thought* (Oliver and Boyd: Edinburgh, London)

MAHABALE, T. S. (1958) 'Resolution of the artificial palm genus *Palmoxylon*: a new approach'. *The Palaeobotanist* **7**, 76-84

MAHESHWARI, P. (1962) 'Contacts between embryology, physiology, and genetics'. *Proceedings of the Summer School of Botany, Darjeeling 1960*, 171-92 (Ministry of Scientific Research and Cultural Affairs: New Delhi)

MANN, G. and WENDLAND, H. (1864) 'On the palms of western Tropical Africa'. *Transactions of the Linnean Society of London* **24**, 421-39

MARTELLI, U. and PICHI-SERMOLLI, R. (1951) 'Les Pandanacées récoltées par Henri Perrier de la Bathie à Madagascar'. *Mémoires de l'Institut Scientifique de Madagascar*, ser. B, 3

MARTIUS, C. F. P. VON (1824) *Palmarum familia ejusque genera* (Lindauer: Munich)

—— (1823-50) *Historia naturalis palmarum*. Vol. 1. Palmas generatim tractat. Vol. 2, Brasiliae palmas singulatim descriptione et icone illustrat. Vol. 3, Expositio palmarum systematica. (Munich)

—— (1839) 'Die Verbreitung der Palmen in der alten Welt'. *Münchner Gelehrten Anzeigen* n.105-18, 1-94

—— (1843-6) 'Palmetum Orbignyanum'. *A. D'Orbigny, Voyage dans l'Amérique medionale*, vol. 7, sect. 3 (Paris)

—— (1860) *Denkrede auf Alexander von Humboldt* (University Press: Munich)

—— EICHLER, A. G. and URBAN I. (1840-1906) *Flora Brasiliensis*. 15 vols. Reprinted 1964-5 (Stechert-Hafner Service Agency Inc.: New York)

McCANN, C. (1935) Ethelbert Blatter, S. J. Obituary. List of publications. *Journal of the Bombay Natural History Society* **37**, 468

McCURRACH, J. C. (1960) *Palms of the world* (Harper and Brothers: New York)

MENARD, H. W. and HAMILTON, E. L. (1963) 'Palaeogeography of the tropical Pacific'. *Pacific Basin Biogeography*, 193–217 (Bishop Museum Press: Honolulu)

MERRILL, E. D. (1917) 'An interpretation of Rumphius's Herbarium Amboinense'. *Bureau of Science Publications* n.9 (Bureau of Printing: Manila)

METZ, C. (1935) 'Bromeliaceae'. *Engler, Das Pflanzenreich* Band IV, n.32 (Wilhelm Engelmann: Leipzig)

MICHALOWSKI, M. (1958) 'The ecology of Paraguayan palms'. *Principes* **2**, 52–8

MOHL, H. VON (1849) *On the structure of the palm stem* (The Ray Society: London)

MOLDENKE, H. N. and MOLDENKE, ALMA L. (1952) *Plants of the Bible* (Chronica Botanica Co.: Waltham, Mass.)

MONOD, TH. (1955) 'Remarques sur un palmier peu connu: Wissmannia carinensis'. *Bulletin de l'Institut Français d'Afrique Noire* ser. A, 338–58

MOORE, H. E. (1951) 'Some American Corypheae'. *Gentes Herbarum* **8**, 209–22

—— (1957a) 'The genus Reinhardtia'. *Principes* **1**, 127–45

—— (1957b) 'Veitchia'. *Gentes Herbarum* **8**, 483–536

—— (1957c) 'Reinhardtia'. *Gentes Herbarum* **8**, 541–76

—— (1963a) 'Iriartiella Wendland emended'. *Gentes Herbarum* **9**, 275–85

—— (1963b) 'Two new palms from Peru'. *Principes* **7**, 107–15

—— (1963c) 'An annotated checklist of cultivated palms'. *Principes* **7**, 119–82

—— and FOSBERG, F. R. (1956) 'The palms of Micronesia and the Bonin Islands'. *Gentes Herbarum* **8**, 432–78

MORRIS, D. (1892) 'On the phenomena concerned in the production of forked and branched palms'. *Journal of the Linnean Society, Botany* **29**, 281–98

NETOLITZKY, F. (1926) 'Anatomie der Angiospermen Samen'. *Handbuch der Pflanzenanatomie*, Band 10, 61–65 (Gebrüder Borntrager: Berlin)

NOE, A. C. (1936) 'Fossil palms. Index of American Palms'. *Field Museum of Natural History, Botanical Series* **14**, 439–56 (Chicago)

OAKLEY, K. P. and MUIR-WOOD, HELEN M. (1964) *The succession of life through geological time* (British Museum, Natural History: London)

PARHAM, J. W. (1964) *Plants of the Fiji Islands* (Government Press: Suva, Fiji)

PEARSON, R. (1964) *Animals and plants of the Cenozoic era* (Butterworths: London)

PERIASAMY, K. (1962) 'Morphological and ontogenetic studies in palms—1. Development of the plicate condition in the palm-leaf'. *Phytomorphology* **12**, 54–64

PETCH, T. (1915 'The effect of lightning on coconut palms'. *Annals of the Royal Botanic Gardens, Peradeniya* **6**, 31–42

PRAKASH, U. (1954) '*Palmocarpon mohgaoeense* sp. nov. A palm fruit from the Deccan Intertrappean Series, India'. *The Palaeobotanist* **3**, 91–6

—— (1961) '*Palmoxylon eocenum* sp. nov.' *The Palaeobotanist* **10**, 6–9

RAWITSCHER, F. (1948) 'The water economy of the vegetation of the "campos cerrados" in southern Brazil'. *Journal of Ecology* **36**, 237–68

—— and RACHID, M. (1946) 'Troncos subterrâneos de plantas brasileiras'. *Annaes de Academia Brasileira de Ciencias* **18**, 261

READ, R. W. (1961) 'Madagascar's three-sided palm—*Neodypsis decaryi*'. *Principes* **5**, 71–4

—— (1963) 'Palm chromosomes'. *Principes* **7**, 85–8

REED, H. S. (1942) *A short history of the plant sciences* (Chronica Botanica Co.; Waltham, Mass.)

REES, A. R. (1963a) 'Germination of palm seeds using a method developed for the oil palm'. *Principes* 7, 27–30

—— (1963b) 'A note on the spines in the oil palm'. *Principes* 7, 30–1

REYNE, A. (1939) 'On the food habits of the coconut crab (*Birgus latro* L.) with notes on its distribution'. *Archives Neerlandaises de Zoologie* 3, 283–320

RHEEDE TOT DRAKENSTEIN, H. VAN (1678–1703) *Hortus indicus malabaricus.* 12 vols. (J. v. Someren and J. v. Dyck: Amsterdam)

RIDLEY, H. N. (1910) 'Symbiosis of ants and plants'. *Annals of Botany* 24, 459–61

—— (1930) *The dispersal of plants throughout the world* (L. Reeve and Co. Ltd: Ashford, Kent)

RUDOLPH, K. (1911) 'Zur Kenntniss der Entfaltungs einrichtungen an Palmenblättern'. *Berichte der Deutschen Botanischen Gesellschaft* 29, 39–47

RUMPHIUS, G. E. (1741–55) *Herbarium amboinense.* 6 vols. Edited by J. Burmann (Meinard Uytwerf: Amsterdam)

RUNCORN, S. K. (1962) *Continental drift* (Academic Press: New York, London)

SAFFORD, W. E. (1905) 'The useful plants of the island of Guam'. *Contributions from the U.S. National Herbarium* 9, 1–416

SANDS, W. N. (1926) 'Observations on the betel nut palm (*Areca catechu* L.)'. *Malayan Agricultural Journal* 14, 202

SARKAR, S. K. (1956) 'Male sterility in palms'. *Agronomia Lusitana* 18, 257–71

—— (1957 'Sex chromosomes in palms'. *Genetica Iberica* 9, 133–42

SCHERY, R. W. (1954) *Plants for man* (George Allen and Unwin Ltd: London)

SCHIMPER, A. F. W. (1903) *Plant geography.* Translated by W. R. Fisher. Revised and edited by P. Groom and I. Bayley Balfour (Clarendon Press: Oxford)

SCHNARF, K. (1933) 'Embryologie der Angiospermen'. *Handbuch der Pflanzenanatomie*, Band 10/2 (Gebrüder Borntraeger: Berlin)

SCHOLANDER, P. F., HEMMINGSEN, E. and GAREY, W. (1961) 'Cohesive lift of sap in the rattan vine'. *Science* 134, 1835–8

SCHOMBURGK, R. (1922) *Travels in British Guiana 1840–1844.* 2 vols. Translated by W. E. Roth (*Daily Chronicle* Office: Georgetown, British Guiana)

SCHOUTE, J. C. (1909) 'Ueber die verästelung bei monokotylen Bäumen. II, Die verästelung von Hyphaene'. *Recueil des Travaux Botaniques Neerlandais* 6, 211–32

—— (1912) 'Ueber das Dickenwachstum der Palmen'. *Annales du Jardin Botanique de Buitenzorg*, ser. 2, 11, 1–209

SCHUMANN, K. (1900) 'Musaceae'. *Engler, Das Pflanzenreich*, Band IV, n.45 (Wilhelm Engelmann: Leipzig)

SEEMANN, B. (1854) *The botany of the voyage of the H.M.S. Herald*, p. 205, pls 45–7 (Lovell Reeve: London)

—— (1856) *Popular history of the palms* (Lovell Reeve: London)

SEIFRIZ, W. (1924) 'The gregarious flowering of the talipot palm, *Corypha umbraculifera*, at Peradeniya, Ceylon'. *Bulletin of the Torrey Botanical Club* 51, 341–50

SEWARD, A. C. and ARBER, E. A. N. (1903) 'Les Nipadites des couches éocenes de la Belgique'. *Memoires du Musée Royale d'Histoire Naturelle de Belgique* 11, 1–16

SHARMA, A. K. and SARKAR, S. K. (1956) 'Cytology of different species of palms and its bearing on the solution of the problems of phylogeny and speciation'. *Genetica* 28, 361–488

SIMMONDS, N. W. (1959) *Bananas* (Longmans: London)

SITHOLEY, R. V. (1954) 'The Mesozoic and Tertiary floras of India—a review'. *The Palaeobotanist* **3**, 55–66

SKINNER, C. M. (1911) *Myths and legends of flowers, trees, fruits, and plants* (J. B. Lippincott Co.: Philadelphia)

SKOTTSBERG, C. (1953) *The natural history of Juan Fernandez and Easter Island.* Vol. 2, Botany (Almquist and Wiksells Boktryckeri A.B.: Uppsala)

SMALL, J. K. (1926) 'The saw palmetto *Serenoa repens'. Journal of the New York Botanical Garden* **27**, 193–202; (1964) *Principes* **8**, 44–6

SMITH, D. (1958) 'The Californian habitat of *Washingtonia filifera'. Principes* **2**, 41–51
—— (1963) 'Growth rates of certain palms'. *Principes* **7**, 7–18

SMITH, J. (1878) *Bible plants* (Hardwicke and Boque: London)

SPIX, J. B. VON and MARTIUS, C. F. P. VON (1824–31) *Reise in Brasilien.* 3 vols (Munich)

SPRUCE, R. (1871) 'Palmae Amazonicae'. *Journal of the Linnean Society of London, Botany* **11**, 65–183

—— (1906) *Notes of a botanist on the Amazon and Andes.* Edited and condensed by A. R. Wallace. 2 vols (Macmillan and Co. Ltd: London)

—— and STEYERMARK, J. A. (1958) 'Flora of Guatemala'. *Field Museum of Natural History, Botanical Series* **24**, 199–299

STEARN, W. T. (1960) 'Humboldt's Essai sur la géographie des plantes'. *Journal of the Society for the Bibliography of Natural History* **3**, 351–57

STEENIS, C. G. G. J. VAN (1952) 'Thesaurus Beccarianus'. *Webbia* **8**, 427–36
—— (1954) 'Pandanus in Malaysian vegetation types'. *Flora Malesiana* **1**, 4, 3–12
—— (1963) 'Transpacific floristic affinities, particularly in the tropical zone'. *Pacific Basin Biogeography*, 219–31

STEENIS-KRUSEMAN, M. J. VAN (1950) 'Malaysian plant collectors and collections, being a cyclopedia of botanical exploration in Malaysia'. *Flora Malesiana* **1**

ST JOHN, H. (1957) 'Notes on Pritchardia'. *Principes* **1**, 161–2

STONE, B. C. (1961) 'The genus *Sararanga* (Pandanaceae)'. *Brittonia* **13**, 212–24

STORY, R. (1959) 'The Pondoland palm'. *Principes* **3**, 103–6

SURRE, C. and ZILLER, R. (1963) 'Le palmier à huile'. *Techniques Agricoles et Productions Tropicales* **2** (G.-P. Maisonneve and Larosse: Paris)

SWINGLE, W. T. (1904) 'The date palm'. *United States Department of Agriculture, Bureau of Plant Industry Bulletin* n. 53

TACKHOLM, VIVI and DRAV, MOHAMED (1950) *Flora of Egypt.* Vol. 2 (Fouad I University Press: Cairo)

TERMIER, H. and G. (1952) *Histoire géologique de la biosphère* (Masson ct Cie.: Paris)

THISELTON-DYER, W. T. (1910) 'Morphological notes XII. Germination of the double coconut'. *Annals of Botany* **24**, 222–30

THOMPSON, R. C. (1949) *A dictionary of Assyrian botany* (The British Academy: London)

THORNE, R. F. (1963) 'Biotic distribution patterns in the tropical Pacific'. *Pacific Basin Biogeography* 311–50 (Bishop Museum Press: Honolulu)

TOMLINSON, P. B. (1959) 'An anatomical approach to the classification of Musaceae'. *Journal of the Linnean Society of London, Botany* **55**, 779–809

—— (1960) 'Seedling leaves in palms and their morphological significance'. *Journal of the Arnold Arboretum* **41**, 414–28

—— (1961a) *Anatomy of monocotyledons II. Palmae* (Clarendon Press: Oxford)

—— (1916b) 'The problem of *Wissmannia*'. *Principes* **5**, 33–4

—— (1962a) 'The leaf-base in palms. Its morphology and mechanical biology'. *Journal of the Arnold Arboretum* **43**, 23–50

—— (1962b) 'Essays on the morphology of palms VII. A digression about spines'. *Principes* **6**, 44–52

—— (1964a) 'Stem structure in arborescent monocotyledons'. *Formation of wood in forest trees*, edited by M. H. Zimmermann, 65–86 (Academic Press, Inc.: New York)

—— (1964b) 'The vascular skeleton of the coconut leaf base'. *Phytomorphology* **14**, 218–30

TRALAU, H. (1964) 'The genus *Nypa* (van Wurmb.)'. *Kungl. Svenska Vetenskapsakademiens Handlingar, Fjärde* serien 10, 1–29

TROLL, W. (1935) 'Vergleichende Morphologie der Fiederblätter'. *Nova Acta Leopoldina* N.F. **2**, 315–455

VAUGHAN, R. E. and WIEHE, P. O. (1953) 'The genus *Pandanus* in the Mascarene Islands'. *Journal of the Linnean Society of London, Botany* **55**, 1–33

VENKATANARAYA, G. (1957) 'On certain aspects of the development of the leaf of *Cocos nucifera* (L.)'. *Phytomorphology* **7**, 297–305

VERDOORN, F. (1945) *Plants and plant science in Latin America* (Chronica Botanica Co.: Waltham, Mass.)

WALLACE, A. R. (1853) *Palm trees of the Amazon* (John van Voorst: London)

—— (1869) *The Malay Archipelago* (Richard Clay and Sons: London)

WARBURG, O. (1900) 'Pandanaceae'. *Engler, Das Pflanzenreich Band IV*, 9 (Wilhelm Engelmann: Leipzig)

WARMING, E. (1909) *Ecology of plants*. Translated by P. Groom and I. Bailey Balfour (Clarendon Press: Oxford)

WEBER, C. (1960) 'Palms on postage stamps'. *Principes* **4**, 9–16

WILLIS, J. G. (1948) *A dictionary of the flowering plants and ferns*. 6th ed. (Cambridge University Press)

WIT, H. C. D. DE (1949) 'Short history of the phytography of Malaysian vascular plants'. *Flora Malesiana* ser. I, **4**, LXXI–CLXI (Noordhoff Kolff N.V.: Djakarta)

—— (1952) 'In memory of G. E. Rumphius (1702–1952)'. *Taxon* **1**, 101–10

WINTON, A. L. (1901) 'The anatomy of the fruit of *Cocos nucifera*'. *American Journal of Science*, series 4, **12**, 265–80

WRIGHT, J. O. (1951) 'Unusual features of the root system of the oil palm in West Africa'. *Nature* **168**, 748

WULFF, E. V. (1943) *An introduction to historical plant geography*. Plant Science Books X (Chronica Botanica Co.: Waltham, Mass.)

ZIMMERMANN, W. (1959) *Die phylogenie der Pflanzen* (Gustav Fischer: Stuttgart)

—— (1962) 'Ein fossiler Palmenstamm aus der Umbegung von Ulm'. *Die Natur* **70**, 1–4

ZIMMERMANN, M. H. and TOMLINSON, P. B. (1965) 'Anatomy of the palm *Rhapis exelsa*'. *Journal of the Arnold Arboretum* **46**, 160–77

# Index